F.

A GUIDEBOOK TO MECHANISM IN
ORGANIC CHEMISTRY

A Guidebook to Mechanism in Organic Chemistry

PETER SYKES
M.SC., PH.D., F.R.I.C.

*Fellow of Christ's College and University
Lecturer in Organic Chemistry in the
University of Cambridge*

LONGMANS

LONGMANS, GREEN AND CO LTD
48 Grosvenor Street, London, W.1
Associated companies, branches and representatives
throughout the world

PRINTED IN GREAT BRITAIN BY
LOWE AND BRYDONE (PRINTERS) LTD, LONDON

FOR
JOYCE

Delocalization – resonance p 12

CONTENTS

FOREWORD

THE great development of the theory of organic chemistry or more particularly of our understanding of the mechanism of the reactions of carbon compounds, which has occurred during the past thirty years or so, has wrought a vast change in outlook over the whole of the science. At one time organic chemistry appeared to the student as a vast body of facts, often apparently unconnected, which simply had to be learnt, but the more recent developments in theory have changed all this so that organic chemistry is now a much more ordered body of knowledge in which a logical pattern can be clearly seen. Naturally enough during the long period of development from the initial ideas of Lapworth and Robinson organic chemical theory has undergone continuous modification and it is only in comparatively recent times that it has become of such evident generality (although doubtless still far from finality) that its value and importance to the undergraduate student has become fully realised. As a result the teaching of organic chemistry has been, to some extent, in a state of flux and a variety of experiments have been made and a substantial number of books produced setting out different approaches to it. While it is the writer's opinion that it is unsatisfactory to teach first the main factual part of the subject and subsequently to introduce the theory of reaction mechanism, he is equally convinced that at the present time it is quite impracticable to concentrate almost entirely on theory and virtually to ignore the factual part of the subject. Organic chemical theory has not yet reached a level at which it permits prediction with any certainty of the precise behaviour of many members of the more complex carbon compounds which are of everyday occurrence in the practice of the science. Sound theory is vital to the well-being of organic chemistry; but organic chemistry remains essentially an experimental science.

In Cambridge we are seeking the middle way, endeavouring to build up both aspects of the subject in concert so that there is a minimum of separation between fact and theory. To achieve this the student is introduced at an early stage to the theoretical principles involved and to the essential reaction mechanisms illustrated by a modest number of representative examples. With this approach is coupled a more factual treatment covering the chemistry of the major groups of carbon compounds. Dr. Sykes [who has been intimately associated with this approach] has now written this aptly-named 'Guidebook' to reaction mechanism which sets out in an admirably lucid way what the student requires as a complement to his factual reading. I warmly commend it as a book which will enable students to rationalise many of the facts of organic chemistry, to appreciate the logic of the subject and in so doing to minimise the memory work involved in mastering it.

A. R. TODD.

26th April, 1961.

PREFACE TO SECOND EDITION

IN preparing this second edition I have been most anxious that it should not increase markedly in size (or price!) for I feel sure that what utility the book has been found to possess stems in no small part from its being short in length (and cheap in price!). I have, therefore, added only those topics which are generally felt to be vital omissions, e.g. nitrosation of amines, diazo-coupling, ester formation and hydrolysis, decarboxylation, etc., but I have also sought to eliminate errors and to clarify the argument throughout, which has involved rewriting many of the sections in whole or in part.

Many readers have been kind enough to write to me and I have where possible adopted their suggestions; in this connection I owe a particular debt to Professor Dr. W. Lüttke of Göttingen and Dr. P. Hocks of Berlin, the translators of the German edition. Mr. G. M. Clarke and Dr. D. H. Marrian of this University have kindly read the proofs of this second edition and they too have made valuable suggestions for which I am most grateful.

PETER SYKES.

Cambridge,
April 1964.

PREFACE

THE last twenty-five years have seen an enormous increase in our knowledge of the reactions of organic compounds and, in particular, of the actual detailed pathway or mechanism by which these reactions take place. This understanding has largely come about from the application of electronic theories—so successful in other fields—to organic chemistry, and has resulted not only in an extremely valuable systematisation and explanation of the vast, disparate mass of existing facts, but has also made it possible to specify, in advance, the conditions necessary for the successful carrying out of many new and useful procedures.

The new approach avoids the learning of vast masses of apparently unconnected facts—which has been *the* characteristic of organic chemistry in the past—and helps and encourages the chemist to think for himself: far from requiring a chemist to know more, it enables him to make infinitely better use of what he already does know. It marks the greater effectiveness of really understanding the underlying principles rather than merely knowing by rote. At the same time it is well to emphasise that the complexity of organic compounds in general is such that the *rigorous* application of quantum-mechanical principles to them is impossible. Assumptions and approximations have to be made before useful generalisations can be worked out and it is at this point that there is particular need for strictly chemical skill and insight: the day of organic chemistry from the armchair is far from being with us yet!

This new and effective way of thinking about organic chemistry has been the subject of several large monographs but a smaller, compact book is still required that introduces the essentials, the very vocabulary of the subject, to the scholarship candidate, to the beginning undergraduate and technical college student, and to the chemist whose professional education has been along strictly classical lines. That is the aim of this book which has grown out of the author's lecture courses at Cambridge and his many years spent in supervising undergraduates.

The minimum of space has purposely been spent on valency theory as such for not only is that adequately treated elsewhere, but the student's real need is to gain as much experience as possible in seeing how theoretical ideas work out in practice: in explaining the course taken by actual reactions. Thus the first chapter is intended to give a succinct statement of the basic principles employed and the rest of the book shows how they work out in explaining the variation of reactivity with structure, the occurrence of three main classes of reagent—electrophiles, nucleophiles and radicals—and their behaviour in the fundamental reactions of organic chemistry—substitution, addition, elimination and rearrangement. In all cases, the examples chosen as illustrations have been kept as simple as possible so that the essential features of the process are not confused by extraneous and inessential detail.

Detailed references to the original literature are not included as the author's experience leads him to believe that in a book of such a size and scope the limited space available can be better employed. A select bibliography is, however, included in which the student's attention is drawn to larger sources of information to which he can now progress and reference is made to the particular virtues of a number of the sources quoted.

I am most grateful to my mentor of many years, Professor Sir Alexander Todd, for his Foreword and to my colleagues Dr. J. Biggs (now of the University of Hull), Dr. V. M. Clark, Dr. A. R. Katritzky, Dr. D. H. Marrian and to my wife, who have read the manuscript in whole or in part and made very many useful suggestions. I should also like to express my gratitude to the Rockefeller Foundation for a grant which enabled me, in 1959, to visit the United States and stay at Harvard University, Northwestern University, the University of Illinois, Oberlin College and the Georgia Institute of Technology to study the teaching of mechanistic organic chemistry to undergraduates and graduate students. Many interesting discussions, particularly with Professors F. G. Bordwell, Nelson J. Leonard and Jack Hine, influenced a number of the ideas developed in this book. My indebtedness to the original literature and to other publications, in particular Ingold's *Structure and Mechanism in Organic Chemistry*, Gould's *Mechanism and Structure in Organic Chemistry*, Alexander's *Ionic Organic Reactions* and Hine's *Physical Organic Chemistry* will be apparent to many who read here. Finally I should like to express my deep appreciation to Longmans, and to the printers for their unfailing patience and for the extreme trouble to which they have gone to produce that rare phenomenon, structural formulae that are both clear and aesthetically satisfying.

Cambridge,
April 1961.

PETER SYKES.

1 STRUCTURE, REACTIVITY AND MECHANISM

THE chief advantage of a mechanistic approach to the vast array of disparate information that makes up organic chemistry is the way in which a relatively small number of guiding principles can be used, not only to explain and interrelate existing facts but to forecast the outcome of changing the conditions under which already known reactions are carried out and to foretell the products that may be expected from new ones. It is the business of this chapter to outline some of these guiding principles and to show how they work. As it is the compounds of carbon with which we shall be dealing, something must first be said about the way in which carbon atoms can form bonds with other atoms, especially with other carbon atoms.

ATOMIC ORBITALS

The carbon atom has, outside its nucleus, six electrons which, on the Bohr theory of atomic structure, were believed to be arranged in orbits at increasing distance from the nucleus. These orbits represented gradually increasing levels of energy, that of lowest energy, the $1s$, accommodating two electrons, the next, the $2s$, also accommodating two electrons, and the remaining two electrons of a carbon atom going into the $2p$ level, which is actually capable of accommodating a total of six electrons.

The Heisenberg indeterminacy principle and the wave-mechanical view of the electron have made us do away with anything so precisely defined as actual orbits, and instead we can now only quote the relative probabilities of finding an electron at various distances from the nucleus. The classical orbits have, therefore, been replaced by three-dimensional *orbitals*, which can be said to represent the shape and size of the space around the nucleus in which there is the greatest probability of finding a particular electron: they are, indeed, a sort of three-dimensional electronic contour. One limitation that theory imposes on such orbitals is that each may accommodate not more than two electrons, these electrons being distinguished from each other by having opposed ('paired') spins.

It can be shown from wave-mechanical calculations that the $1s$ orbital (corresponding to the classical K shell) is spherically symmetrical about the nucleus and that the $2s$ orbital is similarly spherically symmetrical but at a greater distance from the nucleus; there is a region between the two latter orbitals where the probability of finding an electron approaches zero (a *spherical nodal surface*):

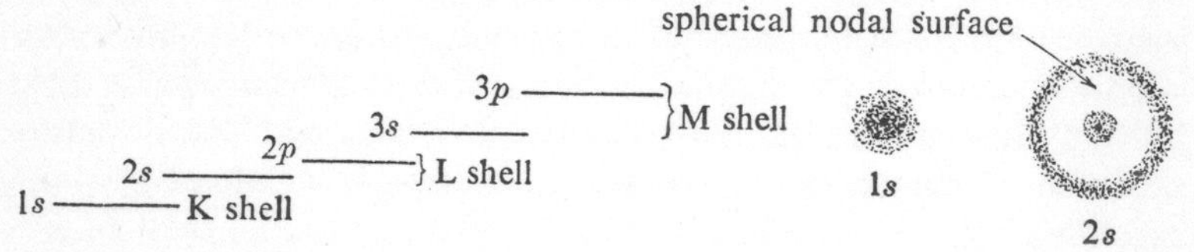

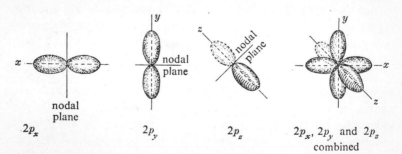

As yet, this marks no radical departure from the classical picture of orbits, but with the $2p$ level (the continuation of the L shell) a difference becomes apparent. Theory now requires the existence of *three* $2p$ orbitals, all of the same energy and shape, arranged mutually at right-angles along notional x, y and z axes and, therefore, designated as $2p_x$, $2p_y$ and $2p_z$, respectively. Further, these three $2p$ orbitals are found to be not spherically symmetrical, like the $1s$ and $2s$, but 'dumb-bell' shaped with a plane, in which there is zero probability of finding an electron (*nodal plane*), passing through the nucleus (at right-angles to the x, y and z axes, respectively) and so separating the two halves of each dumb-bell:

We can thus designate the distribution of the six electrons of the carbon atom, in orbitals, as $1s^2 2s^2\ 2p_x^1 2p_y^1$; orbitals of equal energy (e.g., $2p_x$, $2p_y$, $2p_z$) accommodating a single electron, in turn, before any takes up a second one—the $2p_z$ orbital thus remains unoccupied.

The $2s$ orbital takes up its full complement of two electrons before the $2p$ orbitals begin to be occupied, however, as it is at a slightly lower energy level. This, however, represents the *ground state* of the carbon atom in which only *two* unpaired electrons (in the $2p_x$ and $2p_y$ orbitals) are available for the formation of bonds with other atoms, i.e. at first sight carbon might appear to be only divalent. It is however energetically worthwhile for the carbon atom to assume an *excited state* by uncoupling the $2s^2$ electrons and promoting one of them to the vacant $2p_z$ orbital for, by doing so, it now has *four* unpaired electrons and is thus able to form *four*, rather than only *two*, bonds with other atoms or groups; the large amount of energy produced by forming these two extra bonds considerably outweighs that required (≈ 97 kcal/mole) for the initial $2s^2$ uncoupling and $2s \rightarrow 2p$ promotion. Carbon in order to exhibit its normal and characteristic quadrivalency thus assumes the electron distribution, $1s^2\,2s^1\,2p_x^1\,2p_y^1\,2p_z^1$.

HYBRIDISATION

Carbon does not, however, exert its quadrivalency by the direct use of these four orbitals to form three bonds of one type with the three $2p$ orbitals and one of a different nature with the $2s$ orbital. Calculation shows that by blending these four orbitals so as to form four new, identical and symmetrically disposed orbitals inclined to each other at $109° 28'$ (the normal tetrahedral angle), it is possible to form four stronger, more stable bonds. The observed behaviour of a carbon atom can thus again be justified on energetic grounds. These four new orbitals are designated as sp^3 *hybrids* and the process by which they are obtained as *hybridisation*:

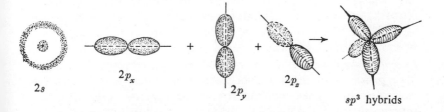

BONDING IN CARBON COMPOUNDS

Bond formation between two atoms is then envisaged as the progressive overlapping of the *atomic* orbitals of the two participating

3

atoms, the greater the possible overlapping, the stronger the bond so formed. When the atoms have come sufficiently close together, it can be shown that their two atomic orbitals are replaced by two *molecular* orbitals, one having less energy and the other more than the sum of the energies of the two separate atomic orbitals. These two new molecular orbitals spread over both atoms and either may contain the two electrons. The molecular orbital of reduced energy is called the *bonding orbital* and constitutes a stable bond between the two atoms; the molecular orbital of increased energy is called the *anti-bonding orbital* and need not here be further considered in the formation of stable bonds between atoms.

In the stable bond so formed the two bonding electrons tend to be concentrated along the line joining the nuclei of the two participating atoms, i.e. the molecular orbital is said to be *localised*. Such localised electrons are often referred to as σ electrons and the covalent bond so formed as a σ bond. Thus on combining with hydrogen, the four hybrid sp^3 atomic orbitals of carbon overlap with the $1s$ atomic orbitals of four hydrogen atoms to form four identical, strong, hybrid sp^3 or σ bonds, making angles of 109° 28′ with each other (the regular tetrahedral angle), in methane. A similar, exactly regular, tetrahedral structure will result with, for example, CCl_4 but with, say, CH_2Cl_2, though the arrangement will remain tetrahedral, it will depart very slightly from exact symmetry; the two large chlorine atoms will take up more room than hydrogen so that the H—C—H and Cl—C—Cl bond angles will differ slightly from 109° 28′ and from each other.

(i) Carbon–carbon single bonds

The combination of two carbon atoms, for example in ethane, results from the overlap of two sp^3 atomic orbitals, one from each carbon atom, to form a strong σ bond between them. The carbon–carbon bond length in saturated compounds is found to be pretty constant— 1·54 Å. We have not, however, defined a unique structure for ethane; the σ bond joining the two carbon atoms is symmetrical about a line joining the two nuclei, and, theoretically, an infinite variety of different structures is still possible, defined by the position of the hydrogens on one carbon atom relative to the position of those on the other. The two extremes of the possible species are known as the *eclipsed* and *staggered* forms; they and the infinite variety of structures lying between them are known as *conformations* of the ethane molecule.

Conformations are defined as different arrangements of the same group of atoms that can be converted into one another without the breaking of any bonds.

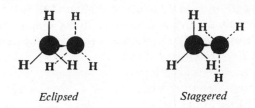

Eclipsed　　　　　　*Staggered*

The staggered conformation is likely to be the more stable of the two for the hydrogen atoms are as far apart as they can get and any interaction is thus at a minimum, whereas in the eclipsed conformation they are suffering the maximum of crowding. The long cherished principle of free rotation about a carbon–carbon single bond is not contravened, however, as it has been shown that the eclipsed and staggered conformations differ by only ≈ 3 kcal/mole in energy content and this is small enough to allow their ready interconversion through the agency of ordinary thermal motions at room temperature. That such crowding *can* lead to a real restriction of rotation about a carbon–carbon single bond has been confirmed by the isolation of two forms of $CHBr_2 \cdot CHBr_2$, though admittedly only at low temperatures where collisions between molecules do not provide enough energy to effect the interconversion.

(ii) Carbon–carbon double bonds

In ethylene each carbon atom is bonded to only *three* other atoms, two hydrogens and one carbon. Strong σ bonds are formed with these three atoms by the use of *three* hybrid orbitals derived by hybridising the $2s$ and, this time, *two* only of the carbon atom's $2p$ atomic orbitals—an atom will normally only mobilise as many hybrid orbitals as it has atoms or groups to form strong σ bonds with. The resultant sp^2 hybrid orbitals all lie in the same plane and are inclined at $120°$ to each other (*plane trigonal orbitals*). In forming the molecule of ethylene, two of the sp^2 orbitals of each carbon atom are seen as overlapping with the $1s$ orbitals of two hydrogen atoms to form two strong σ C—H bonds, while the third sp^2 orbital of each carbon atom is used to form a strong σ C—C bond between them.

5

This then leaves, on each carbon atom, *one unhybridised 2p* atomic orbital at right angles to the plane containing the carbon and hydrogen atoms. These two $2p$ atomic orbitals are parallel to each other and can themselves overlap to form a molecular orbital, spreading over both carbon atoms and situated above and below the plane containing the two carbon and four hydrogen atoms (dotted lines indicate bonds to atoms lying *behind* the plane of the paper and ◄ to those lying in *front* of it):

The electrons occupying this new molecular orbital are known as π electrons and the orbital itself as a π orbital. The new π bond that is thus formed has the effect of drawing the carbon atoms closer together thus the C=C distance in ethylene is 1·33 Å compared with a C—C distance of 1·54 Å in ethane. The lateral overlap of the p orbitals that occurs in forming a π bond is less effective than the linear overlap that occurs in forming a σ bond and the former is thus weaker than the latter. This is reflected in the fact that the energy of a carbon–carbon double bond, though more than that of a single bond is, indeed, less than twice as much. Thus the C—C bond energy in ethane is 83 kcal/mole, while that of C=C in ethylene is only 143 kcal/mole.

The overlap of the two $2p$ atomic orbitals, and hence the strength of the π bond, will clearly be at a maximum when the two carbon and four hydrogen atoms are exactly coplanar, for it is only in this position that the p atomic orbitals are exactly parallel to each other and thus capable of the maximum overlapping. Any disturbance of this coplanar state by twisting about the σ bond joining the two carbon atoms would lead to reduction in π overlapping and hence a decrease in the strength of the π bond: it will thus be resisted. A theoretical justification is thus provided for the long observed resistance to rotation about a carbon–carbon double bond. The distribution of the π electrons in two layers, above and below the plane of the molecule, and extending beyond the carbon–carbon bond axis means that a region of negative charge is effectively waiting there to welcome any electron-seeking reagents (e.g. oxidising agents), so that it comes as no surprise to realise that the characteristic reactions of a carbon–carbon double bond are predominantly with such reagents (*cf.* p. 137). Here the classical picture of a double bond has been superseded by a view in which the two bonds joining the carbon atoms, far from being identical, are believed to be different in nature, strength and position.

(iii) Carbon–carbon triple bonds

In acetylene each carbon atom is bonded to only *two* other atoms, one hydrogen and one carbon. Strong σ bonds are formed with these two atoms by the use of *two* hybrid orbitals derived by hybridising the $2s$ and, this time, *one* only of the carbon atom's $2p$ orbitals. The resultant sp^1 hybrid orbitals are co-linear. Thus, in forming the molecule of acetylene, these hybrid orbitals are used to form strong σ bonds between each carbon atom and one hydrogen atom and between the two carbon atoms themselves, resulting in a linear molecule having *two* unhybridised $2p$ atomic orbitals, at right angles to each other, on each of the two carbon atoms. The atomic orbitals on one carbon atom are parallel to those on the other and can thus overlap with each other resulting in the formation of *two* π bonds in planes at right angles to each other:

The acetylene molecule is thus effectively sheathed in a cylinder of negative charge. The $C{\equiv}C$ bond energy is 194 kcal/mole, so that the increment due to the third bond is less than that occurring on going from a single to a double bond. The $C{\equiv}C$ bond distance is $1 \cdot 20$ Å so that the carbon atoms have been drawn still further together, but here again the decrement on going $C{=}C \rightarrow C{\equiv}C$ is smaller than that on going $C{-}C \rightarrow C{=}C$.

(iv) Conjugated dienes, etc.

An explanation in similar terms can be adduced for the differences in behaviour between dienes (and also in compounds containing more than two double bonds) in which the double bonds are *conjugated* (I) and those in which they are isolated (II):

7

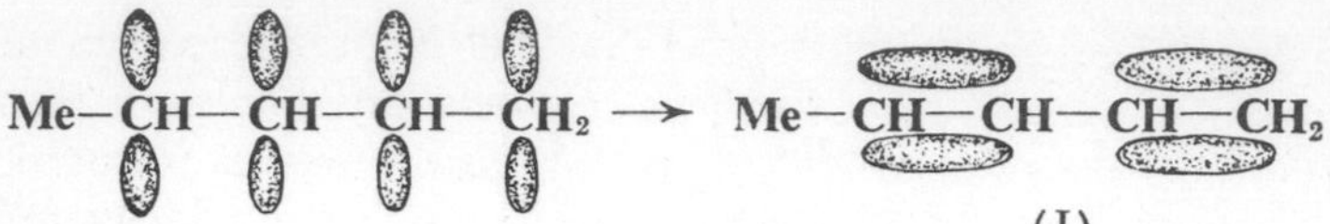

$$Me-CH-CH-CH-CH_2 \rightarrow Me-CH-CH-CH-CH_2$$

(I)

$$CH_2-CH-CH_2-CH-CH_2 \rightarrow CH_2-CH-CH_2-CH-CH_2$$

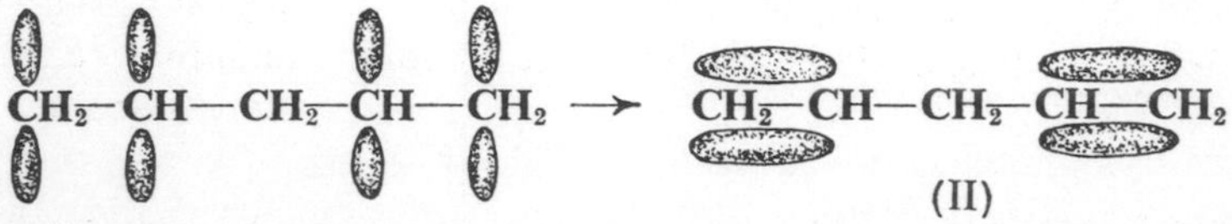

(II)

In either case, overlapping of the *p* atomic orbitals on adjacent carbon atoms can lead to the formation of two localised π bonds as shown, and the compounds would be expected to behave like ethylene, only twice as it were! This adequately represents the observed behaviour of (II) but not of the conjugated compound (I). On looking more closely at (I), however, it is realised that interaction is also possible between the *p* atomic orbitals of the two centre carbon atoms of the conjugated system, as well as between each of these and the *p* orbitals on the outside carbon atoms of the system. An alternative formulation is thus a π orbital covering all four carbon atoms (III)

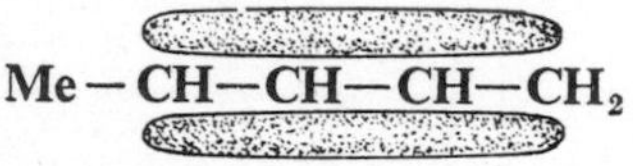

$$Me-CH-CH-CH-CH_2 \qquad CH_2=CH-CH=CH_2$$

(III) (IV)

$$CH_2-CH-CH-CH_2$$

(V)

in which the electrons are said to be *delocalised* as they are now spread over, and are held in common by, the whole of the conjugated system. There will, of course, need to be *two* such delocalised orbitals as no orbital can contain more than two electrons and four electrons are here involved. The result is a region of negative charge above and below the plane containing all the atoms in the molecule.

The better description that this view affords of the properties of conjugated dienes including the possibility of adding, for example, bromine to the ends of the system (1:4-addition) rather than merely to one of a pair of double bonds (1:2-addition) is discussed below (p. 150).

It should, perhaps, be mentioned that such delocalisation can only occur when all the atoms in the diene are essentially in the same plane. For in other positions, (e.g. XIV, p. 13), possible owing to rotation about the central C—C bond, the π atomic orbitals on carbon atoms 2 and 3 would not be parallel and could thus not overlap at all effectively. The effect of the delocalisation that actually takes place is thus to impose considerable restriction on rotation about the central C—C bond, observed as a preferred orientation of the compound.

(v) Benzene and aromaticity

A somewhat similar state of affairs occurs with benzene. The known planar structure of the molecule implies sp^2 hybridisation, with p atomic orbitals, at right angles to the plane of the nucleus, on each of the six carbon atoms (VI):

(VIII)   (VI)   (VII)

Overlapping could, of course, take place 1:2, 3:4, 5:6, or 1:6, 5:4, 3:2 leading to formulations corresponding to the Kekulé structures (e.g. VII) but, in fact, delocalisation takes place as with butadiene, though to a very much greater extent, leading to a cyclic π orbital embracing all six carbon atoms of the ring. Other orbitals in addition to the above are required to accommodate the total of six electrons (*cf.* p. 1), but the net result is annular rings of negative charge above and below the plane of the nucleus (VIII).

Support for this view is provided by the fact that all the carbon–carbon bond lengths in benzene are the same, i.e. all the bonds are of exactly the same character, all being somewhere in between double and single bonds as is revealed by their length, 1·39 Å. The degree of 'multiplicity' of a bond is usually expressed as the *bond order*, which is one for a single, two for a double and three for a triple bond. The relation between bond order and bond length is exemplified by a curve of the type

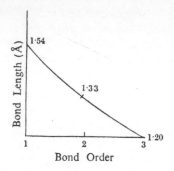

but it will be seen that the relationship is not a linear one and that the bonds in benzene are not midway between double and single bonds in length. The influence of the layer of negative charge on the type of reagents that will attack benzene is discussed below (p. 101).

The relative unreactivity of benzene, as compared with the highly unsaturated system implied in its usual representation and actually observed in a non-cyclic conjugated triene, arises from the stability conferred by the cyclic delocalisation of the π electrons over the six carbon atoms coupled with the fact that the angle between the plane trigonal σ bonds is at its optimum value of 120°. The stability conferred by such cyclic delocalisation also explains why the characteristic reactions of aromatic systems are substitutions rather than the addition reactions that might, from the classical Kekulé structures, be expected and which are indeed realised with non-cyclic conjugated trienes. For addition would lead to a product in which delocalisation, though still possible, could now involve only four carbon atoms and would have lost its characteristic cyclic character (IX; *cf.* butadiene), whereas substitution results in the retention of delocalisation essentially similar to that in benzene with all that it implies (X):

$$\text{Addition (IX)} \quad \xleftarrow{\text{Br}_2} \quad \text{(XI)}^* \quad \xrightarrow{\text{Br}_2} \quad \text{Substitution (X)} + \text{HBr}$$

Addition
(IX)

(XI)

Substitution
(X)

* This symbol has, where appropriate, been used to represent the benzene nucleus as it conveys an excellent impression of the closed, delocalised orbitals from which its characteristic aromaticity stems.

In other words, substitution can take place with overall retention of aromaticity, addition cannot (*cf.* p. 102).

A rough estimate of the stabilisation conferred on benzene by delocalisation of its π electrons can be obtained by comparing its heat of hydrogenation with that of cyclohexene:

The heat of hydrogenation of three isolated double bonds (i.e. bonds between which there is no interaction) in such a cyclic system would thus be $28 \cdot 8 \times 3 = 86 \cdot 4$ kcal/mole. But when benzene is hydrogenated only $49 \cdot 8$ kcal/mole are actually evolved. Thus the interaction of the π electrons in benzene may be said to result in the molecule being *stabler* by $36 \cdot 6$ kcal/mole than if no such interaction took place (the stabilisation arising from similar interaction in conjugated dienes is only ≈ 6 kcal/mole, hence the preference of benzene for substitution rather than addition reactions, *cf.* p. 102). This amount by which benzene is stabilised is referred to as the *delocalisation energy* or, more commonly, the *resonance energy*. The latter, though more widely used, is a highly unsatisfactory term as the word resonance immediately conjures up visions of rapid oscillations between one structure and another, for example the Kekulé structures for benzene, thus entirely misrepresenting the actual state of affairs.

(vi) Conditions necessary for delocalisation

Though the delocalisation viewpoint cannot result in this particular confusion of thought, it may lead to some loss of facility in the actual writing of formulae. Thus while benzene may be written as (XI) as readily as one of the Kekulé structures, the repeated writing of butadiene as (V) becomes tiresome. This has led to the convention of representing molecules that cannot adequately be written as a single classical structure (e.g. (IV)) by a combination of two or more classical structures linked by double-headed arrows; the way in which one is derived from another by movement of electron pairs often being indicated by curved arrows (e.g. (IV) →(XII) or (XIII)), the *tail* of the curved arrow indicating where an electron pair moves *from* and the *head* where it moves *to*:

$$\overset{\frown}{CH_2}=CH-\overset{\frown}{CH}=CH_2 \leftrightarrow \overset{\ominus}{CH_2}-CH=CH-\overset{\oplus}{CH_2}$$
(IV)   (XII)

$$CH_2=CH-CH=CH_2 \leftrightarrow \overset{\oplus}{CH_2}-CH=CH-\overset{\ominus}{CH_2}$$
(IV)   (XIII)

This is the basis of the concept of resonance. The individual classical structures that may readily be written down are referred to as *canonical structures* and the *real, unique* structure of the compound, somewhere 'in between' all of them, being referred to as a *resonance hybrid*. The term *mesomerism* is also used for the phenomenon, though less widely, to avoid the semantic difficulty mentioned above, emphasising that the compound does not have several possible structures which are rapidly interconverted (i.e. it is *not* a sort of extra rapid and reversing tautomerism!), but *one* structure only, 'in between' the classical structures that can more readily be written (meso implying 'in between').

A certain number of limitations must be borne in mind, however, when considering delocalisation and its representation through two or more classical structures as above. Broadly speaking, the more canonical structures that can be written for a compound, the greater the delocalisation of electrons and the more stable the compound will be. These structures must not vary too widely from each other in energy content, however, or those of higher energy will contribute so little to the hybrid as to make their contribution virtually irrelevant. Structures involving separation of charge (e.g. XII and XIII) may be written but, other things being equal, these are usually of higher energy content than those in which such separation has not taken place (e.g. IV), and hence contribute correspondingly less to the hybrid. The structures written must all contain the same number of paired electrons and the constituent atoms must all occupy essentially the same positions relative to each other in each canonical structure.

If delocalisation is to be significant, all atoms attached to unsaturated centres must lie in the same plane or nearly so. This requirement has already been referred to for butadiene (p. 9), for if the molecule takes up a position such as (XIV)

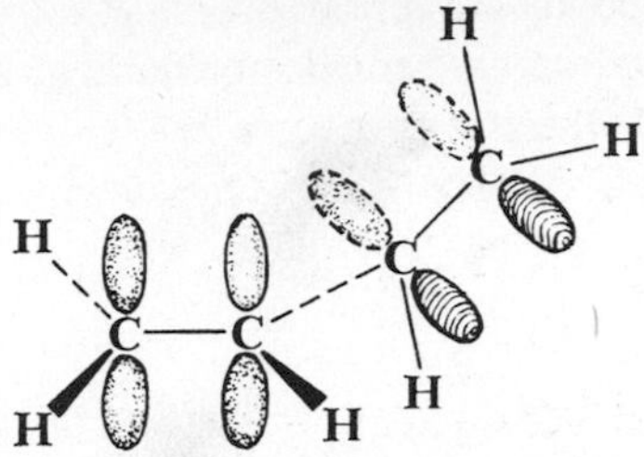

(XIV)

the p atomic orbitals on C_2 and C_3 are no longer parallel, cannot therefore overlap, and delocalisation is thus prevented. Some overlap will still take place if the orbitals are not exactly parallel, but overlapping, with its consequent stabilisation, decreases fairly rapidly as the parallel position is departed from. Examples where delocalisation, with consequent stabilisation, is actually prevented by steric factors are discussed subsequently (p. 22).

The delocalisation that is so effective in promoting the stability of aromatic compounds results when there are no *partially* occupied orbitals of the same energy. The complete filling of such orbitals can be shown to occur with $2 + 4n$ π electrons, and 6π electrons ($n = 1$) is the arrangement that occurs by far the most commonly in aromatic compounds. 10π electrons ($n = 2$) are present in naphthalene (delocalisation energy, 61 kcal/mole) and 14π electrons ($n = 3$) in anthracene and phenanthrene (delocalisation energies, 84 and 91 kcal/mole, respectively) and though these substances are not monocyclic like benzene, the introduction of the trans-annular bonds that makes them bi- and tri-cyclic, respectively, seems to cause relatively little perturbation so far as delocalisation of the π electrons over the cyclic group of ten or fourteen carbon atoms is concerned.

THE BREAKING AND FORMING OF BONDS

A covalent bond between two atoms can essentially be broken in the following ways:

$$R:X \begin{array}{l} \nearrow R\cdot + \cdot X \\ \rightarrow R:^{\ominus} + X^{\oplus} \\ \searrow R^{\oplus} + :X^{\ominus} \end{array}$$

In the first case each atom separates with one electron leading to the formation of highly reactive entities called free radicals, owing their reactivity to their unpaired electron; this is referred to as *homolytic fission* of the bond. Alternatively, one atom may hold on to both electrons, leaving none for the other, the result in the above case being a negative and a positive ion, respectively. Where **R** and **X** are not identical, the fission can, of course, take place in either of two ways, as shown above, depending on whether **R** or **X** retains the electron pair. Either of these processes is referred to as *heterolytic fission*. Formation of a covalent bond can, of course, take place by the reversal of any of these processes.

Such free radicals or ion pairs are formed transiently as reactive intermediates in a very wide variety of organic reactions as will be shown below. Reactions involving radicals tend to occur in the gas phase and in solution in non-polar solvents and to be catalysed by light and by the addition of other radicals (p. 231). Reactions involving ionic intermediates take place more readily in solution in polar solvents. Many of these ionic intermediates can be considered as carrying their charge on a carbon atom, though the ion is often stabilised by delocalisation of the charge, to a greater or lesser extent, over other carbon atoms or atoms of different elements:

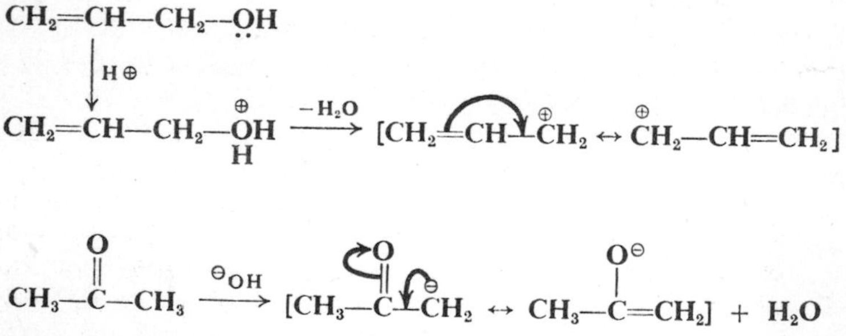

$$CH_2{=}CH{-}CH_2{-}\overset{..}{\underset{..}{O}}H$$

$$\Big\downarrow H \oplus$$

$$CH_2{=}CH{-}CH_2{-}\overset{\oplus}{\underset{H}{O}}H \xrightarrow{-H_2O} [CH_2{=}CH{-}\overset{\oplus}{C}H_2 \leftrightarrow \overset{\oplus}{C}H_2{-}CH{=}CH_2]$$

$$CH_3{-}\overset{O}{\overset{\|}{C}}{-}CH_3 \xrightarrow{\ominus OH} [CH_3{-}\overset{O}{\overset{\|}{C}}{-}\overset{\ominus}{C}H_2 \leftrightarrow CH_3{-}\overset{O\ominus}{\underset{}{C}}{=}CH_2] + H_2O$$

When a positive charge is carried on carbon the entity is known as a *carbonium ion* and when a negative charge, a *carbanion*. Though such ions may be formed only transiently and be present only in minute concentration, they are nevertheless often of paramount importance in controlling the reactions in which they participate.

FACTORS AFFECTING ELECTRON-AVAILABILITY IN BONDS AND AT INDIVIDUAL ATOMS

In the light of what has been said above, any factors that influence the relative availability of electrons (the *electron density*) in particular bonds or at particular atoms in a compound will greatly affect its reactivity towards a particular reagent; for a position of high electron availability will be attacked with difficulty if at all by, for example, $^{\ominus}$OH, whereas a position of low electron availability is likely to be attacked with ease, and vice versa with a positively charged reagent. A number of such factors have been recognised.

(i) Inductive effect

In a covalent single bond between unlike atoms the electron pair forming the σ bond is never shared absolutely equally between the two atoms; it tends to be attracted a little more towards the more electronegative atom of the two. Thus in an alkyl halide

$$-\overset{|}{\underset{|}{C}}\!\!\!\Longrightarrow Cl \qquad -\overset{|}{\underset{|}{\overset{\delta+}{C}}}\!\!-\overset{\delta-}{Cl} \qquad \overset{|}{\underset{|}{C}}\!\!\to Cl$$

$$\text{(XV)} \qquad\qquad \text{(XVI}a) \qquad\qquad \text{(XVI}b)$$

the electron density tends to be greater nearer chlorine than carbon (XV) as the former is the more electronegative; this is generally represented in classical formulae by (XVI*a*) or (XVI*b*). If the carbon atom bonded to chlorine is itself attached to further carbon atoms, the effect can be transmitted further:

$$\underset{4}{C}\!\!-\!\!\underset{3}{C}\!\!-\!\!\underset{2}{C}\!\!\to\!\!\underset{1}{C}\!\!\leftrightarrow\!\!Cl$$

The effect of the chlorine atom's partial appropriation of the electrons of the carbon–chlorine bond is to leave C_1 slightly electron-deficient; this it seeks to rectify by, in turn, appropriating slightly more than its share of the electrons of the σ bond joining it to C_2, and so on down the chain. The effect of C_1 on C_2 is less than the effect of Cl on C_1, however, and the transmission quickly dies away in a saturated chain, usually being too small to be noticeable beyond C_2.

Most atoms and groups attached to carbon exert such *inductive effects* in the same direction as chlorine, i.e. they are electron-withdrawing, owing to their being more electronegative than carbon, the

15

major exception being alkyl groups which are electron-donating.*
Though the effect is quantitatively rather small, it is responsible for
the increase in basicity that results when one of the hydrogen atoms
of ammonia is replaced by an alkyl group (p. 49), and, in part at any
rate, for the readier substitution of the aromatic nucleus in toluene
than in benzene. Several suggestions have been made to account for the
electron-donating abilities of CH_3, CH_2R, CHR_2 and CR_3, none of
which is wholly convincing and the matter can be said to be unsettled.

All inductive effects are permanent polarisations in the ground
state of the molecule and are therefore manifested in its physical
properties, for example, its dipole moment.

(ii) Mesomeric or conjugative effect

This is essentially a further statement of the electron redistribution
that can take place in unsaturated and especially in conjugated
systems via their π orbitals. An example is the carbonyl group (p. 158)
whose properties are not entirely satisfactorily represented by the
classical formulation (XVII), nor by the extreme polar structure
(XVIII), that may be derived from it by an electron shift as shown:

| (XVII) | (XVIII) | (XIX) |

The actual structure is somewhere in between, i.e. a resonance hybrid
of which the above are the canonical forms, perhaps best represented
by (XIX) in which the π electrons are drawn preferentially towards
oxygen rather than carbon. If the carbonyl group is conjugated with
a $>C=C<$ bond, the above polarisation can be transmitted further
via the π electrons:

(XX)

* The metal atoms in, for example, lithium alkyls and Grignard reagents,
both of which compounds are largely covalent, are also electron-donating, leading
to negatively polarised carbon atoms in each case: $R \rightarrow Li$ and $R \rightarrow Mg \cdot Hal$
(*cf.* p. 170).

Delocalisation takes place (XX), so that an electron-deficient atom results at C_3, as well as at C_1 as in a simple carbonyl compound. The difference between this transmission via a conjugated system and the inductive effect in a saturated system is that here the effect suffers much less diminution by its transmission; C_3 is almost as positive as C_1 was in (XIX).

The stabilisation that can result by delocalisation of a positive or negative charge in an ion via its π orbitals can be a potent feature in making the formation of the ion possible in the first place (*cf.* p. 40). It is, for instance, the stabilisation of the phenoxide ion (XXI) by delocalisation of its charge via the delocalised π orbitals of the nucleus that is largely responsible for the acidity of phenol, i.e. the ease with which it will lose a proton in the first place (*cf.* p. 41):

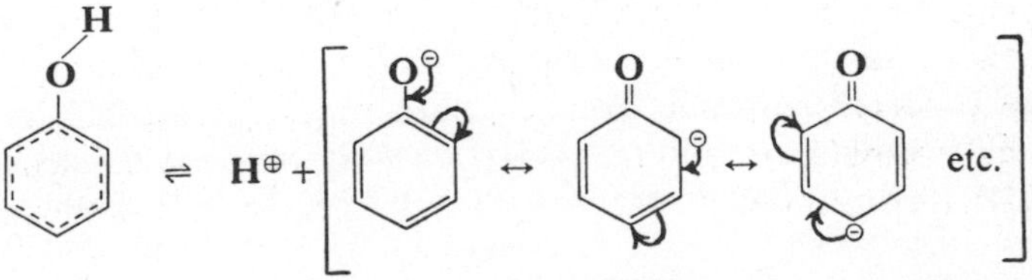

(XXI)

An apparently similar delocalisation can take place in undissociated phenol itself involving an unshared electron pair on the oxygen atom

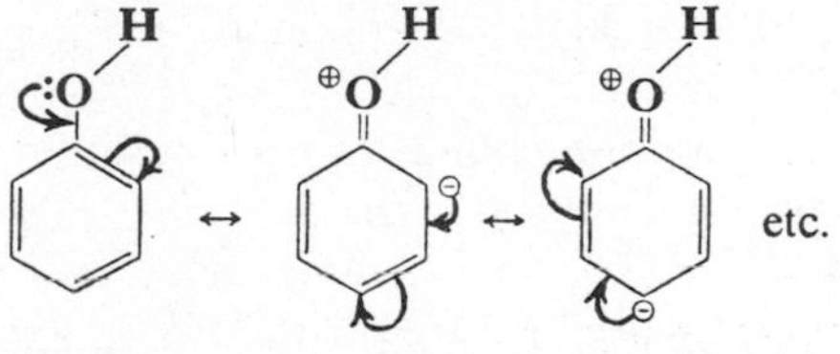

but this involves separation of charge and will thus be correspondingly less effective than the stabilisation of the phenoxide ion which does not.

Similar stabilisation of the anion with respect to the neutral molecule is not shared by benzyl alcohol, which is thus no more acidic than aliphatic alcohols, for the intervening saturated carbon atom prevents interaction with the π orbitals of the nucleus:

17

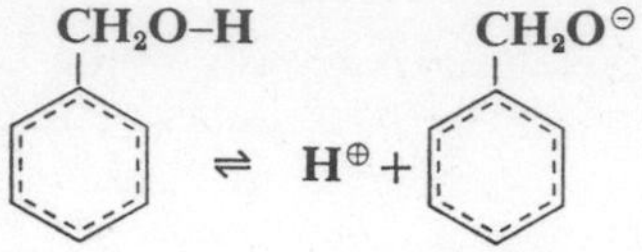

$$CH_2O{-}H \qquad\qquad CH_2O^{\ominus}$$

$$\rightleftharpoons \quad H^{\oplus} +$$

(XXII)

In other words, the phenoxide ion (XXI) is stabilised with respect to the phenol molecule whereas the benzyl oxide ion (XXII) is not so stabilised with respect to the benzyl alcohol molecule. A somewhat similar situation occurs in the dissociation of the carboxylic acids:

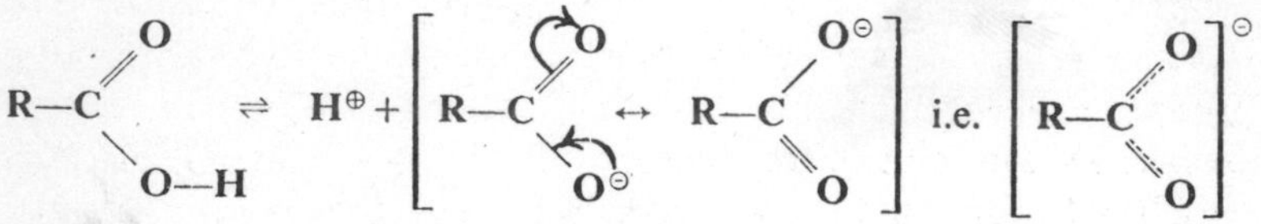

(XXIII)

The more the carboxylate ion (XXIII) is stabilised with respect to the undissociated acid molecule, the more readily the latter will lose a proton and the stronger the acid will then be. Here again delocalisation can take place in the undissociated molecule

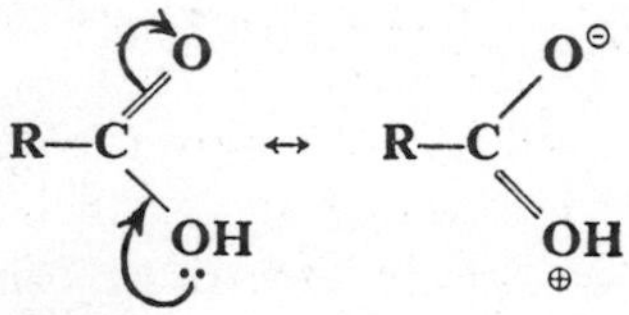

and contributes to its stability but it requires separation of charge and so will be less effective than that in the carboxylate anion which does not. It will be observed that the stabilisation effected in the carboxylate ion will be particularly marked as the two canonical structures that can be written are of equal energy.

The most common examples of mesomeric effects are encountered in substituted aromatic systems: the π electrons of suitable substituents interact with the delocalised π orbitals of the nucleus and thus profoundly influence its reactivity, i.e. its aromaticity. The delocalised π orbitals of the benzene nucleus are particularly effective in transmitting the electrical influence of a substituent from one part of the molecule to another:

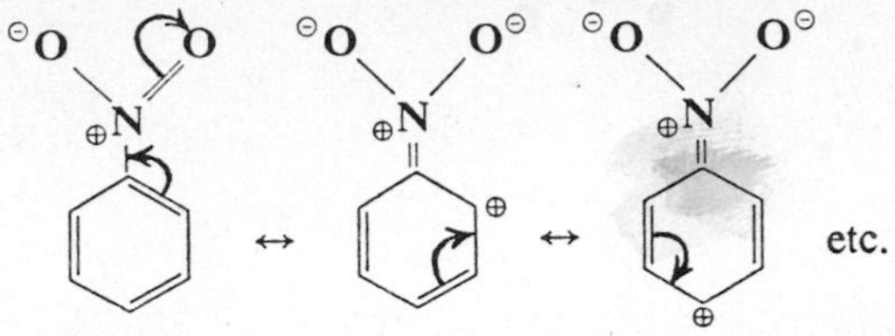

Thus the nitro group in nitrobenzene lowers the density of negative charge over the nucleus, as compared with benzene itself: it is an *electron-withdrawing group*, in contrast to the negatively charged oxygen atom in the phenoxide ion (XXI), which is an *electron-donating group*. Because of the presence of an electron-withdrawing group, nitrobenzene will be less readily attacked than benzene itself by positive ions or electron-deficient reagents (oxidising agents such as $KMnO_4$, for example) which, as will be seen below (p. 101), are exactly the type of reagents involved in normal aromatic substitution reactions.

Mesomeric, like inductive, effects are permanent polarisations in the ground state of the molecule and are therefore manifested in the physical properties of the compounds in which they occur. The essential difference between inductive and mesomeric effects is that the former occur essentially in saturated groups or compounds, the latter in unsaturated and, especially, conjugated compounds. The former involve the electrons in σ bonds, the latter those in π bonds and orbitals. Inductive effects are transmitted over only quite short distances in saturated chains before dying away, whereas mesomeric effects may be transmitted from one end to the other of quite large molecules provided that conjugation (i.e. delocalised π orbitals) is present through which they can proceed. Either effect influences the behaviour of compounds in both essentially static and dynamic situations: in both the position of equilibria and rates of reaction, in the strength of acids and bases as much as in the reactivity of alkyl halides or the relative ease of substitution of different aromatic species.

(iii) Time-variable effects

Some workers have sought to distinguish between effects such as the two considered above which are permanent polarisations manifested in the ground state of the molecule and changed distributions of electrons that may result either on the close approach of a reagent or, more especially, in the transition state, lying between reactants and products, that may result from its initial attack. These time-variable factors corresponding to the permanent effects discussed above have been named the *inductomeric* and *electromeric* effects, respectively. Any such effects can be looked upon as *polarisabilities* rather than as polarisations, for the distribution of electrons reverts to that of the ground state of the molecule attacked if either of the reactants is removed without reaction being allowed to take place or, if a transition state is actually formed, it decomposes to yield the starting materials again.

Such time-variable effects, being only temporary, will not, of course, be reflected in the physical properties of the compounds concerned. It has proved impossible to distinguish experimentally between permanent and time-variable effects in a number of cases, but it cannot be too greatly emphasised that despite the difficulties in distinguishing what proportions of a given effect are due to permanent and to time-variable factors, the actual close approach of a reagent may have a profound effect in enhancing reactivity in a reactant molecule and so in promoting reaction.

(iv) Hyperconjugation

The inductive effect of alkyl groups is normally found to be in the order

$$CH_3 \rightarrow - \; < \; Me \rightarrow -CH_2 \rightarrow - \; < \; \begin{matrix} Me \searrow \\ CH \rightarrow - \\ Me \nearrow \end{matrix} \; < \; \begin{matrix} Me \searrow \\ Me \rightarrow -C \rightarrow - \\ Me \nearrow \end{matrix}$$

as would be expected. When, however, the alkyl groups are attached to an unsaturated system, e.g. a double bond or a benzene nucleus, this order is found to be disturbed and in the case of some conjugated systems actually reversed. It thus appears that alkyl groups are capable, in these circumstances, of giving rise to electron release by a mechanism different from the inductive effect and of which methyl is the most successful exponent. This has been explained as proceeding by an extension of the conjugative or mesomeric effect, delocalisation taking place in the following way:

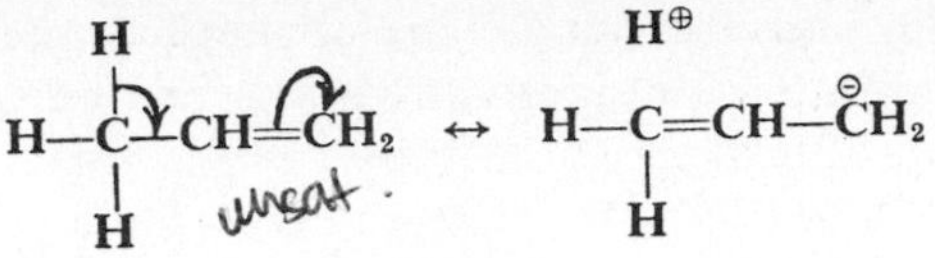

(XXIV)

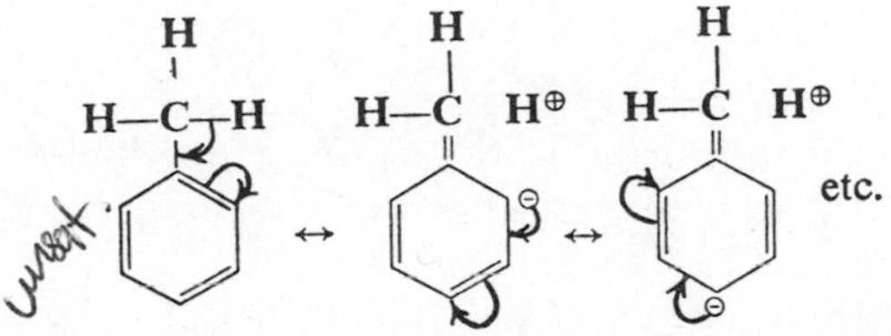

(XXV)

This effect has been called *hyperconjugation* and has been used successfully to explain a number of otherwise unconnected phenomena. It should be emphasised that it is not suggested that a proton actually becomes free in (XXIV) or (XXV), for if it moved from its original position one of the conditions necessary for delocalisation to occur would be controverted (p. 12).

The reason for the reversal of electron-donating ability in going **Me → Et → isoPr → t-Bu** is that hyperconjugation depends for its operation on hydrogen attached to carbon atoms α- to the unsaturated system. This is clearly at a maximum with **Me** (XXIV) and non-existent with **t-Bu** (XXVIII), provided it is assumed that no similar effect of comparable magnitude occurs in **C—C** bonds,

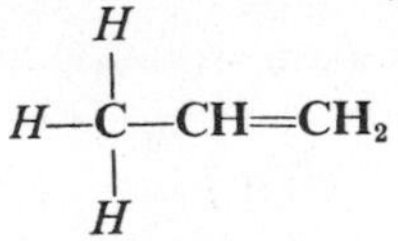

$$H-\underset{\underset{H}{|}}{\overset{\overset{H}{|}}{C}}-CH=CH_2 \qquad Me-\underset{\underset{H}{|}}{\overset{\overset{H}{|}}{C}}-CH=CH_2 \qquad Me-\underset{\underset{H}{|}}{\overset{\overset{Me}{|}}{C}}-CH=CH_2$$

(XXIV) 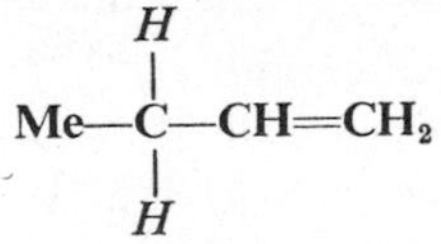   (XXVI) 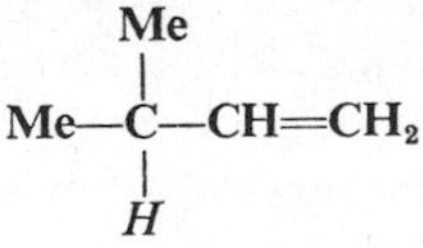   (XXVII)

$$Me-\underset{\underset{Me}{|}}{\overset{\overset{Me}{|}}{C}}-CH=CH_2$$

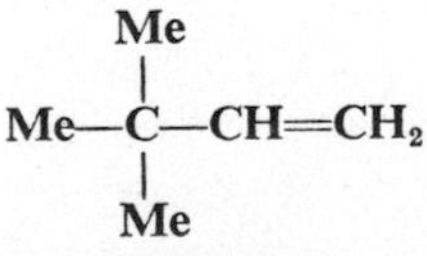

(XXVIII)

hence the increased electron-donating ability of methyl groups under these conditions. This is believed to be the reason for the increased stabilisation of olefines in which the double bond is not terminal compared with isomeric compounds in which it is, i.e. (XXIX) in which there are nine α-hydrogen atoms compared with (XXX) in which there are only five:

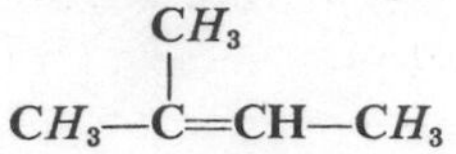

$$\underset{(XXIX)}{CH_3-\overset{\overset{\displaystyle CH_3}{|}}{C}=CH-CH_3} \qquad\qquad \underset{(XXX)}{Me-CH_2-\overset{\overset{\displaystyle CH_3}{|}}{C}=CH_2}$$

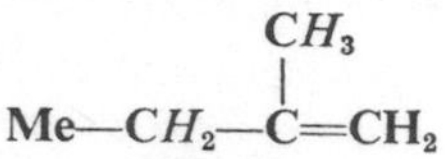

This leads to their preferential formation in reactions which could lead to either compound on introduction of the double bond and even to the fairly ready isomerisation of the less into the more stable compound.

Although hyperconjugation has proved useful on a number of occasions, its validity is not universally accepted and a good deal of further work needs to be done on its theoretical justification.

STERIC EFFECTS

We have to date been discussing factors that may influence the relative availability of electrons in bonds or at particular atoms in a compound, and hence influence that compound's reactivity. The working or influence of these factors may, however, be modified or even nullified by the operation of steric factors; thus effective delocalisation via π orbitals can only take place if the p or π orbitals on the atoms involved in the delocalisation can become parallel or fairly nearly so. If this is prevented, significant overlapping cannot take place and delocalisation fails to occur. A good example of this is provided by dimethylaniline (XXXI) and its 2,6-dialkyl derivatives, e.g. (XXXII). The NMe_2 group in (XXXI), being electron-donating (due to the unshared electron pair on nitrogen interacting with the delocalised π orbitals of the nucleus), activates the nucleus towards attack by the diazonium cation $PhN_2^{\oplus}$, i.e. towards azo-coupling, leading to preferential substitution at *o*- and, more particularly, *p*-positions (*cf.* p. 119):

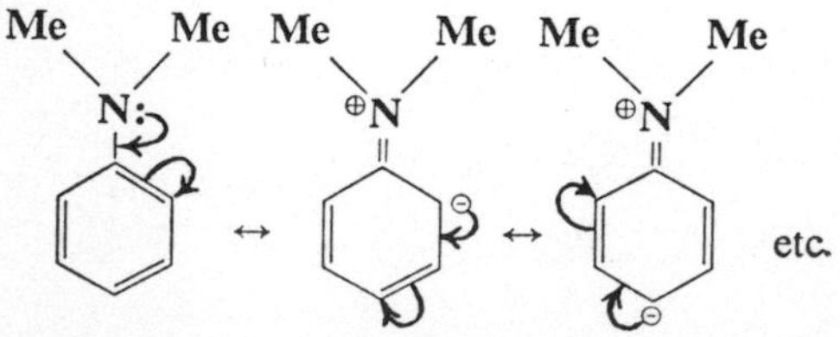

(XXXI)

The 2,6-dimethyl derivative (XXXII) does not couple under these conditions, however, despite the fact that the methyl groups that have been introduced are too far away for their not very considerable bulk to interfere directly with attack at the *p*-position. The failure to couple at this position is, in fact, due to the two methyl groups in the *o*-positions to the NMe_2 interfering sterically with the two methyl groups attached to nitrogen and so preventing these lying in the same plane as the benzene nucleus. This means that the *p* orbitals of nitrogen and the ring carbon atom to which it is attached are prevented from becoming parallel to each other and their overlapping is thus inhibited. Electronic interaction with the nucleus is thus largely prevented and transfer of charge to the *p*-position, with consequent activation to attack by $PhN_2^{\oplus}$ as in (XXXI), does not now take place:

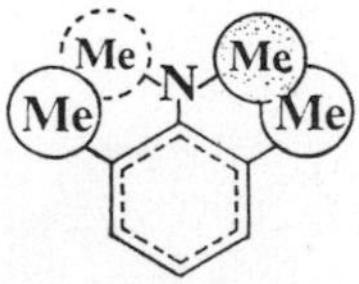

(XXXII)

The most common steric effect, however, is the classical 'steric hindrance' in which it is apparently the sheer bulk of groups that is influencing the reactivity of a site in a compound directly and not by promoting or inhibiting electron-availability. This has been investigated closely in connection with the stability of the complexes formed by trimethylboron with a wide variety of amines. Thus the complex (XXXIII) formed with triethylamine dissociates extremely readily whereas the complex (XXXIV) with quinuclidine, which can be looked upon as having three ethyl groups on nitrogen that are 'held back' from interfering sterically with attack on the nitrogen atom, is very stable:

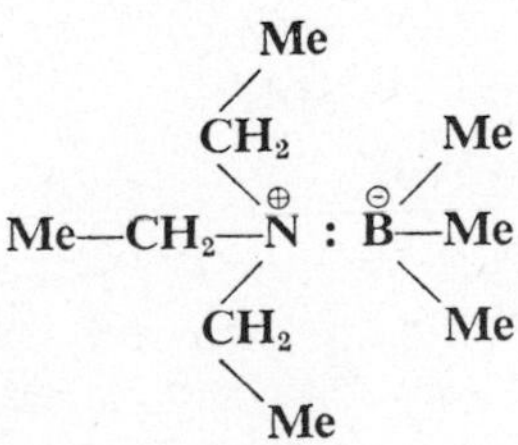

(XXXIII) 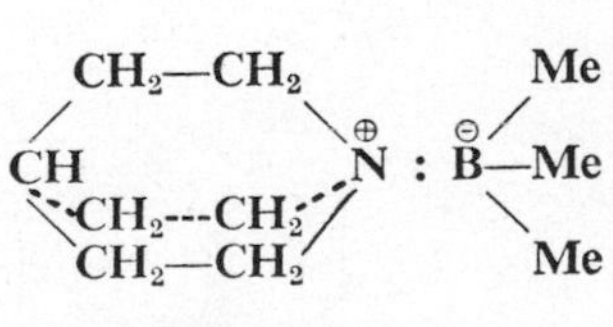   (XXXIV)

That this difference is not due to differing electron availability at the nitrogen atom in the two cases is confirmed by the fact that the two amines differ very little in their strengths as bases (*cf*. p. 56): the uptake of a proton constituting very much less of a steric obstacle than the uptake of the relatively bulky **BMe₃**.

More familiar examples of steric inhibition, however, are probably the difficulties met with in esterifying tertiary acids (XXXV) and 2,6-disubstituted benzoic acids (XXXVI*a*)

$$R_3C \cdot CO_2H$$

(XXXV)   (XXXVI*a*)   (XXXVI*b*)

and then in the hydrolysis of the esters, or other derivatives such as amides, once made. That this effect is indeed steric is suggested by its being much greater in magnitude than can be accounted for by any influence the alkyl substituents might be expected to have on electron availability and also by its non-occurrence in the aromatic species if these substituents are in the *m*- or *p*-positions. Further, if the carboxyl group is moved away from the nucleus by the introduction of a **CH₂** group, the new acid (XXXVI*b*) may now be esterified as readily as the unsubstituted species: the functional group is now beyond the steric range of the methyl substituents.

It should be emphasised that such steric inhibition is only an extreme case and any factors which disturb or inhibit a particular orientation of the reactants with respect to each other, short of preventing their close approach, can also profoundly affect the rate of reactions: a state of affairs that is often encountered in reactions in biological systems.

CLASSIFICATION OF REAGENTS

Reference has already been made to electron-donating and electron-withdrawing groups, their effect being to render a site in a molecule electron-rich or electron-deficient, respectively. This will clearly influence the type of reagent with which the compound will most readily react. An electron-rich compound, such as phenoxide ion, (XXXVII)

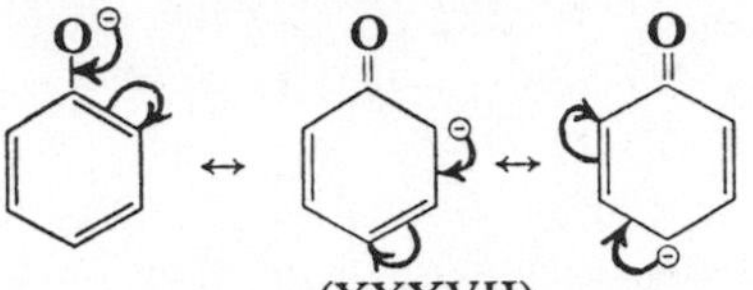

(XXXVII)

will tend to be most readily attacked by positively charged ions such as $PhN_2^{\oplus}$, the diazonium cation, or by other species which, though not actually ions themselves, possess an atom or centre which is electron-deficient, for example the sulphur atom in sulphur trioxide:

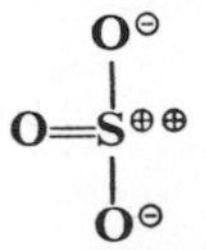

Azo-coupling (p. 112) or sulphonation (p. 108) takes place on a carbon atom of the nucleus rather than on oxygen because of the charge-transfer from oxygen to carbon that can take place as shown above and because of the greater stability of the carbon rather than the oxygen-substituted products.

Conversely, an electron-deficient centre, such as the carbon atom in methyl chloride (XXXVIII)

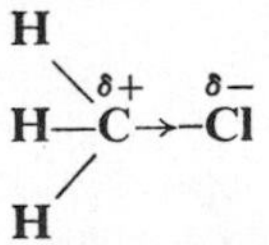

(XXXVIII)

will tend to be most readily attacked by negatively charged ions such as $^{\ominus}OH$, $^{\ominus}CN$, etc., or by other species which, though not actually ions themselves, possess an atom or centre which is electron-rich, for example the nitrogen atom in ammonia or amines, $H_3N:$ or $R_3N:$. It must be emphasised that only a *slightly* unsymmetrical distribution of electrons is required for a reaction's course to be dominated: the presence of a full-blown charge on a reactant certainly helps matters along but is far from being essential. Indeed the requisite unsymmetrical charge distribution may be induced by the mutual polarisation of reagent and substrate on their close approach as when bromine adds to ethylene (p. 137).

In reactions of the first type the reagent is looking for a position in the substrate to be attacked where electrons are especially readily available; such reagents are thus referred to as *electrophilic reagents* or *electrophiles*. In reactions of the second type the reagent is looking for a position where the atomic nucleus is short of its normal complement of orbital electrons and is anxious to make it up; the reagents employed are thus referred to as *nucleophilic reagents* or *nucleophiles*.

This differentiation can be looked upon as a special case of the acid/base idea. The classical definition of acids and bases is that the former are proton-donors and the latter proton-acceptors. This was made more general by Lewis who defined acids as compounds prepared to accept electron pairs and bases as substances that could provide such pairs. This would include a number of compounds not previously thought of as acids and bases, e.g. boron trifluoride (XXXIX)

$$
\begin{array}{cc}
\text{F} \qquad \text{Me} & \text{F} \qquad \text{Me} \\
\diagdown \qquad \diagup & \diagdown \ominus \oplus \diagup \\
\text{F—B} + :\text{N—Me} & \rightleftharpoons \quad \text{F—B:N—Me} \\
\diagup \qquad \diagdown & \diagup \qquad \diagdown \\
\text{F} \qquad \text{Me} & \text{F} \qquad \text{Me} \\
\text{(XXXIX)} & \text{(XL)}
\end{array}
$$

which acts as an acid by accepting the electron pair on nitrogen in trimethylamine to form the complex (XL), and is therefore referred to as a *Lewis acid*. Electrophiles and nucleophiles in organic reactions can be looked upon essentially as acceptors and donors, respectively, of electron pairs from and to other atoms, most frequently *carbon*. Electrophiles and nucleophiles also, of course, bear a relationship to oxidising and reducing agents for the former can be looked upon as electron-acceptors and the latter as electron-donors. A number of the more common electrophiles and nucleophiles are listed below.

Electrophiles

$H^{\oplus}$, $H_3O^{\oplus}$, HNO_3, H_2SO_4, HNO_2 (i.e. $^{\oplus}NO_2$, SO_3 and $^{\oplus}NO$ respectively), $PhN_2^{\oplus}$

BF_3, $AlCl_3$, $ZnCl_2$, $FeCl_3$, Br_2, $\overset{*}{I}$—Cl, $\overset{*}{N}O$—Cl, $\overset{*}{C}N$—Cl

$$
\underset{*}{>}C=O, \quad R-\overset{\overset{\displaystyle O}{\|}}{\underset{*}{C}}-Cl, \quad R-\overset{\overset{\displaystyle O}{\|}}{\underset{*}{C}}-O-\overset{\overset{\displaystyle O}{\|}}{C}-R, \quad \underset{*}{C}O_2
$$

Nucleophiles

$HO^\ominus, RO^\ominus, RS^\ominus, Hal^\ominus, HSO_3^\ominus, {}^\ominus CN, R \cdot C \equiv C^\ominus, {}^\ominus CH(CO_2Et)_2$

(XLI)

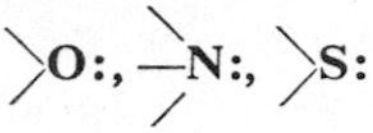

$$\rangle O:, \ —\!N:, \ \rangle S:$$

$R \cdot MgBr, \ RLi, \ LiAl\overset{*}{H}_4, \ *\langle\rangle\!-\!O^\ominus$

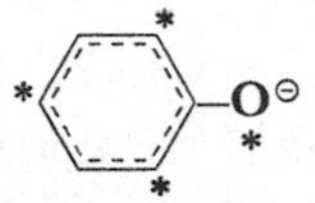

Where a reagent is starred, the star indicates the atom that accepts electrons from, or donates electrons to, the substrate as the case may be. It rapidly becomes apparent that no clear distinction can be made between what constitutes a reagent and what a substrate, for though HNO_3, ${}^\ominus OH$, etc., are normally thought of as reagents, the diethyl malonate carbanion (XLI) could, at will, be either reagent or substrate, when reacted with, for example, an alkyl halide. The reaction of the former on the latter is a nucleophilic attack, while that of the latter on the former would be looked upon as an electrophilic attack; but from the standpoint of whichever reactant a reaction itself is viewed, its essential nature is not for a moment in doubt.

It should not be forgotten, however, that reactions involving free radicals as the reactive entities are also known. These are much less susceptible to variations in electron density in the substrate than are reactions involving polar intermediates, but they are greatly affected by the addition of small traces of substances that either liberate or remove radicals. They are considered in detail below (p. 240).

TYPES OF REACTION

Within this classification there are essentially four kinds of reaction which organic compounds can undergo:

(*a*) Displacement (or substitution) reactions.
(*b*) Addition reactions.
(*c*) Elimination reactions.
(*d*) Rearrangements.

In (*a*) it is displacement from carbon that is normally referred to but the atom displaced can be either hydrogen or another atom or group. In electrophilic substitution reactions it is often hydrogen that is

27

displaced, classical aromatic substitution (p. 101) being a good example:

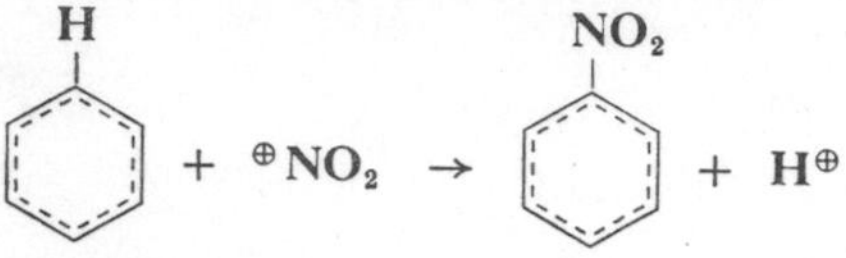

$$\text{[benzene with H]} + {}^{\oplus}NO_2 \rightarrow \text{[benzene with } NO_2\text{]} + H^{\oplus}$$

In nucleophilic substitution reactions, it is often an atom other than hydrogen that is displaced (pp. 58, 132):

$$NC^{\ominus} + R\text{—}Br \rightarrow NC\text{—}R + Br^{\ominus}$$

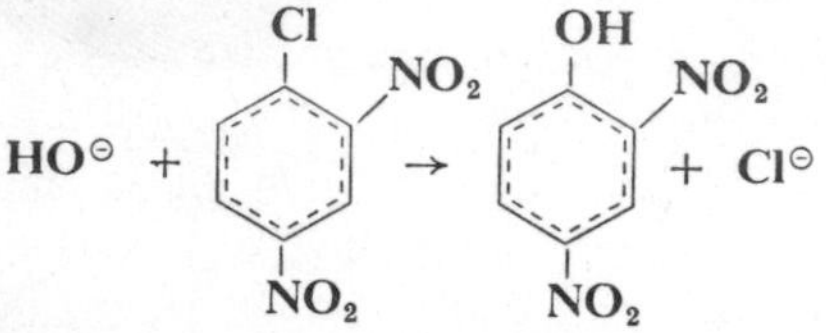

$$HO^{\ominus} + \text{[benzene with Cl, } NO_2, NO_2\text{]} \rightarrow \text{[benzene with OH, } NO_2, NO_2\text{]} + Cl^{\ominus}$$

but nucleophilic displacement of hydrogen is also known (p. 130)

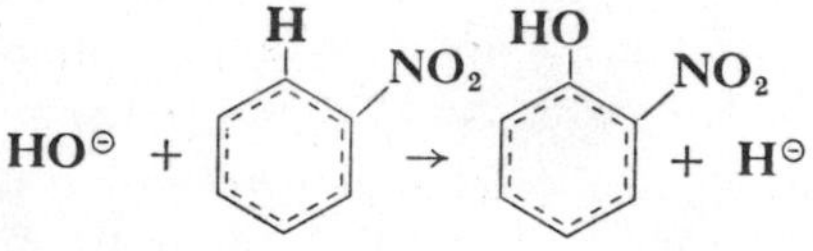

$$HO^{\ominus} + \text{[benzene with H, } NO_2\text{]} \rightarrow \text{[benzene with HO, } NO_2\text{]} + H^{\ominus}$$

though hydride ion is not actually liberated as such as will be seen subsequently (p. 131). Radical-induced displacement reactions are also known, for example the halogenation of alkanes (*cf.* p. 248).

Addition reactions, too, can be electrophilic, nucleophilic or radical-induced depending on whether the process is initiated by an electrophile, a nucleophile or a radical. Addition to simple carbon-carbon double bonds is normally either an electrophilic or radical reaction; an example is the addition of **HBr**

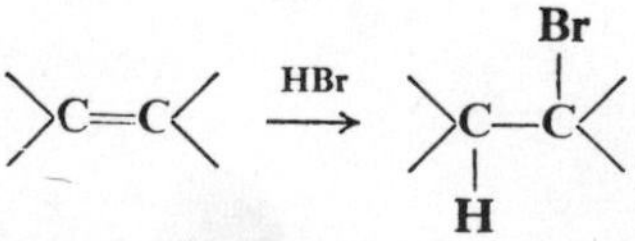

$$\text{>C=C<} \xrightarrow{\text{HBr}} \text{>C—C<} \text{ (Br, H)}$$

which can be initiated by the attack of either $H^{\oplus}$ (p. 141) or $Br\cdot$ (p. 244) on the double bond. By contrast, the addition reactions exhibited by the carbonyl group in simple aldehydes and ketones are usually nucleophilic in character (p. 158). An example is the base-catalysed formation of cyanhydrins in liquid **HCN**:

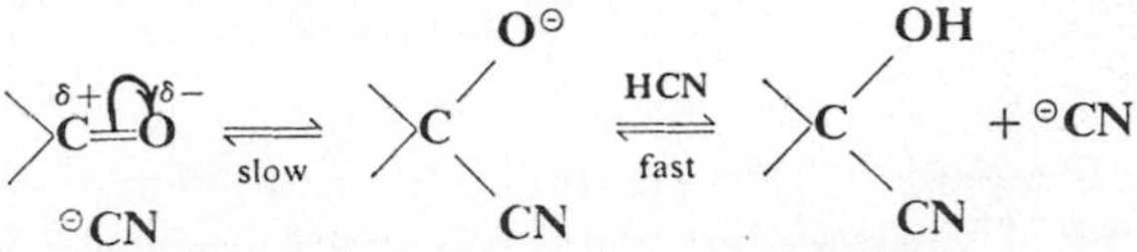

$$\underset{\ominus CN}{\overset{\delta+\quad\delta-}{>C=O}} \underset{slow}{\rightleftharpoons} \underset{CN}{>C}\overset{O^{\ominus}}{\diagup} \underset{fast}{\overset{HCN}{\rightleftharpoons}} \underset{CN}{>C}\overset{OH}{\diagup} + {}^{\ominus}CN$$

Elimination reactions are, of course, essentially the reversal of addition reactions; the most common is the loss of atoms or groups from adjacent carbon atoms to yield olefines:

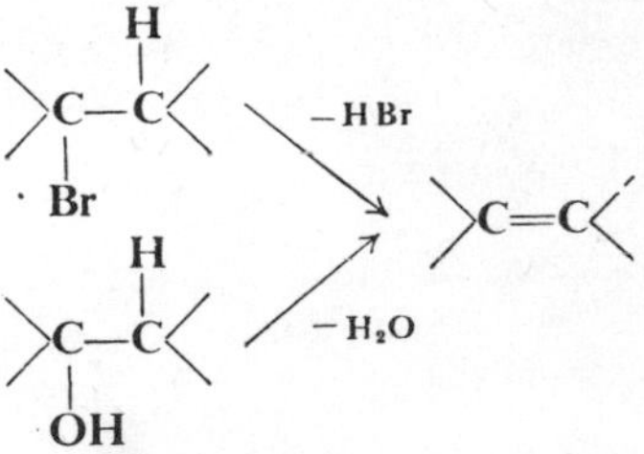

$$\begin{array}{c} >C-C< \\ \cdot \ Br \end{array} \quad \overset{-HBr}{\searrow} \quad >C=C< \\ \begin{array}{c} >C-C< \\ OH \end{array} \quad \overset{-H_2O}{\nearrow}$$

Rearrangements may also proceed via electrophilic, nucleophilic or radical intermediates and can involve either the mere migration of a functional group (p. 86) as in the allylic system

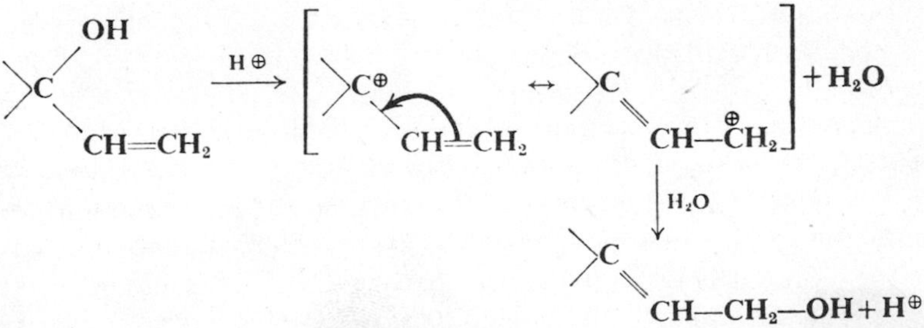

$$>C\overset{OH}{\diagdown}_{CH=CH_2} \xrightarrow{H\oplus} \left[>C^{\oplus}\diagdown_{CH=CH_2} \leftrightarrow >C\diagdown_{CH-\overset{\oplus}{C}H_2} \right] + H_2O$$

$$\downarrow H_2O$$

$$>C\diagdown_{CH-CH_2-OH} + H^{\oplus}$$

or the actual rearrangement of the carbon skeleton of a compound as in the pinacol (XLII) → pinacolone (XLIII) change (p. 90):

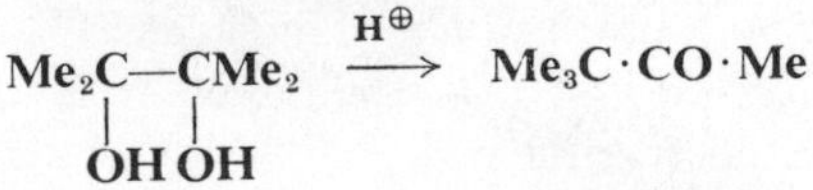

$$\underset{\underset{OH\ OH}{|\quad|}}{Me_2C-CMe_2} \xrightarrow{H^{\oplus}} Me_3C\cdot CO\cdot Me$$

$$(XLII) \qquad\qquad (XLIII)$$

29

The actual rearrangement step is often followed by a displacement, addition or elimination reaction before a final, stable product is obtained.

ENERGETICS OF REACTION

The general path followed by the reactants in an organic reaction as they are converted into products is normally too complex to be followed in complete detail, but useful comments can be made on the sequence of changes involved, and particularly on their energetics. Broadly speaking, reactions proceed most readily when the products constitute a more stable state than the original reactants, the difference being the *free energy of reaction*, ΔF; nevertheless it is seldom, if ever, that the change involves, energetically, a mere direct run downhill (XLIV): the more usual picture is that an 'energy hump' has to be surmounted on the way (XLV):

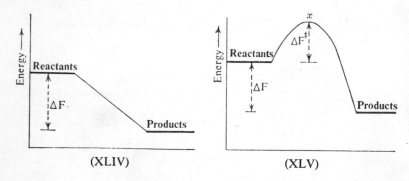

(XLIV)   (XLV)

The horizontal co-ordinate in the above diagrams, often called the *reaction co-ordinate*, need have no exact quantitative significance and merely represents the sequence of the reaction. It will be seen that in order for reaction to proceed in (XLV), energy will have to be supplied to the reactants in order to carry them over the hump. This energy is required, essentially, to stretch and ultimately to break any bonds as may be necessary in the reactants. This proceeds more readily in molecules that have absorbed energy and so become activated; the well-known increase in reaction rates as the temperature is raised, is indeed, due to the larger proportion of molecules in an activated state as the temperature rises. A probability factor is also involved as molecules, although activated, will often only react with each other if they are in a particular orientation or configuration and only a certain proportion of the activated molecules will satisfy this condition. In addition to the straightforward energy term, an *entropy* factor is also involved expressing essentially the relative randomness, and hence probability, of the initial and final states of the reaction, i.e. of reactants and products. The amount of work necessary to get the reactants up the top of the hump, including both the energetic and probability factors, is called the *free energy of activation*, $\Delta F^{\ddagger}$.

The top of the energy hump, x, corresponds to the least stable configuration through which the reactants pass on their way to products and this is generally referred to as the *transition state* or *activated complex*. It should be emphasised that this is merely a state that is passed through in a dynamic process and the transition state is *not* an intermediate that can actually be isolated. A typical transition state is (XLVI) met with in the alkaline hydrolysis of methyl iodide

$$HO^{\ominus} + H\text{-}C\text{-}I \ \rightarrow \ \left[\begin{array}{c} H \quad H \\ \overset{\delta-}{HO}\text{----}C\text{----}\overset{\delta-}{I} \\ H \end{array} \right] \ \rightarrow \ HO\text{-}C\text{-}H + I^{\ominus}$$

(XLVI)

in which the C—OH bond is being formed before the C—I bond is completely broken and the three hydrogen atoms are passing through a configuration in which they all lie in one plane (at right angles to the plane of the paper). This reaction is discussed in detail below (p. 66).

It will be realised from what has already been said that in discussing the influence of structural factors, both electronic and steric, on the reactivity of compounds, it is more pertinent to consider what effect these factors will have on the *transition state* in a reaction rather than on the ground state of the reactant molecule. For any factor that serves to stabilise the transition state, i.e. to lower its energy content, lowers $\Delta F^{\ddagger}$ (the height of the hump that has to be surmounted) and so offers an easier and less demanding path for the reaction to traverse. It is at this point that the time-variable, i.e. polarisability factors (p. 19), consequent on the close approach of reagent and substrate, may exert their most potent, and possibly determining, effect on the course of a reaction. Steric effects are also of the utmost significance at this point, for a transition state in which the groups are highly crowded will be notably loth to form and the reaction, therefore, rendered that much more difficult and, hence, less likely to proceed. The exact nature of the transition state is not always known with certainty, however, and the influence of structural factors on reactivity can then only be considered, less satisfactorily, with reference to the original reactant molecule.

Many common reactions are, however, less simple than this, proceeding not through a single transition state as in (XLV) but involving the formation of one, or more, actual intermediates as in the two-stage process (XLVII):

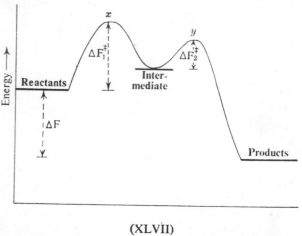

(XLVII)

This is essentially two separate reactions, reactants → intermediate with a free energy of activation of $\Delta F_1^{\ddagger}$ and intermediate → products, with $\Delta F_2^{\ddagger}$; the free energy of the overall reaction being ΔF. The stage with the higher free energy of activation—the first, with $\Delta F_1^{\ddagger}$ in the above case—will usually be the slower and, therefore, *rate-determining* step of the overall reaction, for clearly the overall reaction cannot proceed more rapidly than its slowest stage and it will be this that will be measured in a kinetic investigation of the overall reaction. The degree of real difference between an activated complex and an actual intermediate depends on the depth of the dip or energy minimum characterising the latter. If it is sufficiently pronounced the intermediate may actually be isolated as in the Hofmann reaction, in which salts of the anion (XLVIII) may be recovered during the conversion of an N-bromoamide to an isocyanate (*cf.* p. 93):

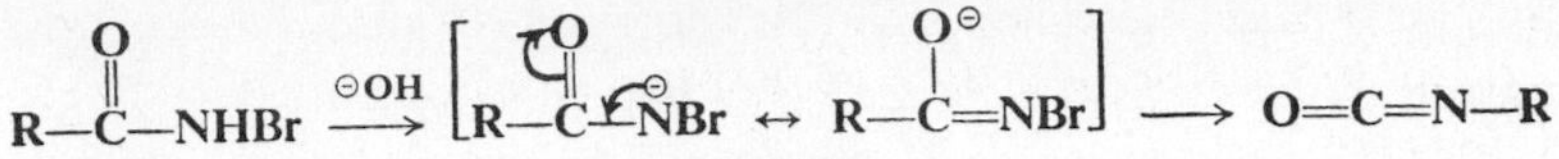

$$R\overset{\text{O}}{\overset{\|}{-}C}-NHBr \xrightarrow{\ominus OH} \left[R\overset{\text{O}}{-}C\overset{\ominus}{=}NBr \leftrightarrow R\overset{\text{O}^{\ominus}}{-}C=NBr \right] \longrightarrow O=C=N-R$$

(XLVIII)

But as the minimum becomes less marked, the intermediate will become correspondingly less stable (*b*) and, therefore, less likely to be isolable until finally the minimum is indistinguishable (*c*), when transition state and intermediate become synonymous (XLIX):

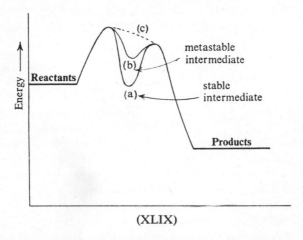

(XLIX)

It should, however, be emphasised that we are not forced to rely on actual isolation—which is a relatively rare occurrence—for the identification of an intermediate. Physical, particularly spectroscopic, methods supply us with a very effective and delicate alternative which has proved immensely helpful in the investigation of reaction mechanisms.

INVESTIGATION OF REACTION MECHANISMS

It is seldom, if ever, possible to provide complete and entire information about the course that is traversed by any chemical reaction: too much is involved. Sufficient data can nevertheless often be gathered to show that one theoretically possible mechanism is just not compatible with the experimental results, or to demonstrate that one mechanism is a good deal more likely than another. The largest body of work has certainly come from kinetic studies on reactions, but the interpretation of kinetic data in mechanistic terms is not always quite as simple as might, at first sight, be supposed. Thus in a very simple case, if the aqueous hydrolysis of the alkyl halide, $R \cdot Hal$, is found to follow the kinetics

$$\text{Rate} \propto [R \cdot Hal]$$

it is not safe to conclude that the rate-determining step does *not* involve the participation of water because $[H_2O]$ does not figure in the rate equation, for if water is being used as the solvent its concentration would remain virtually unchanged whether or not it actually participated in the reaction. Its participation might be revealed by carrying out the hydrolysis with only a small concentration of water in another solvent; then the hydrolysis may be found to follow the kinetics

$$\text{Rate} \propto [R \cdot Hal]\ [H_2O]$$

but the actual mechanism by which the reaction proceeds may have changed on altering the environment, so that we are not, of necessity, any the wiser about what *really* went on in the aqueous solution to begin with!

The vast majority of organic reactions are carried out in solution and quite small changes in the solvent used can have the profoundest effects on reaction rates and mechanisms. Particularly is this so when ionic intermediates, for example carbonium ions and carbanions, are involved for such ions normally carry an envelope of solvent molecules about with them, which greatly affects their stability (and hence their ease of formation), and which is highly influenced by the composition and nature of the solvent employed.

Light may be thrown on reaction mechanisms from sources other than kinetic experiments, however. Thus a study of alternative or by-products in a reaction can often be of value. A case in point is the elimination reaction (p. 189) that often accompanies a substitution reaction (p. 201) in the action of alkali on alkyl halides and which can be interpreted in some instances as involving a carbonium ion (L) as a common intermediate:

$$R \cdot CH_2 \cdot CH_2 \cdot Hal \rightarrow Hal^\ominus + R \cdot CH_2 \cdot \overset{\oplus}{C}H_2$$
$$\text{(L)}$$

$H_2O \nearrow \quad R \cdot CH_2 \cdot CH_2 \cdot OH + H^\oplus \quad$ *Substitution*

$-H^\oplus \searrow \quad R \cdot CH = CH_2 \quad$ *Elimination*

In some cases, for example the Hofmann reaction mentioned above, intermediates can actually be isolated, but where this is not possible, various potential intermediates can be introduced into the reaction to see whether any of them will speed it up, as a true intermediate in the process should. Alternatively, another species of molecule may be introduced into the system in an endeavour to fix or trap a transient intermediate. An example of this is provided in reactions proceeding via radical intermediates where, by introducing an olefine into the system, the radical intermediate induces polymerisation of the olefine and is itself thereby fixed at the end of the polymer chain (*cf.* p. 247):

$$Ra\cdot + CH_2{=}CH_2 \rightarrow Ra{-}CH_2{-}CH_2\cdot \xrightarrow{nCH_2=CH_2} \text{Polymer}$$

The use of isotopes has also shed a good deal of light on a number of difficult mechanistic problems. Thus the aqueous hydrolysis of esters could proceed, in theory, by cleavage at (*a*)—alkyl/oxygen cleavage, or (*b*)—acyl/oxygen cleavage:

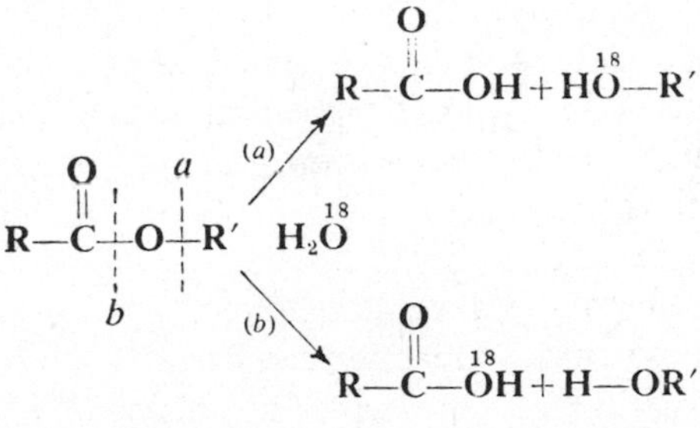

If the reaction is carried out in water enriched in the isotope ^{18}O, (*a*) will lead to an alcohol which is ^{18}O enriched and an acid which is not, while (*b*) will lead to an ^{18}O enriched acid but a normal alcohol. Most esters are found to yield an ^{18}O enriched acid indicating that hydrolysis, under these conditions, proceeds via acyl/oxygen cleavage. It should, of course, be emphasised that these results only have validity provided neither acid nor alcohol can, after formation, itself exchange oxygen with water enriched in ^{18}O, as has in fact been shown to be the case. Heavy water, D_2O, has been much used in a rather similar way, especially to investigate whether particular hydrogen atoms participate in a given reaction. Thus in the Cannizzaro reaction with benzaldehyde (p. 167)

$$\underset{H_2O}{\overset{\ominus OH}{\longrightarrow}}$$

Ph—C—H + Ph—C—H $\overset{\ominus OH}{\underset{H_2O}{\longrightarrow}}$ Ph—C—O$^\ominus$ + Ph—C—OH

the question arises of whether the second hydrogen atom that becomes attached to carbon in the benzyl alcohol formed comes from the solvent (water) or from a second molecule of benzaldehyde. Carrying out the reaction in D_2O leads to the formation of *no* **Ph·CHD·OH**, indicating that the second hydrogen could not have come from the solvent and must, therefore, arise by direct transfer from a second molecule of aldehyde.

Compounds suitably 'labelled' with deuterium, or the radioactive hydrogen isotope tritium, have also been used to decide whether a particular **C—H** bond is broken during the rate-determining stage of a reaction. Thus in the nitration of nitrobenzene (p. 105)

$$O_2N \cdot C_6H_4 {-} H \overset{\oplus NO_2}{\longrightarrow} O_2N \cdot C_6H_4 \cdot NO_2 + H^\oplus$$

a **C—H** bond is broken and a **C—NO$_2$** bond formed, and the question arises whether either or both processes are involved in the rate-determining step of the reaction. Repeating the nitration on deuterium- and tritium-labelled nitrobenzene shows that there is no detectable difference in the rate at which the three compounds react, thus indicating that **C—H** bond fission cannot be involved in the rate-determining step as it can be shown that if it were there would be a considerable slowing in reaction rate on going **C—H → C—D → C—³H** (*kinetic isotope effect*).

Another technique that has been of the utmost value is observing the stereochemical course followed by a number of chemical reactions. Thus the addition of bromine, and a number of other reagents, to suitable olefines has been found to yield *trans* products

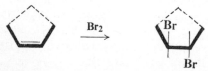

indicating that the bromine cannot add on directly as **Br—Br** for this would clearly lead to a *cis* product. The prevalence of *trans* addition reactions also provides further information about the mechanism of the reactions (p. 139). Many elimination reactions also take place more readily with the *trans* member of a pair of *cis/trans* isomerides, as seen in the conversion of *syn* and *anti* aldoxime acetates to nitriles:

$$
\begin{array}{ccc}
\underset{\substack{\diagup \\ \text{Me·CO·O}}}{\overset{\substack{\text{Ph} \qquad \text{H} \\ \diagdown \diagup \\ \text{C} \\ \| \\ \text{N:} }}{}}
& \underset{\substack{\text{easily}}}{\overset{\ominus \text{OH}}{\longrightarrow}} \quad \overset{\text{Ph}}{\underset{\text{N}}{\overset{|}{\underset{\|}{\text{C}}}}} \quad \underset{\substack{\text{less} \\ \text{readily}}}{\overset{\ominus \text{OH}}{\longleftarrow}}
& \overset{\substack{\text{Ph} \qquad \text{H} \\ \diagdown \diagup \\ \text{C} \\ \| \\ :\text{N} \diagdown \\ \text{O·OC·Me}}}{}
\end{array}
$$

Anti   Syn

This again sets limitations to which any mechanism advanced for the reaction will have to conform.

A study of the fate of asymmetric centres in optically active compounds has also been of great value, particularly in the case of nucleophilic substitution at a saturated carbon atom, for example, in the hydrolysis of alkyl halides (p. 66). Thus reaction via the type of transition state that we have already mentioned (XLVI, p. 31), will lead to a product having the opposite configuration to the starting material as the asymmetric centre will have been 'turned inside out':

$$
\text{HO}^{\ominus} + \text{R}' \!\!\overset{\text{R}}{\underset{\text{R}''}{\text{C}}}\!\!-\!\text{I} \;\rightarrow\; \left[\begin{array}{c} \text{R}' \qquad \text{R} \\ \delta^- \quad \diagdown \quad \delta^- \\ \text{HO}\text{-----}\text{C}\text{-----}\text{I} \\ | \\ \text{R}'' \end{array} \right] \;\rightarrow\; \text{HO}\!-\!\overset{\text{R}}{\underset{\text{R}''}{\text{C}}}\!\!\blacktriangleleft\text{R}' + \text{I}^{\ominus}
$$

This establishes a test by which the occurrence of this type of mechanism may be detected (p. 66).

The degree of success with which a suggested mechanism can be said to describe the course of a particular reaction is not determined solely by its ability to account for the known facts; the acid test is how successful it is at forecasting a change of rate, or even in the nature of the products formed, when the conditions under which the reaction is carried out or the structure of the substrate are changed. Some of the suggested mechanisms we shall encounter measure up to these criteria better than do others, but the overall success of a mechanistic approach to organic reactions is demonstrated by the way in which the application of a few relatively simple guiding principles can bring light and order to bear on a vast mass of disparate information about equilibria, reaction rates and the relative reactivity of organic compounds. We shall now go on to consider some simple examples of this.

2 THE STRENGTHS OF ACIDS AND BASES

MODERN electronic theories of organic chemistry have been highly successful in a wide variety of fields in relating behaviour with structure, but nowhere has this been more marked than in accounting for the relative strengths of organic acids and bases. According to the definition of Arrhenius, acids are compounds that yield hydrogen ions, $H^{\oplus}$, in solution while bases yield hydroxide ions, $^{\ominus}OH$. Such definitions are reasonably adequate if reactions in water only are to be considered, but the acid/base relationship has proved so useful in practice that the concepts of both acids and bases have become considerably more generalised. Thus Brønsted defined acids as substances that would give up protons, i.e. *proton donors*, while bases were *proton acceptors*. The first ionisation of sulphuric acid in aqueous solution is then looked upon as:

$$H_2SO_4 + H_2O \rightleftharpoons H_3O^{\oplus} + HSO_4^{\ominus}$$

Acid	*Base*	*Con-jugate acid*	*Con-jugate base*

Here water is acting as a base by accepting a proton and is thereby converted into its so-called *conjugate acid*, $H_3O^{\oplus}$, while the acid, H_2SO_4, by donating a proton is converted into its *conjugate base*, $HSO_4^{\ominus}$.

The more generalised picture provided by Lewis who defined acids as molecules or ions capable of co-ordinating with unshared electron pairs, and bases as molecules or ions which have such unshared electron pairs available for co-ordination, has already been referred to (p. 26). Lewis acids include such species as boron trifluoride (I) which reacts with trimethylamine to form a solid salt (m.p. 128°):

$$
\begin{array}{ccc}
\text{Me} & \text{F} & \text{Me F} \\
| & | & \overset{\oplus}{|} \quad \overset{\ominus}{|} \\
\text{Me—N:} & \text{B—F} & \rightleftharpoons \quad \text{Me—N:B—F} \\
| & | & | \quad | \\
\text{Me} & \text{F} & \text{Me F}
\end{array}
$$

(I)

38

Other common examples are aluminium chloride, stannic chloride, zinc chloride, etc. We shall, at this point, be concerned essentially with proton acids and the effect of structure on the strength of a number of organic acids and bases will now be considered in turn. Compounds in which a C—H bond is ionised will be considered subsequently (p. 210), however.

ACIDS

(i) pK_a

The strength of an acid, HX, in water, i.e. the extent to which it is dissociated, may be estimated by considering the equilibrium:

$$H_2O: + HX \rightleftharpoons H_3O^\oplus + X^\ominus$$

Then the equilibrium constant is given by

$$K_a \approx \frac{[H_3O^\oplus][X^\ominus]}{[HX]}$$

the concentration of water being taken as constant as it is present in such large excess. It should be emphasised that K_a, the *acidity constant* of the acid in water, is only approximate if concentrations instead of activities have been used. The constant is influenced by the composition of the solvent in which the acid is dissolved (see below) and by other factors but it does, nevertheless, serve as a useful guide to acid strength. In order to avoid writing negative powers of 10, K_a is generally converted into pK_a (p$K_a = -\log_{10} K_a$); thus while K_a for acetic acid in water at 25° is $1 \cdot 79 \times 10^{-5}$, p$K_a = 4 \cdot 76$. The *smaller* the numerical value of pK_a, the *stronger* is the acid to which it refers.

(ii) Effect of solvent

The influence of the solvent on the dissociation of acids (and of bases) can be profound; thus hydrogen chloride which is a strong acid in water is not ionised in benzene. Water is a most effective ionising solvent on account (*a*) of its high dielectric constant, and (*b*) of its ion-solvating ability. The higher the dielectric constant of a solvent the smaller the electrostatic energy of any ions present in it; hence the more stable such ions are in solution.

Ions in solution strongly polarise solvent molecules near them and the greater the extent to which this can take place, the greater the stability of the ion, which is in effect stabilising itself by spreading its charge. Water is extremely readily polarised and ions stabilise themselves in solution by collecting around themselves a solvation envelope of water molecules.

Water has the advantage of being able to function as an acid or a base with equal facility, which further increases its usefulness and versatility as an ionising solvent. It does however have the disadvantage as an ionising solvent for organic compounds that some of them are insufficiently soluble in the unionised form to dissolve in it in the first place.

(iii) The origin of acidity in organic compounds

Acidity in an organic compound, **YH**, may be influenced by

(*a*) The strength of the **Y—H** bond,
(*b*) The electronegativity of **Y**,
(*c*) Factors stabilizing **Y**$^\ominus$ compared with **YH**,

but of these (*a*) is normally found to be of little significance. The effect of (*b*) is reflected in the fact that the **pK_a** of methanol, **CH$_3$O—H**, is ≈ 16 while that of methane, **H$_3$C—H**, is ≈ 50, oxygen being considerably more electronegative than carbon. By contrast, the **pK_a** of formic acid,

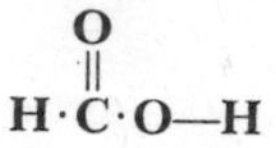

$$\overset{\displaystyle O}{\underset{\displaystyle H \cdot C \cdot O—H}{\|}}$$

is $3 \cdot 77$. This is in part due to the electron-withdrawing carbonyl group enhancing the electron affinity of the oxygen atom to which the incipient proton is attached but much more important is the stabilisation possible in the resultant formate anion compared with the undissociated formic acid molecule:

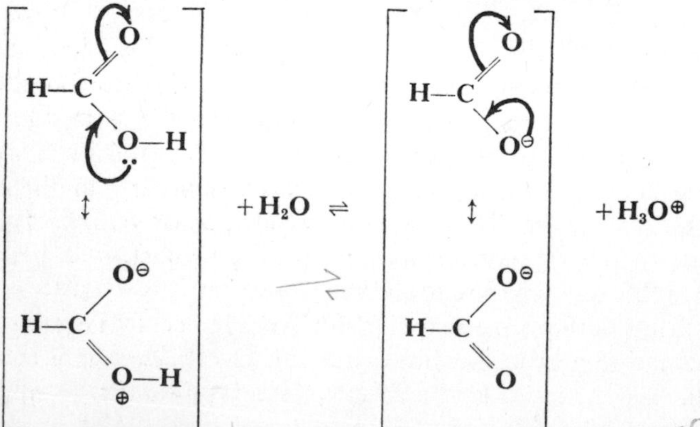

[handwritten margin notes:] carboxylic acids

[handwritten note below left structure:] not as stabilized due to seperation of charge

[handwritten note below right structure:] resonance stabilized

[handwritten note bottom right:] good acid Y$^\ominus$ more stable than Y

There is extremely effective delocalisation, with consequent stabilisation, in the formate anion involving as it does two canonical structures of identical energy and though delocalisation can take place in the formic acid molecule also, this involves separation of charge and will consequently be much less effective as a stabilising influence (*cf.* p. 12). The effect of this differential stabilisation is somewhat to discourage the recombination of proton with the formate anion, the ⇌ is to this extent displaced to the right, and formic acid is, by organic standards, a moderately strong acid.

With alcohols there is no such factor stabilising the alkoxide ion, $RO^{\ominus}$, relative to the alcohol itself and alcohols are thus very much less acidic than carboxylic acids. With phenols, however, there is again the possibility of relative stabilisation of the anion (II) by delocalisation of its negative charge through interaction with the π orbitals of the aromatic nucleus:

(II)

Delocalisation also occurs in the undissociated phenol molecule (*cf.* p. 17) but, involving charge separation, is less effective than in the anion (II), thus leading to some reluctance on the part of the latter to recombine with a proton. Phenols are indeed found to be stronger acids than alcohols (the pK_a of phenol itself is $9 \cdot 95$) but considerably weaker than carboxylic acids. This is due to the fact that delocalisation of the negative charge in the carboxylate anion involves structures of identical energy content (see above), and of the centres involved two are highly electronegative oxygen atoms; whereas in the phenoxide ion (II) the structures involving negative charge on the nuclear carbon atoms are likely to be of higher energy content than the one in which it is on oxygen and, in addition, of the centres here involved only one is a highly electronegative oxygen atom. The relative stabilisation of the anion with respect to the undissociated molecule is thus likely to be less effective with a phenol than with a carboxylic acid leading to the lower relative acidity of the former.

(iv) Simple aliphatic acids

The replacement of the non-hydroxylic hydrogen atom of formic acid by an alkyl group would be expected to produce a weaker acid as the electron-donating inductive effect of the alkyl group will reduce the residual electron affinity of the oxygen atom carrying the incipient proton and so reduce the strength of the acid. In the anion the increased electron availability on oxygen will serve to promote its recombination with proton as compared with the formate/formic acid system:

$$\left[Me \rightarrow C \begin{array}{c} O \\ O \end{array} \right]^{\ominus} < \left[H - C \begin{array}{c} O \\ O \end{array} \right]^{\ominus}$$

The $\rightleftharpoons$ is thus shifted to the left compared with formic acid/formate and it is found that the pK_a of acetic acid is $4 \cdot 76$, compared with $3 \cdot 77$ for formic acid. Further substitution of alkyl groups in acetic acid has much less effect than this first introduction and, being now essentially a second-order effect, the influence on acid strength is not always regular, steric and other influences also playing a part; pK_a values are observed as follows:

$$Me_2CH \cdot CO_2H \qquad Me_3C \cdot CO_2H$$
$$4 \cdot 86 \qquad\qquad 5 \cdot 05$$

$$CH_3 \cdot CO_2H \quad Me \cdot CH_2 \cdot CO_2H$$
$$4 \cdot 76 \qquad\quad 4 \cdot 88$$

$$Me \cdot (CH_2)_2 \cdot CO_2H \quad Me \cdot (CH_2)_3 \cdot CO_2H$$
$$4 \cdot 82 \qquad\qquad\quad 4 \cdot 86.$$

If there is a doubly bonded carbon atom adjacent to the carboxyl group the acid strength is increased. Thus acrylic acid, $CH_2{=}CH \cdot CO_2H$, has a pK_a of $4 \cdot 25$ compared with $4 \cdot 88$ for the saturated analogue, propionic acid. This is due to the fact that the unsaturated α-carbon atom is sp^2 hybridised, which means that electrons are drawn closer to the carbon nucleus than in a saturated, sp^3 hybridised atom due to the rather larger s contribution in the sp^2 hybrid. The result is that sp^2 hybridised carbon atoms are less electron donating than saturated sp^3 hybridised ones, and so acrylic acid though still weaker than formic acid is stronger than propionic. The effect is much more marked with the sp^1 hybridised carbon atom of a triple bond, thus the pK_a of propiolic acid, $HC{\equiv}C \cdot CO_2H$, is $1 \cdot 84$. An analogous situation occurs with the hydrogen atoms of ethylene and acetylene; those of the former are little more acidic than the hydrogens in ethane, whereas those of acetylene are sufficiently acidic to be readily replaceable by a number of metals.

(v) Substituted aliphatic acids

The effect of introducing electron-withdrawing substituents into fatty acids is more marked. Thus halogen, with an inductive effect acting in the opposite direction to alkyl, would be expected to increase the strength of an acid so substituted, and this is indeed observed as pK_a values show:

$$CH_3 \rightarrow -CO_2H$$
$$4 \cdot 76$$

$$F \leftarrow CH_2 \leftarrow CO_2H$$
$$2 \cdot 66$$

$$Cl \leftarrow CH_2 \leftarrow CO_2H$$
$$2 \cdot 86$$

$$Br \leftarrow CH_2 \leftarrow CO_2H$$
$$2 \cdot 90$$

$$I \leftarrow CH_2 \leftarrow CO_2H$$
$$3 \cdot 16$$

$$\begin{array}{c} Cl \\ \nwarrow \\ CH \leftarrow CO_2H \\ \nearrow \\ Cl \end{array}$$
$$1 \cdot 29$$

$$\begin{array}{c} Cl \\ | \\ Cl \leftarrow C \leftarrow CO_2H \\ | \\ Cl \end{array}$$
$$0 \cdot 65$$

The action of this effect results in increased stabilisation of the substituted anion, by spreading of its charge,

acidity

$$\left[F \leftarrow CH_2 \leftarrow C \underset{O}{\overset{O}{\diagdown}} \right]^{\ominus} \ggg \left[CH_3 \rightarrow C \underset{O}{\overset{O}{\diagdown}} \right]^{\ominus}$$

F pulls e's away from Oxy. leaving more positive Oxy. which readily drops Hyd. proton (H⁺)

and the halogenated acids are thus stronger than their unsubstituted analogues. The relative effect of the different halogens is in the expected order, fluorine being the most electronegative (electron-withdrawing) and producing a hundredfold increase in strength of fluoracetic acid as compared with acetic acid itself. The effect is very much greater than that produced, in the opposite direction, by the introduction of an alkyl group, and the introduction of further halogens still produces large increases in acid strength: trichloracetic is thus a very strong acid.

The introduction of a halogen further away than in the α-position to the carboxyl group has much less effect, its inductive effect quickly dying in a saturated chain as the following pK_a values show:

$$Me \cdot CH_2 \cdot CH_2 \cdot CO_2H \qquad Me \cdot CH_2 \cdot CHCl \cdot CO_2H$$
$$4 \cdot 82 \qquad\qquad\qquad 2 \cdot 84$$

$$Me \cdot CHCl \cdot CH_2 \cdot CO_2H \qquad CH_2Cl \cdot CH_2 \cdot CH_2 \cdot CO_2H$$
$$4 \cdot 06 \qquad\qquad\qquad 4 \cdot 52$$

Other electron-withdrawing groups, e.g. $R_3\overset{\oplus}{N}-$, $-CN$, $-NO_2$, $>CO$, $-CO_2R$ increase the strength of fatty acids, as also do hydroxyl and methoxyl groups; the unshared electrons on the oxygen atoms of the last two groups are not able to exert a mesomeric effect in the opposite direction to their inductive effect owing to the intervening saturated carbon atom. These effects are seen in the pK_a values:

$$O_2N \leftarrow CH_2 \leftarrow CO_2H \qquad\qquad EtO_2C \leftarrow CH_2 \leftarrow CO_2H$$
$$1 \cdot 68 \qquad\qquad\qquad\qquad 3 \cdot 35$$

$$Me_3\overset{\oplus}{N} \leftarrow CH_2 \leftarrow CO_2H \qquad\qquad Me \cdot CO \leftarrow CH_2 \leftarrow CO_2H$$
$$1 \cdot 83 \qquad\qquad\qquad\qquad 3 \cdot 58$$

$$NC \leftarrow CH_2 \leftarrow CO_2H \qquad\qquad Me\overset{\cdot\cdot}{O} \leftarrow CH_2 \leftarrow CO_2H$$
$$2 \cdot 47 \qquad\qquad\qquad\qquad 3 \cdot 53$$

$$H\overset{\cdot\cdot}{O} \leftarrow CH_2 \leftarrow CO_2H$$
$$3 \cdot 83$$

(vi) Phenols

Analogous effects can be observed with substituted phenols, the presence of electron-withdrawing groups in the nucleus increasing their acidity. In the case of a nitro-group, the inductive effect will fall off with distance as we go o- $\rightarrow m$- $\rightarrow p$-nitrophenol but there will be an electron-withdrawing mesomeric effect when the nitro-group is in the o- or p-, but not in the m-position, and this, too, will promote ionisation by stabilisation of the resultant anion. We might therefore expect o- and p-nitrophenols to be more acidic than the m-compound which is, in fact, found to be the case:

	pK_a
$C_6H_5 \cdot OH$	$9 \cdot 9$
$o\text{-}O_2N \cdot C_6H_4 \cdot OH$	$7 \cdot 2$
$m\text{-}O_2N \cdot C_6H_4 \cdot OH$	$8 \cdot 35$
$p\text{-}O_2N \cdot C_6H_4 \cdot OH$	$7 \cdot 14$
$2\text{:}4\text{-}(O_2N)_2 \cdot C_6H_3 \cdot OH$	$4 \cdot 01$
$2\text{:}4\text{:}6\text{-}(O_2N)_3 \cdot C_6H_2 \cdot OH$	$1 \cdot 02$

Handwritten marginal notes:

NO_2 stabalizes anion in 2 ways.
1) By pulling e's away from O xy
2) anion is resor stabalized.

$X = NO_2$, F, etc

Thus picric acid is a very strong acid. The effect of introducing electron-donating alkyl groups is small:

	pK_a
$C_6H_5 \cdot OH$	9·95
$o\text{-Me} \cdot C_6H_4 \cdot OH$	10·28
$m\text{-Me} \cdot C_6H_4 \cdot OH$	10·08
$p\text{-Me} \cdot C_6H_4 \cdot OH$	10·19

The resulting substituted phenols are very slightly weaker acids, but the effect is marginal and irregular, indicating that the effect of such substituents in destabilising the phenoxide ion by disturbing the interaction of its negative charge with the delocalised π orbitals of the aromatic nucleus is small, as might have been expected.

(vii) Aromatic carboxylic acids

Benzoic acid, with a pK_a of 4·20, is a stronger acid than its saturated analogue cyclohexane carboxylic acid ($pK_a = 4\cdot 87$) indicating that a phenyl group, like a double bond, is here exerting an electron-withdrawing effect—compared with a saturated carbon atom—on the carboxyl group, due to the sp^2 hybridised carbon atom to which the carboxyl group is attached (p. 42). Benzoic acid is nevertheless weaker than formic acid ($pK_a = 3\cdot 77$), showing that the phenyl group exerts an *overall electron-donating* effect compared with hydrogen. The difficulty in forecasting the relative effects a phenyl group will have on electron-density in the undissociated acid and in its anion arises from the fact that its π electron system can act as an electron source or an electron sink at will, depending on the nature of the group to which it is attached. This is well illustrated by its equally effective stabilisation of the phenoxide anion, $PhO^{\ominus}$ (p. 17) and the benzyl carbonium ion $Ph \cdot \overset{\oplus}{C}H_2$ (p. 63).

The introduction of alkyl groups has very little effect on the strength of benzoic acid (*cf.* similar introduction in aliphatic acids)

	pK_a
$C_6H_5 \cdot CO_2H$	4·20
$m\text{-Me} \cdot C_6H_4 \cdot CO_2H$	4·24
$p\text{-Me} \cdot C_6H_4 \cdot CO_2H$	4·34

but electron-withdrawing groups increase its strength, the effect, as with the phenols, being most pronounced when they are in the *o*- and *p*-positions:

45

	pK_a
$C_6H_5 \cdot CO_2H$	4·20
$o\text{-}O_2N \cdot C_6H_4 \cdot CO_2H$	2·17
$m\text{-}O_2N \cdot C_6H_4 \cdot CO_2H$	3·45
$p\text{-}O_2N \cdot C_6H_4 \cdot CO_2H$	3·43
$3\!:\!5\text{-}(O_2N)_2 \cdot C_6H_3 \cdot CO_2H$	2·83

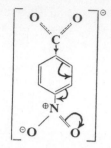

The particularly marked effect with o-NO$_2$ is probably due to the very short distance over which the powerful inductive effect is operating.

The presence of groups such as **OH**, **OMe** or halogen having an electron-withdrawing inductive effect but an electron-donating mesomeric effect when in the o- and p-positions may, however, cause the p-substituted acids to be weaker than the m- and, on occasion, weaker even than the unsubstituted acid itself, e.g. p-hydroxybenzoic acid:

pK_a of X·C$_6$H$_4$·CO$_2$H

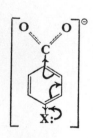

	H	Cl	Br	OMe	OH
o-	4·20	2·94	2·85	4·09	2·98
m-	4·20	3·83	3·81	4·09	4·08
p-	4·20	3·99	4·00	4·47	4·58

It will be noticed that this compensating effect becomes more pronounced in going Cl $\approx$ Br $\rightarrow$ OH, i.e. in increasing order of readiness with which the atom attached to the nucleus will part with its electron pairs. The behaviour of o-substituted acids is, as seen above, often anomalous. Their strength is sometimes considerably greater than expected due to direct interaction of the adjacent groups, e.g. intramolecular hydrogen bonding stabilises the anion (IV) from salicyclic acid (III) by delocalising its charge, an advantage not shared by the *m*- and *p*-isomers nor by *o*-methoxybenzoic acid:

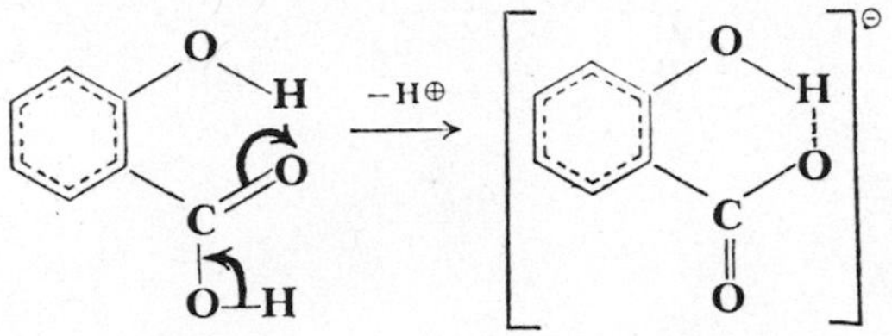

(III)   (IV)

The effect is even more pronounced where hydrogen bonding can occur with a hydroxyl group in both *o*-positions and 2,6-dihydroxybenzoic acid has a **pK_a** of 1·30.

(viii) Dicarboxylic acids

As the carboxyl group itself has an electron-withdrawing inductive effect, the presence of a second such group in an acid would be expected to make it stronger, as shown by the following **pK_a** values:

$H \cdot CO_2H$ 3·77	$HO_2C \cdot CO_2H$ 1·23
$CH_3 \cdot CO_2H$ 4·76	$HO_2C \cdot CH_2 \cdot CO_2H$ 2·83
$CH_3 \cdot CH_2 \cdot CO_2H$ 4·88	$HO_2C \cdot CH_2 \cdot CH_2 \cdot CO_2H$ 4·19
$C_6H_5 \cdot CO_2H$ 4·17	$HO_2C \cdot C_6H_4 \cdot CO_2H$ *o*- 2·98 *m*- 3·46 *p*- 3·51

The effect is very pronounced but falls off sharply as soon as the carboxyl groups are separated by more than one saturated carbon atom. Maleic acid (V) is a much stronger acid than fumaric (VI) (**pK_a^1** is 1·92 compared with 3·02) due to the hydrogen bonding that can take place with the former, but not the latter, stabilising the anion (*cf.* salicylic acid):

next page

47

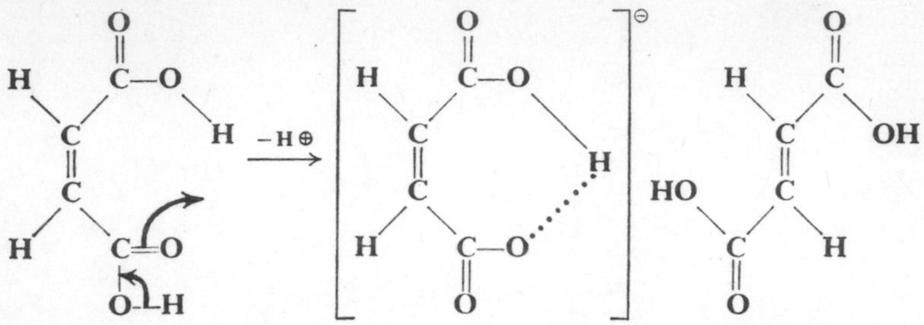

(V)   (VI)

The second dissociation of fumaric occurs more readily than that of maleic acid, however (pK_a^2 is $4\cdot38$ compared with $6\cdot23$) because of the greater difficulty in removing the proton from the negatively charged cyclic system of the latter. Oxalic, malonic and succinic acids are each weaker in their second dissociations than formic, acetic and propionic acids, respectively, because the second proton has to be removed from a negatively charged species containing an electron-donating substituent, i.e. $^{\ominus}O_2C$, which will destabilise the anion with respect to the undissociated acid as compared with the unsubstituted system:

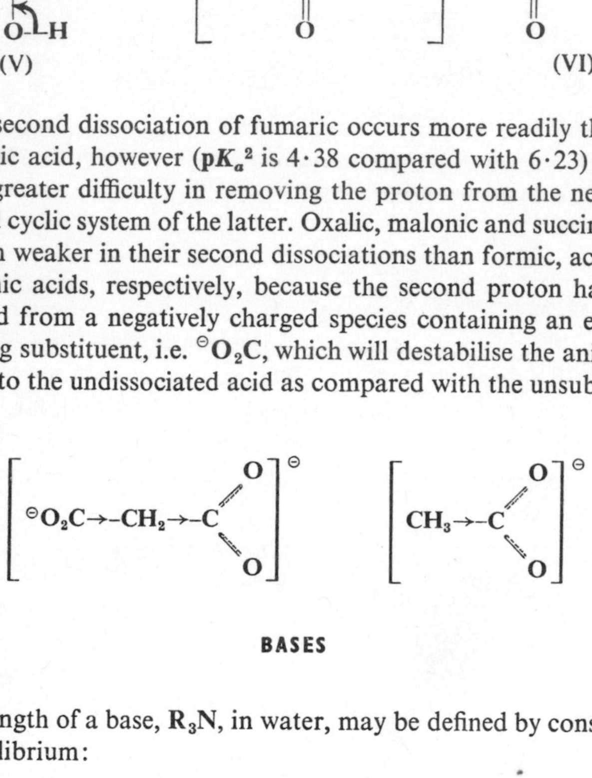

BASES

(i) pK_b

The strength of a base, R_3N, in water, may be defined by considering the equilibrium:

$$R_3N: + HOH \rightleftharpoons R_3\overset{\oplus}{N}:H + {}^{\ominus}OH$$

Then the equilibrium constant, in water, is given by

$$K_b \approx \frac{[R_3\overset{\oplus}{N}H][{}^{\ominus}OH]}{[R_3N]}$$

the concentration of water being taken as constant as it is present in such large excess. As with K_a, K_b is, on the grounds of convenience, usually expressed as pK_b ($pK_b = -\log_{10} K_b$), then the *smaller* the numerical value of pK_b, the *stronger* is the base to which it refers. The strengths of bases may also be expressed in terms of pK_a, thus providing a continuous scale for acids *and* bases. K_a (and hence pK_a) for a base R_3N is a measure of the readiness with which $R_3\overset{\oplus}{N}H$ will part with a proton

$$R_3\overset{\oplus}{N}H + H_2O \rightleftharpoons R_3N + H_3O^\oplus$$

i.e. of the acidity of $R_3\overset{\oplus}{N}H$, and is defined by:

$$K_a \approx \frac{[R_3N][H_3O^\oplus]}{[R_3\overset{\oplus}{N}H]}$$

pK_b values in water may be converted into pK_a by use of the relation:

$$pK_a + pK_b = 14 \cdot 00 \text{ (at } 25°)$$

(ii) Aliphatic bases

As increasing strength in nitrogenous bases is related to the readiness with which they are prepared to take up protons and, therefore, to the availability of the unshared electron pair on nitrogen, we should expect to see an increase in basic strength as we go: $NH_3 \rightarrow R \cdot NH_2 \rightarrow R_2NH \rightarrow R_3N$, due to the increasing inductive effect of successive alkyl groups making the nitrogen atom more negative. An actual series of amines have pK_b values as follows, however:

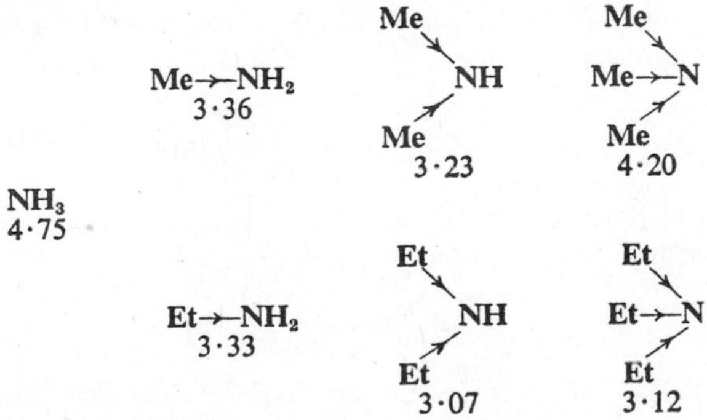

It will be seen that the introduction of an alkyl group into ammonia increases the basic strength markedly as expected, ethyl having a very slightly greater effect than methyl. The introduction of a second alkyl group further increases the basic strength but the net effect of introducing the second alkyl group is much less marked than with the first. The introduction of a third alkyl group to yield a tertiary amine, however, *decreases* the basic strength in both the series quoted.

This is due to the fact that the basic strength of an amine in water is determined not only by electron-availability on the nitrogen atom, but also by the extent to which the cation, formed by uptake of a proton, can undergo solvation and so becomes stabilised. The more hydrogen atoms attached to nitrogen in the cation, the greater the possibilities of solvation via hydrogen bonding between these and water:

$$R_2\overset{\oplus}{N} \quad > \quad R_3\overset{\oplus}{N}H \leftarrow :O$$

Thus as we go along the series $NH_3 \rightarrow R \cdot NH_2 \rightarrow R_2NH \rightarrow R_3N$, though the inductive effect will *increase* the basicity, progressively less stabilisation of the cation by hydration will occur, which will tend to *decrease* the basicity. The net effect of introducing successive alkyl groups thus becomes progressively smaller, and an actual changeover takes place on going from a secondary to a tertiary amine. If this is the real explanation, no such changeover should occur if measurements of basicity are made in a solvent in which hydrogen-bonding cannot take place; it has, indeed, been found that in chlorobenzene the order of basicity of the butylamines is

$$Bu \cdot NH_2 \quad < \quad Bu_2NH \quad < \quad Bu_3N$$

though their pK_b values in water are $3 \cdot 39, 2 \cdot 72$ and $4 \cdot 13$, respectively.

Quaternary alkylammonium salts, e.g. $R_4N^{\oplus}I^{\ominus}$, are known, on treatment with moist silver oxide—'AgOH'—to yield basic solutions comparable in strength with the mineral alkalis. This is readily understandable for the base so obtained, $R_4N^{\oplus \ominus}OH$, is bound to be completely ionised as there is no possibility, as with tertiary amines etc., of reverting to an unionised form:

$$R_3\overset{\oplus}{N}H + {}^{\ominus}OH \rightarrow R_3N: + H_2O$$

The effect of introducing electron-withdrawing groups, e.g. Cl, NO_2, close to a basic centre is, naturally, to decrease the basicity, due to their electron-withdrawing inductive effect (see substituted anilines below, p. 53); thus

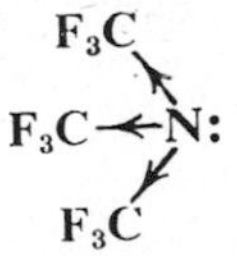

$$F_3C \overset{F_3C}{\underset{F_3C}{\longleftarrow}} N:$$

is virtually non-basic due to the three powerfully electron-withdrawing CF_3 groups.

The change is particularly pronounced with groups such as $\diagup C{=}O$ when these are adjacent to the basic centre for they are then able to act via a mesomeric effect:

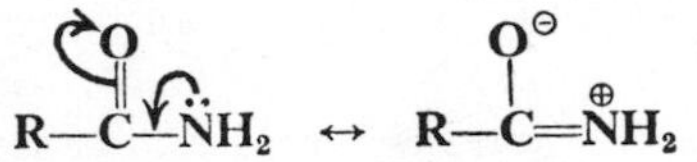

$$R-\overset{O}{\overset{\|}{C}}-\ddot{N}H_2 \leftrightarrow R-\overset{O^{\ominus}}{\overset{|}{C}}{=}\overset{\oplus}{N}H_2$$

Thus amides are only very weakly basic in water (pK_b for acetamide $= 14\cdot5$) and if two $\diagup C{=}O$ groups are present, the resultant imides, far from being basic, are often sufficiently acidic to form alkali metal salts, e.g. phthalimide:

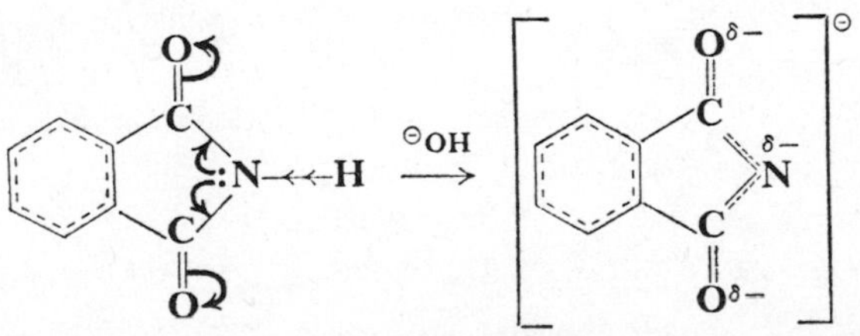

$$\left[\begin{array}{c} \text{structure with } N{-}\cdots{-}H, \ {}^{\ominus}OH \longrightarrow \text{ delocalised anion} \end{array} \right]^{\ominus}$$

The effect of delocalisation in *increasing* the basic strength of an amine is seen in guanidine, $HN{=}C(NH_2)_2$, which, with the exception of the quaternary alkylammonium hydroxides above, is among the strongest organic bases known, having too small a pK_b in water for it to be accurately measured. Both the neutral molecule and the cation, $\overset{\oplus}{H_2N}=C(NH_2)_2$, resulting from its protonation, are stabilised by delocalisation

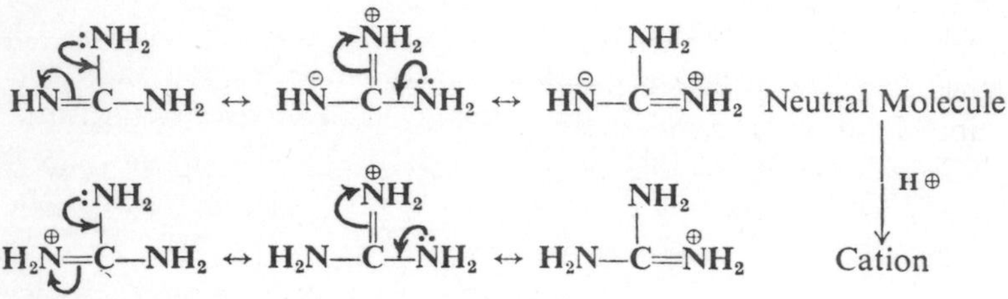

but in the cation the positive charge is spread symmetrically by the contribution to the hybrid of three exactly equivalent structures of equal energy. No comparably effective delocalisation occurs in the neutral molecule (in which two of the contributing structures involve separation of charge) with the result that the cation is greatly stabilised with respect to it, thus making protonation 'energetically profitable' and guanidine an extremely strong base.

(iii) Aromatic bases

The exact reverse of the above is seen with aniline which is a very weak base, having a pK_b of $9 \cdot 38$ compared to $4 \cdot 75$ for ammonia and $3 \cdot 46$ for methylamine. In aniline, the unshared electron pair on nitrogen can interact with the delocalised π orbitals of the nucleus:

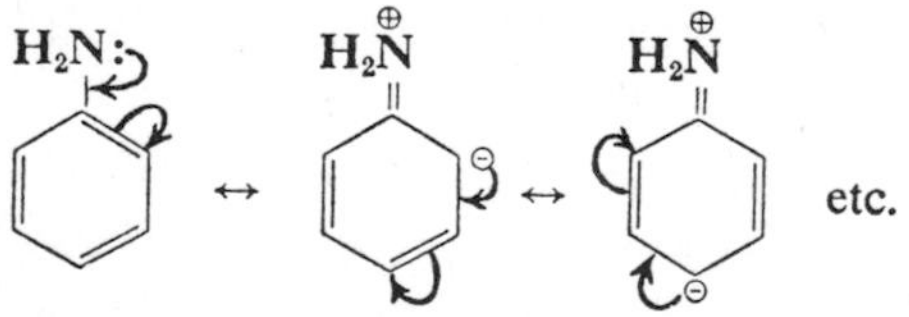

If the aniline is protonated, any such interaction, with resultant stabilisation, is prohibited, as the electron pair on nitrogen is no longer unshared:

(VII)

Here the aniline molecule is stabilised with respect to the anilinium cation (VII) and it is, therefore, 'energetically *un*profitable' for aniline to take up a proton; it thus functions as a base with the utmost reluctance which is reflected in its pK_b of $9 \cdot 38$, compared with that of cyclohexylamine, $3 \cdot 32$. The effect is naturally more pronounced when further phenyl groups are introduced on nitrogen; thus diphenyl-amine, Ph_2NH is an extremely weak base ($pK_b = 13 \cdot 2$) while triphenyl-amine, Ph_3N is, by ordinary standards, not basic at all.

The overriding importance of this mesomeric destabilising of the anilinium cation (VII) with respect to the aniline molecule in determining the basic strength of aniline is confirmed by the relatively small and irregular effects produced in pK_b when methyl groups are introduced on the nitrogen atom or in the ring; for these groups would not be expected to influence markedly the interaction of the nitrogen's unshared pair with the delocalised π orbitals of the benzene nucleus (*cf.* the small effect produced by introducing alkyl groups into the nucleus of phenol, p. 45). Thus the substituted anilines have pK_b values:

$Ph \cdot NH_2$	$Ph \cdot NHMe$	$Ph \cdot NMe_2$	$Me \cdot C_6H_4 \cdot NH_2$	
$9 \cdot 38$	$9 \cdot 60$	$9 \cdot 62$	*o-*	$9 \cdot 62$
			m-	$9 \cdot 33$
			p-	$9 \cdot 00$

The small, base-strengthening inductive effect they usually exert is not large enough to modify the destabilisation of the cation to any significant extent. A group with a more powerful inductive effect, e.g. NO_2, has rather more influence. This is intensified when the nitro group is in the *o-* or *p-*position for the interaction of the unshared electron pair of nitrogen with the delocalised π orbitals of the benzene nucleus is then enhanced and the cation even further destabilised with respect to the neutral molecule resulting in further weakening of the base. Thus the nitro-anilines have pK_b values:

$Ph \cdot NH_2$	$O_2N \cdot C_6H_4 \cdot NH_2$	
$9 \cdot 38$	*o-*	$14 \cdot 28$
	m-	$11 \cdot 55$
	p-	$13 \cdot 02$

The extra base-weakening effect when the substituent is in the *o-*position is due in part to the short distance over which its inductive effect is operating and also to direct interaction, both steric and by hydrogen bonding, with the NH_2 group (*cf.* the case of *o*-substituted benzoic acids, p. 47). *o*-Nitroaniline is such a weak base that its salts are largely hydrolysed in aqueous solution, while 2,4-dinitroaniline is insoluble in aqueous acids, and 2,4,6-trinitroaniline resembles an amide; it is indeed called picramide and readily undergoes hydrolysis to picric acid.

With substituents such as **OH** and **OMe** having unshared electron pairs, an electron-donating, i.e. base-strengthening, mesomeric effect can be exerted from the *o*- and *p*-, but not from the *m*-position with the result that the *p*-substituted aniline is a stronger base than the corresponding *m*-compound. The *m*-compound is a weaker base than aniline itself due to the electron-withdrawing inductive effect exerted by the oxygen atom in each case. As so often, the effect of the *o*-substituent remains somewhat anomalous due to direct interaction with the NH_2 group by both steric and polar effects. The substituted anilines have pK_b values as follows:

$Ph \cdot NH_2$	$HO \cdot C_6H_4 \cdot NH_2$		$MeO \cdot C_6H_4 \cdot NH_2$	
9·38	*o*-	9·28	*o*-	9·51
	m-	9·83	*m*-	9·80
	p-	8·50	*p*-	8·71

An interesting case is provided by 2,4,6-trinitroaniline (VIII) and 2,4,6-trinitrodimethylaniline (IX), the latter being about forty thousand times as strong as the former while aniline itself is only about twice as strong as dimethylaniline. This is due to the fact that the influence of nitro groups in the substituted dimethylaniline (IX) is essentially confined to their inductive effects. The dimethylamino group is sufficiently large to interfere sterically with the very large nitro groups in both *o*-positions, and the *p* orbitals on the nitrogen atoms of both NMe_2 and NO_2 groups are thus prevented from becoming parallel to the orbitals of the nuclear carbon atoms. As a consequence, mesomeric shift of unshared electrons from the amino-nitrogen atom to the oxygen atom of the nitro groups via the delocalised orbitals of the nucleus (*cf.* p. 52) is also prevented, and base-weakening by mesomeric electron-withdrawal does not, therefore, occur.

In trinitro-aniline (VIII), however, the NH_2 group is sufficiently small for no such limitation to be imposed and hydrogen-bonding between the o-NO_2 groups and the hydrogens of the NH_2 may help to hold these groups in the required orientation: the p orbitals may become parallel and interact; and the base is thus enormously weakened by the very powerful electron-withdrawing mesomeric effects of the three nitro groups:

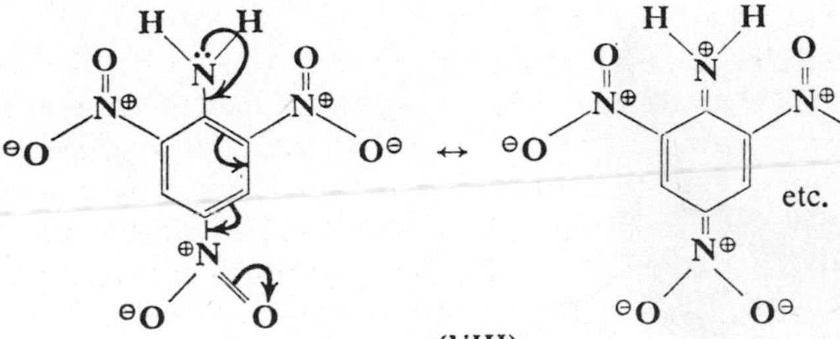

(VIII)

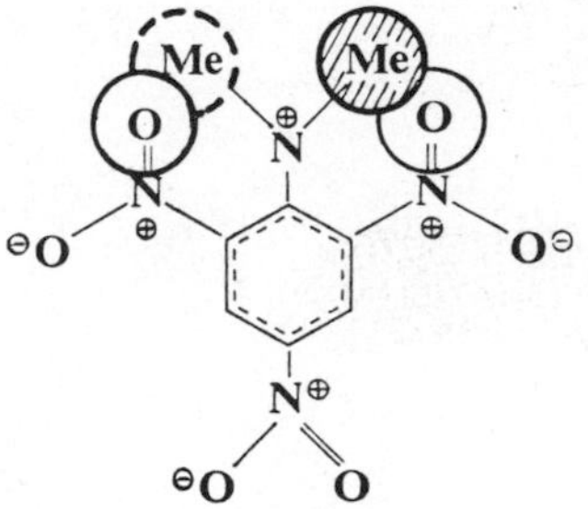

(IX)

(iv) Heterocyclic bases

Pyridine, C_5H_5N, , (pK_b 8·96) is a very much weaker base than the aliphatic tertiary amines (e.g. pK_b of $Et_3N = 3·12$) and this weakness is found to be characteristic of bases in which the nitrogen atom is multiply bonded. This is due to the fact that as the nitrogen atom becomes progressively more multiply bonded its lone-pair of electrons is accommodated in an orbital that has progressively more s character; they are thus drawn closer to the nitrogen nucleus and held more tightly by it, thereby becoming less available for forming a bond with proton, with a consequent decline in the basicity of the compound. As we go $\geq$N → $\searrow$N → ≡N in, for example, R_3N →

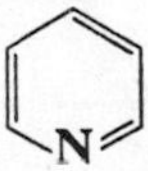

$C_5H_5N \rightarrow R \cdot C \equiv N$, the unshared pairs are in sp^3, sp^2 and sp^1 orbitals, respectively, and the declining basicity is reflected in the two pK_b values quoted above and the fact that the basicity of alkyl cyanides is too small to measure.

With quinuclidine, however,

the unshared electron pair is again in an sp^3 orbital and its pK_b (3·42) is almost identical with that of triethylamine (3·12).

Pyrrole (X) is found to exhibit some aromatic character (though this is not so pronounced as with benzene or pyridine) and does not behave like a conjugated diene as might otherwise have been expected:

$$
\begin{array}{c}
HC\text{---}CH \\
\| \quad\quad \| \\
HC \quad\quad CH \\
\diagdown \ddot{N} \diagup \\
H \\
(X)
\end{array}
$$

For such aromaticity to be achieved, six π electrons of the ring atoms must occupy stable delocalised orbitals. This necessitates the contribution of *two* electrons by the nitrogen atom and, though the completed orbitals will be deformed towards nitrogen because of the more electronegative nature of that atom as compared with carbon, nitrogen's electron pair will thus not be available for taking up a proton:

(X)

The situation resembles that already encountered with aniline (p. 52) in that the cation (XI), obtained if protonation is forced upon pyrrole (protonation is shown as taking place on nitrogen, but it may occur on the α-carbon atom as happens with C-alkylated pyrroles),

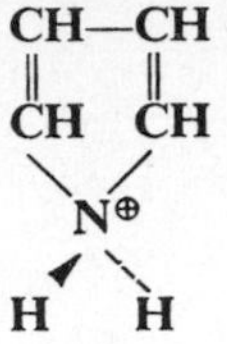

$$\begin{array}{cc}
CH\!\!-\!\!CH \\
\| \quad \| \\
CH \quad CH \\
\diagdown \quad \diagup \\
N^{\oplus} \\
\diagup \quad \diagdown \\
H \quad \quad H
\end{array}$$

(XI)

is destabilised with respect to the neutral molecule (X); but the effect is here more pronounced, for to function as a base pyrrole has to lose *all* its aromatic character and consequent stability. This is reflected in its pK_b of $\approx 13 \cdot 6$ compared with $9 \cdot 38$ for aniline; it is thus only a very weak base and functions as an acid, albeit a very weak one, in that the hydrogen atom attached to nitrogen may be removed by a strong base, e.g. $^{\ominus}NH_2$.

No such considerations can, of course, apply to the fully-reduced pyrrole, pyrrolidine

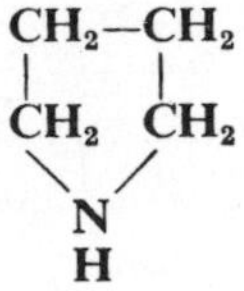

$$\begin{array}{cc}
CH_2\!\!-\!\!CH_2 \\
| \quad \quad | \\
CH_2 \quad CH_2 \\
\diagdown \quad \diagup \\
N \\
H
\end{array}$$

which has a pK_b of $2 \cdot 73$, closely similar to that of diethylamine, $3 \cdot 07$.

3 NUCLEOPHILIC SUBSTITUTION AT A SATURATED CARBON ATOM

A TYPE of reaction that has probably received more study than any other—largely due to the monumental work of Ingold and his school—is nucleophilic substitution at a saturated carbon atom: the classical displacement reaction exemplified by the conversion of an alkyl halide to an alcohol by the action of alkali:

$$HO^\ominus + R\text{---}Hal \rightarrow HO\text{---}R + Hal^\ominus$$

Investigation of the kinetics of such reactions has shown that there are essentially two extreme types, one in which

$$\text{Rate} \propto [R \cdot Hal][^\ominus OH] \tag{1}$$

and another in which:

$$\text{Rate} \propto [R \cdot Hal] \text{ i.e. is independent of } [^\ominus OH] \tag{2}$$

In many examples the kinetics are mixed, showing both types of rate law simultaneously, or are otherwise complicated, but cases are known which do exemplify the simple relations shown above.

RELATION OF KINETICS TO MECHANISM

The hydrolysis of methyl bromide in aqueous alkali has been shown to proceed according to equation (1) and this is interpreted as involving the participation of both halide and hydroxyl ion in the rate-determining (i.e. slowest) step of the reaction. Ingold has suggested a transition state in which the attacking hydroxyl ion becomes partially bonded to the reacting carbon atom before the incipient bromide ion has become wholly detached from it; thus part of the energy necessary to effect the breaking of the C—Br bond is then supplied by that produced in forming the HO—C bond. Calculation shows that an approach by the hydroxyl ion along the line of centres of the carbon and bromine atoms is that of lowest energy requirement. This can be represented:

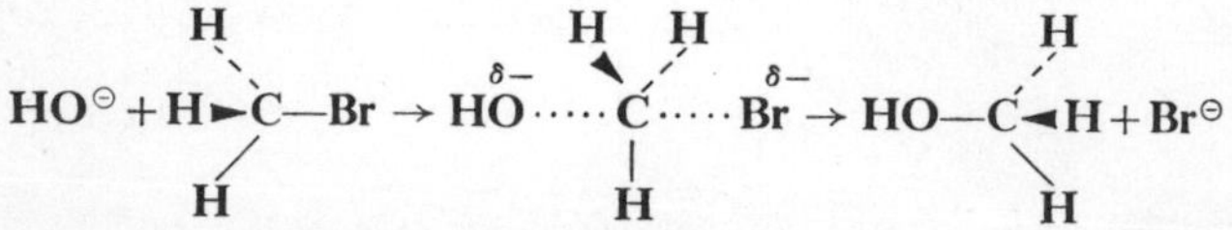

$$HO^\ominus + H\text{---}\underset{\underset{H}{|}}{\overset{\overset{H}{|}}{C}}\text{---}Br \rightarrow HO\cdots\overset{\delta-}{\underset{H}{\overset{H\ \ H}{C}}}\cdots\overset{\delta-}{Br} \rightarrow HO\text{---}\underset{\underset{H}{|}}{\overset{\overset{H}{|}}{C}}\text{---}H + Br^\ominus$$

Transition state

58

The negative charge is spread in the transition state in the course of being transferred from hydroxyl to bromine, and the hydrogen atoms attached to the carbon atom attacked pass through a position in which they all lie in one plane (at right angles to the plane of the paper as drawn here). This type of mechanism has been named by Ingold S_N2, standing for Substitution Nucleophilic bimolecular.

A certain element of confusion is to be met with both in text-books and in the literature over the use of the term bimolecular, particularly in its confusion with second order as applied to reactions. It is probably simplest to reserve the latter purely for a description of the type of kinetic equation that a reaction follows: thus equation (1) represents a second order reaction, being first order in each reactant and equation (2) represents a first order reaction; while molecularity is reserved for a description of the mechanism proposed, being used in the sense of specifying the number of species that are actually undergoing covalency changes in the rate-determining stage. Thus, hydrolysis of methyl bromide under the conditions specified, not only exhibits second order kinetics but, as represented mechanistically, is clearly a bimolecular reaction.

By contrast, the hydrolysis of t-butyl chloride in alkali is found kinetically to follow equation (2), i.e. as the rate is independent of [$^\ominus$OH], this can play no part in the rate-determining step. This has been interpreted as indicating that the halide undergoes slow ionisation (in fact, completion of the $R \rightarrow Hal$ polarisation that has already been shown to be present in such a molecule) as the rate-determining step, followed by rapid, non rate-determining attack by $^\ominus$OH or, if that is suitable, by solvent, the latter often predominating:

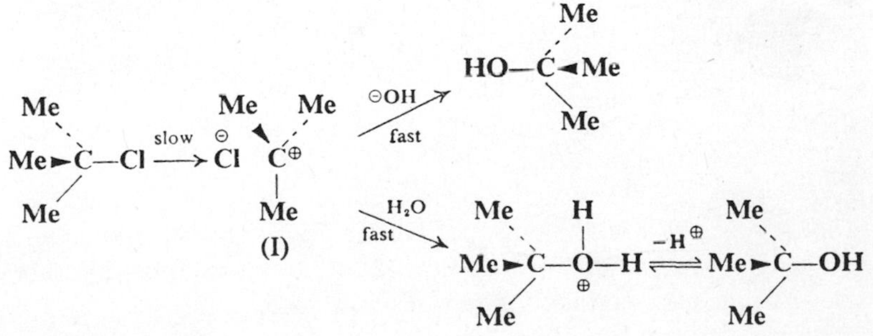

This type of mechanism has been named S_N1, i.e. Substitution Nucleophilic **uni**molecular. The energy necessary to effect the initial ionisation is largely recovered in the energy of solvation of the ions so formed. The cation (I) in which the carbon atom carries a positive charge is a carbonium ion and during its formation the initially tetrahedral carbon atom collapses to a more stable planar state in which the three methyl groups are as far apart as they can get; attack by $^{\ominus}$OH or solvent can then take place from either side. If this assumption of a planar state is inhibited by steric or other factors (*cf.* p. 65), the carbonium ion will be formed only with difficulty if at all, i.e. ionisation, and hence reaction by the S_N1 mechanism, may then not take place.

Kinetics alone can, in some cases, be an insufficient guide as to which mechanism is being followed, unless the reaction is investigated under more than one set of conditions. Thus where the solvent can act as a nucleophilic reagent, e.g. H_2O under S_N2 conditions:

$$\text{Rate} \propto [R \cdot Hal][H_2O].$$

But as $[H_2O]$ is effectively constant, the rate becomes proportional to $[R \cdot Hal]$ and study of the kinetics in water alone would erroneously suggest that the reaction was of the S_N1 type. Such attack by the solvent, in this case H_2O, is known as *solvolysis*.

EFFECT OF SOLVENT

The solvent in which a reaction is carried out may exert a profound effect on the mechanism by which such reaction takes place. So far as the hydrolysis or solvolysis of a given halide is concerned, the more polar the solvent employed the more likely is the reaction to proceed via the S_N1 rather than the S_N2 mode, and such changeovers, as the solvent is varied, are well known. This change in mechanism is in part due to a solvent of high dielectric constant promoting ionisation but also to the fact that ions so produced will become highly solvated in suitable solvents, e.g. water. This solvation process is attended by the liberation of considerable amounts of energy which may go a long way towards providing the energy necessary for ionisation, which is thus further promoted. That such solvation effects are of great importance is confirmed by the fact that though S_N1 reactions are not unknown in the vapour phase, where solvation of ions is naturally impossible, they are very much less common than those in solution.

For a halide that undergoes hydrolysis by the S_N1 mode in a number of different solvents, the rate of hydrolysis is observed to increase as the solvent becomes more polar and/or a better medium for solvating ions: thus the rate of hydrolysis (S_N1) of t-butyl chloride is 30,000 times as fast in 50 per cent aqueous ethanol as in ethanol alone. The effect of change of solvent on a halide whose hydrolysis proceeds by the S_N2 mechanism throughout is much less marked and the direction of the effect on rate of reaction is not always readily predictable. This difference in the effect of change of solvent on reaction rate in the two cases may be of help in determining whether a particular displacement reaction is proceeding by the S_N1 or S_N2 mechanisms.

EFFECT OF STRUCTURE

An interesting contrast is provided by hydrolysis of the series of halides:

$$CH_3{-}Br \qquad Me{-}CH_2{-}Br \qquad \underset{Me}{\overset{Me}{\diagdown}}CH{-}Br \qquad Me{-}\underset{Me}{\overset{Me}{\diagup}}C{-}Br$$

The first and last members are described in the literature as undergoing ready hydrolysis, the two intermediate members being more resistant. Measurement of rates of hydrolysis with dilute alkali in aqueous ethanol gives the plot

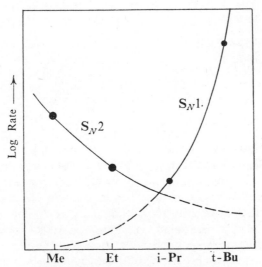

Based on Ingold, *Structure and Mechanism in Organic Chemistry*, by permission of Cornell University Press.

and further kinetic investigation shows a change in order of reaction, and hence presumably of mechanism, as the series is traversed. Thus methyl and ethyl bromide show second order kinetics, isopropyl bromide shows a mixture of second and first order, with the former predominating—the total rate here being a minimum for the series—while t-butyl bromide exhibits first order kinetics.

The reason for the changeover is not far to seek: methyl groups exert an inductive effect as already mentioned (p. 15), so that in $Me \rightarrow CH_2 - Br$ the carbon atom attached to bromine will be more negative than that in $CH_3 - Br$, it will thus be less susceptible to attack by $^\ominus OH$ and the S_N2 mechanism will be inhibited. This effect will be more pronounced in $\begin{smallmatrix}Me_\searrow\\Me^\nearrow\end{smallmatrix} CH - Br$ and S_N2 attack will be further inhibited, but transmission of some of the negative charge accumulated on carbon to the bromine atom will promote ionisation, i.e. attack on the carbon atom by the S_N1 mechanism will be facilitated. By the time $\begin{smallmatrix}Me_\searrow\\Me \rightarrow\\Me^\nearrow\end{smallmatrix} C - Br$ is reached, S_N2 attack is entirely inhibited, but that by S_N1 is now considerably promoted, a complete changeover in the mechanistic type of the reaction has been effected and the overall rate increases. The stability of the carbonium ion produced on going $\overset{\oplus}{C}H_3 \rightarrow Me \cdot \overset{\oplus}{C}H_2 \rightarrow Me_2 \overset{\oplus}{C}H \rightarrow Me_3 \overset{\oplus}{C}$ will be increasingly promoted by hyperconjugation

$$H \overset{\frown}{-}CH_2 - \overset{\overset{\displaystyle CH_3}{|}}{\underset{\underset{\displaystyle CH_3}{|}}{C^\oplus}} \quad \leftrightarrow \quad \overset{\oplus}{H} \quad CH_2 = \overset{\overset{\displaystyle CH_3}{|}}{\underset{\underset{\displaystyle CH_3}{|}}{C}} \quad etc$$

via the hydrogen atoms attached to the α-carbons, the above series of ions having 0, 3, 6 and 9 such hydrogen atoms, respectively. Such hyperconjugative stabilisation can only take place in a planar ion, hence the need for a carbonium ion to be able to attain such a planar state if it is to be formed at all (*cf.* p. 84). This increasing stabilisation of the carbonium ion as the series is traversed will naturally further promote the S_N1 mechanism at the expense of S_N2.

There will also be an increasing steric resistance to S_N2 as the series is traversed. Not only will $^\ominus OH$ find it more difficult to attack the carbon atom attached to bromine as the former becomes more heavily substituted, but the S_N2 mechanism involves a transition state in which there are *five* groups around the carbon atom attacked, while the S_N1 intermediate involves only *three*, and even these at their maximum distance apart in a planar state. The divergence between the two will naturally increase, with consequent favouring of S_N1 at the expense of S_N2, as alkyl substitution at the carbon atom being attacked is increased.

A similar change of mechanism is observed, but considerably sooner, in traversing the series:

$$CH_3—Cl \quad Ph \cdot CH_2—Cl \quad Ph_2CH—Cl \quad Ph_3C—Cl$$

S_N1 hydrolysis is here observed at the second member and with $Ph_3C—Cl$ the ionisation is so pronounced that the compound shows electrical conductivity when dissolved in liquid SO_2. The reason for the greater promotion of ionisation, with consequent more rapid changeover to the S_N1 mechanism, is the considerable stabilisation of the carbonium ion that is here possible by delocalisation of the positive charge

i.e. a classical example of an ion stabilised by charge delocalisation via the agency of the delocalised π orbitals of the benzene nucleus (*cf.* the negatively charged phenoxide ion, p. 17). In terms of overall reactivity, benzyl chloride is rather similar to t-butyl chloride; the effect will become progressively more pronounced, and S_N1 attack further facilitated, with Ph_2CHCl and Ph_3CCl as the possibilities of delocalising the positive charge are increased in the carbonium ions obtainable from these halides.

Similar carbonium ion stabilisation can occur with allyl halides:

$$CH_2{=}CH—CH_2Cl \rightarrow [CH_2{=}CH—\overset{\oplus}{C}H_2 \leftrightarrow \overset{\oplus}{C}H_2—CH{=}CH_2] + Cl^{\ominus}$$

S_N1 attack is thus promoted and allyl, like benzyl, halides are normally extremely reactive as compared with e.g. $CH_3 \cdot CH_2 \cdot CH_2Cl$ and $Ph \cdot CH_2 \cdot CH_2 \cdot CH_2Cl$ respectively where such carbonium ion stabilisation cannot take place.

By contrast, vinyl halides such as $CH_2=CH-Cl$ and halogeno-benzenes are very unreactive. The reason in each case is that some overlap occurs between the p orbital on chlorine and an orbital on the adjacent carbon atom:

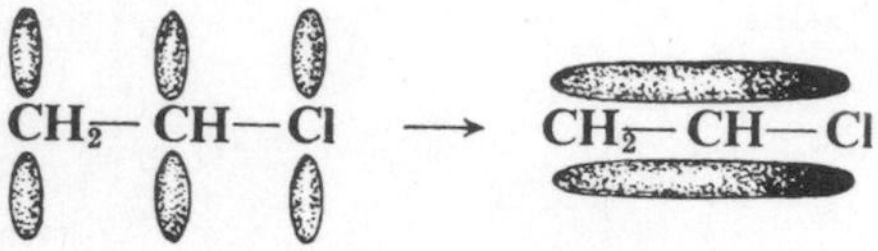

i.e.

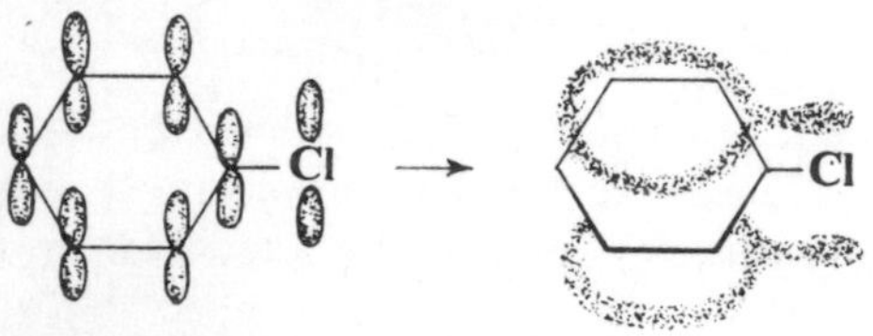

i.e. 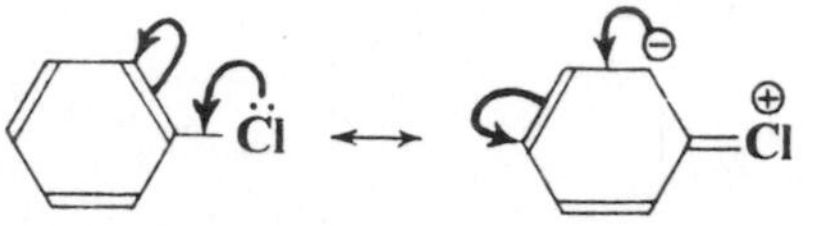 etc.

The effect is to make this carbon atom more negative and hence less readily attacked by, e.g. $^\ominus OH$, and also to introduce a certain amount of double bond character into the linkage between carbon and chlorine (confirmed by the slightly shorter $C-Cl$ bond distances observed in the above compounds compared with $Me \cdot CH_2-Cl$); features that will discourage attack by either S_N1 or S_N2 mechanisms.

The influence of steric factors on mechanism is particularly observed when substitution takes place at the β-position. Thus in the series

$$CH_3-CH_2-Hal \qquad Me-CH_2-CH_2-Hal \qquad \begin{matrix} Me \\ \diagdown \\ CH-CH_2-Hal \\ \diagup \\ Me \end{matrix}$$

$$\begin{matrix} Me \\ \diagdown \\ Me-C-CH_2-Hal \\ \diagup \\ Me \end{matrix}$$

it is found that the S_N2 reaction rate falls as we pass along the series, the drop being particularly marked as we go from the isobutyl to the neopentyl halide, in which attack 'from the back' by e.g. $^{\ominus}OH$ on the α-carbon atom along the line of centres might be expected to be very highly hindered. The main factor inhibiting S_N2 attack is however the highly crowded transition state

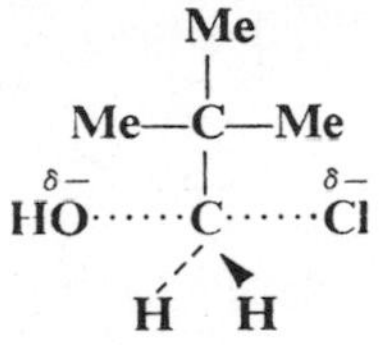

that would have to be formed. The drop in rate probably owes little to the inductive effect of the increasing number of substituent methyl groups owing to the interposition of a saturated carbon atom (the β-carbon) between them and the carbon atom (α-) to be attacked.

A very interesting example of the effect of structure on the reactivity of a halide is provided by 1-bromotriptycene (II):

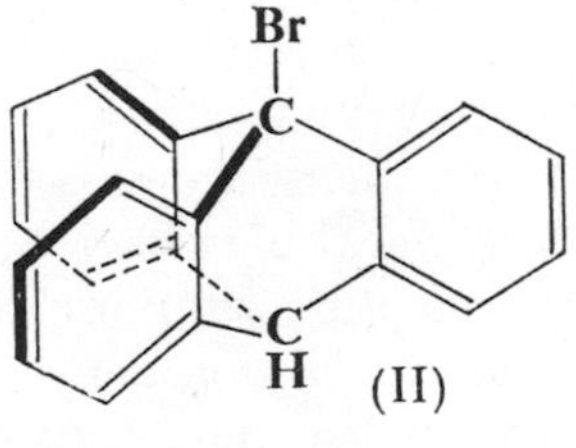

The bromine atom in this compound is virtually inert to nucleophiles. S_N2 'attack from the back' is inhibited sterically by the cage-like structure, and the formation of a transition state, in which the three groups attached to the carbon atom attacked must pass through a co-planar arrangement, is prevented as this atom is held rigidly in position by the substituents attached to it. S_N1 attack is also inhibited because the carbonium ion that would be formed by ionisation is unable to stabilise itself for, being unable to achieve coplanarity with its substituents, charge-delocalisation with them (p. 84) cannot take place.

The hydrolysis of an optically active halide presents some interesting stereochemical features. Thus considering both mechanisms in turn:

(i) S_N2 mechanism

$$HO^\ominus + R' \blacktriangleright \overset{R}{\underset{R''}{\overset{|}{C}}} - Br \rightarrow HO \cdots\cdots \overset{R' \quad R}{\underset{R''}{\overset{\searrow \; \nearrow}{C}}} \cdots\cdots Br \rightarrow HO - \overset{R}{\underset{R''}{\overset{|}{C}}} \blacktriangleleft R' + Br^\ominus$$

Dextro, i.e. (+)   ?

It will be seen that the arrangement or pattern of the three groups attached to the carbon atom attacked has been effectively turned inside out. The carbon atom is said to have undergone reversal or, as more usually expressed, *inversion* of its *configuration* (the pattern or arrangement in space of the groups attached to it). Indeed, if the product could be the bromide instead of the corresponding alcohol it would be found to rotate the plane of polarisation of plane polarised light in the opposite direction (i.e. laevo or (−)) to the starting material for it would, of course, be its mirror image. The actual product is the alcohol, however, and we are unfortunately not able to tell merely by observing its direction of optical rotation whether it has the same or the opposite configuration to the bromide from which it was derived; for compounds, other than mirror images, having opposite configurations do not necessarily exhibit opposite directions of optical rotation, any more than do compounds having the same configuration necessarily exhibit the same direction of optical rotation. Thus in order to confirm that the above S_N2 reaction is, in practice, actually attended by an inversion of configuration, as the theory requires, it is necessary to have an independent method for relating the configuration of, e.g., a halide and the corresponding alcohol.

(ii) Determination of relative configuration

This turns essentially on the fact that if an asymmetric compound undergoes a reaction in which a bond joining one of the groups to the asymmetric centre is broken, then the centre may—though it need not of necessity—undergo inversion of configuration; while if the compound undergoes reaction in which no such bond is broken then the centre will preserve its configuration intact. Thus in the series of reactions on the asymmetric alcohol (III)

$$
\begin{array}{c}
R \\
R' \!\!\succ\!\! C\!-\!OH \\
R'' \quad (+) \\
(III)
\end{array}
\xrightarrow{\; p\text{-Me}\cdot C_6H_4\cdot SO_2\cdot Cl \;}
\begin{array}{c}
R \\
R' \!\!\succ\!\! C\!-\!O\cdot SO_2\cdot C_6H_4\cdot Me\text{-}p \\
R'' \\
(IV)
\end{array}
\xrightarrow{\; Cl^{\ominus} \;}
\begin{array}{c}
R \\
Cl\!-\!C\!\!\prec\!\! R' \\
R'' \\
(VII)
\end{array}
$$

$Me\cdot CO_2{}^{\ominus}$

$$
\begin{array}{c}
R \\
HO\!-\!C\!\!\prec\!\! R' \\
R'' \\
(VI) \; (-)
\end{array}
\xleftarrow{\; {}^{\ominus}OH \;}
\begin{array}{c}
R \\
Me\cdot CO\cdot O\!-\!C\!\!\prec\!\! R' \\
R'' \\
(V)
\end{array}
$$

formation of an ester with toluene p-sulphonyl chloride is known not to break the C—O bond of the alcohol,* hence the tosylate (IV) must have the same configuration as the original alcohol. Reaction of this ester with acetate ion is known to be a replacement in which p-$Me\cdot C_6H_4\cdot SO_2\cdot O^{\ominus}$ is expelled and $Me\cdot CO\cdot O^{\ominus}$ introduced,* hence the C—O bond *is* broken in this reaction and inversion of configuration can take place in forming the acetate (V). Alkaline hydrolysis of the acetate (V→VI) can be shown not to involve fission of the alkyl-oxygen C—O linkage,† so the alcohol (VI) must have the same configuration as the acetate (V). As (VI) is found to be the mirror image of the starting material, an inversion of configuration must have taken place during the series of reactions and it can only have taken place during the reaction of acetate ion with the tosylate (IV). A number of further reactions with the tosylate show that an inversion of configuration takes place with a variety of anions and hence it may be concluded with a considerable degree of confidence that it takes place on reaction with chloride ion, so that the chloride (VII), like the acetate (V), has the opposite configuration to the original alcohol (III). Now that it is thus possible to show that S_N2 reactions are normally attended by inversion of configuration, independent demonstration that a particular reaction takes place by an S_N2 mechanism is often used to relate the configuration of product and starting material in that reaction.

* That such is the case may be shown by using an alcohol with ^{18}O in the ·OH group and showing that this atom is not eliminated on forming the tosylate; it is, however, eliminated when the tosylate is reacted with $Me\cdot CO_2{}^{\ominus}$.

† Hydrolysis of an acetate in which the alcohol-oxygen atom is labelled with ^{18}O fails to result in its replacement, showing that the alkyl–oxygen bond is not broken in the hydrolysis (*cf.* p. 35).

(iii) S_N1 mechanism

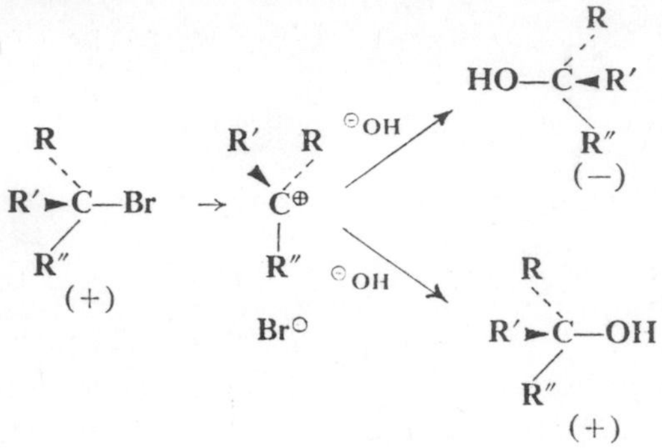

As the carbonium ion formed in the slow, rate-determining stage of the reaction is planar, it is to be expected that subsequent attack by a nucleophilic reagent such as $^{\ominus}$OH or the solvent (e.g. H_2O) will take place with equal readiness from either side of the planar ion leading, in fact, to a 50/50 mixture of species having the same and the opposite configuration as the starting material, i.e. that racemisation will take place yielding an optically inactive ($\pm$) product.

What actually happens, depends on how rapidly the attack by a nucleophile follows on the initial ionisation step. If the second reaction follows closely upon the first, it may be that the receding anion, e.g. $Br^{\ominus}$, may still be only a few molecular diameters away and thus attack by an approaching nucleophile is inhibited on the side of the carbonium ion to which the bromine was originally attached. Attack on the 'backside' of the carbonium ion is unaffected, however, and will thus preponderate, leading to more inversion than retention of configuration in the product, i.e. racemisation with some inversion will be observed in the product.

What is thus observed in practice, under S_N1 conditions, may range from virtually complete racemisation to almost total inversion of configuration depending on how rapidly attack by a nucleophile follows on the initial ionisation. The most common situation is mainly racemisation attended by some inversion, the relative proportions of the two seen with a particular substrate being profoundly influenced by the conditions under which the reaction is carried out. If the solvent can act as a nucleophile, e.g. H_2O, attack is likely to be more rapid, because of its very large relative concentration, than if the presence of an added nucleophile, $Y^{\ominus}$, is necessary, thus leading to a relatively higher proportion of inversion. A good solvating solvent such as water is particularly effective in this respect because of the rapidity with which the incipient carbonium ion collects a solvating envelope around itself.

(iv) $S_N i$ mechanism

Despite what has been said above of replacement reactions leading to inversion of configuration or racemisation or, in some cases, a mixture of both, a few cases are known of reactions that proceed with retention of configuration, i.e. in which the starting material and product have the same configuration. One case in which this has been shown to occur is in the replacement of **OH** by **Cl** by the use of thionyl chloride. This reaction has been shown to follow second order kinetics, i.e. rate $\propto [\mathbf{R \cdot OH}][\mathbf{SOCl_2}]$, but it clearly cannot proceed according to an unmodified $S_N 2$ mechanism for this would lead to inversion of configuration which is not observed. It has been interpreted mechanistically as follows:

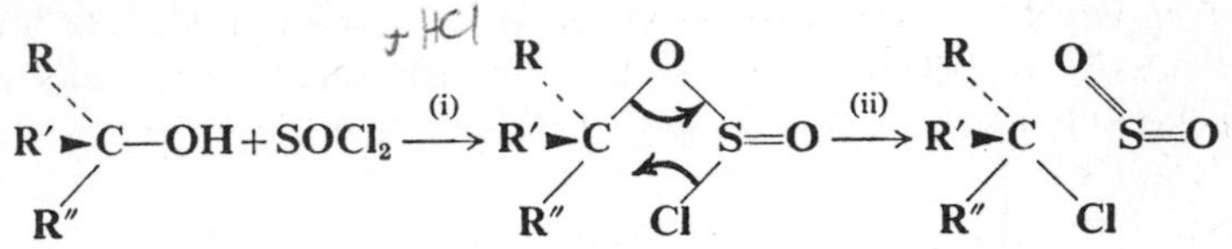

(VIII)

No change in configuration can take place in stage (i) as the **C—O** bond is not broken and in the second stage, where this bond is broken, attack by **Cl** takes place from the same side of the carbon atom because of the orientation of the intermediate (VIII). A close study of the reaction has suggested that the second stage exhibits some $S_N 1$ character in that the breakdown of (VIII) probably proceeds through an ion pair (*cf.* p. 80):

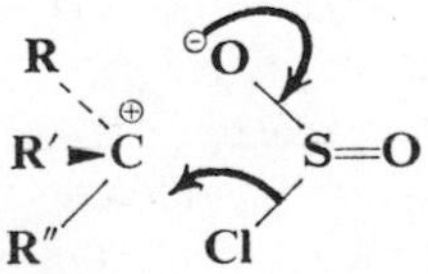

The chlorosulphite anion then breaks down to SO_2 and $Cl^{\ominus}$ so rapidly that $Cl^{\ominus}$ is available for frontal attack on the carbonium ion before the

69

latter has had time to collapse to the planar state, thus leading to a product having the same configuration as the starting material. This is admittedly an *ad hoc* explanation but support for it has been obtained by the fact that compounds such as (VIII), alkyl chlorosulphites, can actually be isolated and then shown to undergo extremely ready conversion to alkyl halide $+ SO_2$. If, however, the reaction is carried out in the presence of base, e.g. pyridine, the hydrogen chloride liberated in forming the chlorosulphite in stage (i) is converted to $Cl^\ominus$; this then readily attacks (VIII) 'from the back' with the expulsion of $^\ominus O \cdot SO \cdot Cl$. The reaction is now of a normal S_N2 type, proceeding with inversion, and the somewhat specialised S_Ni (Substitution Nucleophilic internal) mechanism, with retention of configuration, is no longer observed.

(v) Neighbouring group participation

There are also a number of other cases of replacement reactions in which retention of configuration takes place but these can all be shown to have one feature in common: an atom, close to the carbon undergoing the displacement reaction, which carries a negative charge or has an unshared pair of electrons, i.e. which can act as an 'internal' nucleophilic reagent. Thus in the alkaline hydrolysis of the β-chlorohydrin (IX)

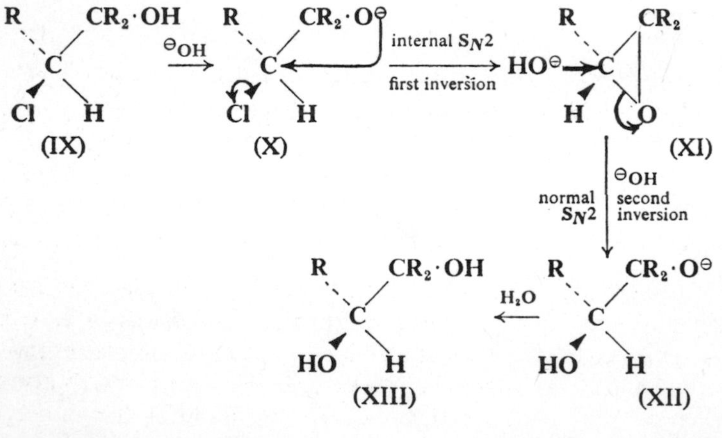

the first stage is conversion of the **OH** to the corresponding alkoxide ion (X). This ion, acting as a nucleophile, then attacks the carbon atom carrying chlorine 'from the back' in an internal S_N2 reaction that results in inversion of configuration at this carbon and the formation of the cyclic intermediate (XI), an alkylene oxide or epoxide. The three-membered ring is then reopened by the action of $^{\ominus}OH$, attack taking place at the less heavily substituted of the two carbon atoms (i.e. the one that originally carried the chlorine in this case) as this will be the more positive of the two, its electron availability being enhanced by the inductive effect of only one rather than of two alkyl groups. This attack will also be of the S_N2 type, from the side to which the chlorine was originally attached, resulting in a second inversion of configuration at this carbon atom. The reaction is completed by conversion of the alkoxide ion (XII) to the alcohol (XIII). This alcohol will have the same configuration as the original chloride (IX) but it would hardly be true to say that the overall reaction had proceeded with retention of configuration for, in fact, the *apparent* retention of configuration has been brought about by two successive inversions. This, of course, distinguishes such a reaction type from S_Ni which is attended by a *real* retention of configuration.

Evidence for this overall picture of the reaction is provided by the actual isolation of the epoxides postulated as intermediates and the demonstration that they may be hydrolysed under the conditions of the reaction and with results as observed above.

A similar apparent retention of configuration occurs in the hydrolysis of α-halogenated acids in dilute alkaline solution

(XIV)

but here the suggested cyclic intermediate (XIV), an α-lactone, has not actually been isolated. If the reaction is carried out in extremely concentrated base, $[^{\ominus}OH]$ is then large enough to compete effectively with the internal attack by $-CO_2^{\ominus}$ and the normal one stage S_N2 reaction then yields a product whose configuration has undergone inversion. At intermediate concentrations of base both reactions take place, i.e. retention of configuration with a varying degree of racemisation is observed.

Even if no stereochemical point is at issue, participation of neighbouring groups can be of interest because of their possible effect on the rate of reaction. Thus $ClCH_2 \cdot CH_2 \cdot SEt$ may be hydrolysed approximately 10,000 times as rapidly as $ClCH_2 \cdot CH_2 \cdot OEt$ under the same conditions. This is far too large a difference for it to be due to inductive or steric effects in such simple molecules and is thought to arise from the rate-determining formation of a cyclic sulphonium salt (XV) which, being highly strained, undergoes extremely ready and rapid hydrolysis:

$$
\text{EtS:} \overset{\curvearrowright}{} CH_2 \overset{\curvearrowleft}{} Cl \xrightarrow[\text{determining}]{\text{rate-}} \overset{\oplus}{EtS} - CH_2 \xrightarrow[\substack{\text{very} \\ \text{rapid}}]{H_2O} \text{EtS:} \quad CH_2 - OH
$$
$$
\underset{CH_2}{} \qquad \underset{\substack{CH_2 \\ {}^{\ominus}Cl \ \ (XV)}}{} \qquad \underset{CH_2}{} \quad + H^{\oplus}
$$

The oxygen in the ether, $ClCH_2 \cdot CH_2 \cdot OEt$, being more electronegative, does not part with its unshared electrons so readily as sulphur, hence no cyclic salt is formed and the chlorine undergoes hydrolysis by a normal displacement reaction. Suitable nitrogen-containing compounds also show such enhanced ease of hydrolysis proceeding via ethyleneimmonium ions such as (XVI):

$$
Me_2N: \overset{\curvearrowright}{} CH_2 \overset{\curvearrowleft}{} Cl \xrightarrow[\text{determining}]{\text{rate}} \overset{\oplus}{Me_2N} - CH_2 \xrightarrow[\text{rapid}]{{}^{\ominus}OH} Me_2N: \quad CH_2 - OH
$$
$$
\underset{CH_2}{} \qquad \underset{\substack{CH_2 \\ {}^{\ominus}Cl \ \ (XVI)}}{} \qquad \underset{CH_2}{}
$$

Their hydrolysis normally proceeds less rapidly than that of similar sulphur compounds, however, reflecting the greater stability of the cyclic nitrogen, as compared with the cyclic sulphur, intermediates.

These features are of interest in relation to the classical vesicant agents of chemical warfare such as mustard gas itself, $S(CH_2 \cdot CH_2Cl)_2$ and the related nitrogen mustards such as $MeN(CH_2 \cdot CH_2Cl)_2$. The cyclic immonium derivatives obtained as intermediates during the hydrolytic destruction of the latter have the additional hazard of being powerful neurotoxins.

EFFECT OF ENTERING AND LEAVING GROUPS

Changing the nucleophilic reagent employed, i.e. *the entering group*, is not going to alter the rate of an S_N1 displacement reaction, e.g. of a halide, for this reagent does not take part in the rate-determining step of the reaction. With an S_N2 displacement, however, the more strongly nucleophilic the reagent the more the reaction will be promoted. The 'nucleophilicity' of the reagent can broadly be equated with the extent to which it has available electrons, i.e. with its basic strength. This parallel, though useful, is by no means exact, however, for in a displacement reaction an ion such as $Y^\ominus$ is usually showing nucleophilicity for carbon while when acting as a base it is exhibiting nucleophilicity for hydrogen and nucleophilic attack on carbon is usually much more subject to steric influences than is coordination with a proton. The parallel can however be used as a general guide with fair success, particularly if the *attacking atom* of the nucleophiles considered is the same in each case. Thus strong bases such as $EtO^\ominus$ and $HO^\ominus$ are more strongly nucleophilic agents than weak bases such as $Me \cdot CO_2{}^\ominus$. From what has already been said about the effect of change of reagent on the two types of mechanism, it follows that in the displacement of any particular atom or group, the more powerfully nucleophilic the reagent employed the greater is the chance of the reaction proceeding by the S_N2 route. Thus as the series H_2O, $Me \cdot CO_2{}^\ominus$, $PhO^\ominus$, $HO^\ominus$, $EtO^\ominus$ is traversed, it may well be that a displacement reaction of $R \cdot Hal$ which started by being S_N1 with H_2O or $Me \cdot CO_2{}^\ominus$ has changed over to S_N2 by the time $EtO^\ominus$ is reached.

So far as change of *attacking atom* in a nucleophile is concerned, it is broadly true, within a single group or subgroup of the periodic table, that the larger the atom the greater its nucleophilic reactivity; thus decreasing reactivities $I^\ominus > Br^\ominus > Cl^\ominus > F^\ominus$ and $RS^\ominus > RO^\ominus$ are observed. This is probably due to the fact that as the atom increases in size, the hold the nucleus has on the peripheral electrons decreases, with the result that they become more readily polarisable leading to bonding interaction at greater internuclear distances. Also the larger the ion or group the less its solvation energy, which means the less energy that has to be supplied to it in order to remove, in whole or in part, its envelope of solvent molecules so as to get it into a condition in which it will attack a carbon atom. It is a combination of these two factors which makes the large $I^\ominus$ a better nucleophile than the small $F^\ominus$, despite the fact that the latter is a considerably stronger base than the former.

So far as the *leaving group*, i.e. the one expelled or displaced, in an S_N2 reaction is concerned, the more easily the C-leaving group bond can be distorted the more readily the transition state will be formed, so here again ready polarisability is an advantage. Thus ease of expulsion decreases in the series $I^\ominus > Br^\ominus > Cl^\ominus > F^\ominus$; this, of course, exemplifies the well-known decrease in reactivity seen as we go from alkyl iodide to alkyl fluoride. The fact that $I^\ominus$ can both attack and be displaced so readily means that it is often used as a catalyst in nucleophilic reactions, the desired reaction being facilitated via successive attacks on and displacements from the centre under attack:

$$RCl + H_2O \xrightarrow{\text{slow}} R \cdot OH + H^\oplus + Cl^\ominus$$

$$RCl + I^\ominus \xrightarrow[\text{fast}]{} Cl^\ominus + RI$$

$$I^\ominus + H^\oplus + R \cdot OH$$

The overall effect is thus facilitation of the hydrolysis of **RCl**, which does not readily take place directly, via the easy formation of **RI** ($I^\ominus$ as an effective attacking agent) followed by its ready hydrolysis ($I^\ominus$ as an effective leaving agent).

In general terms, it can be said that the more basic the leaving group the less easily can it be displaced by an attacking nucleophile; thus strongly basic groups such as $RO^\ominus$, $HO^\ominus$, $H_2N^\ominus$ and $F^\ominus$, bound to carbon by small atoms that may not readily be polarised, cannot normally be displaced under ordinary conditions. They can, however, be displaced in acid solution due to initial protonation providing a positively charged species (rather than a neutral molecule) for the nucleophile to attack, and resulting in readier displacement of the much less basic **YH** rather than $Y^\ominus$:

$$R \cdot \overset{..}{O}H \xrightarrow{H^\oplus} R \cdot \underset{\oplus}{\overset{H}{\overset{..}{O}}}H \xrightarrow{Br^\ominus} RBr + H_2O$$

Thus even the extremely tightly held fluorine in alkyl fluorides may be displaced by nucleophilic reagents in concentrated sulphuric acid solution. The use of hydrogen iodide to cleave ethers

$$Ph \cdot \overset{..}{O} \cdot R \xrightarrow{H^\oplus} Ph \cdot \underset{\oplus}{\overset{H}{\overset{..}{O}}} \cdot R \xrightarrow{I^\ominus} Ph \cdot OH + RI$$

is due to the fact that $I^\ominus$ is the most powerful nucleophile that can be obtained in the strongly acid solution that is necessary to make reaction possible.

The leaving group in an S_N1 reaction determines the reaction rate; the lower the energy of the C-leaving group bond and the greater the tendency of the leaving group to form an anion, the more readily the reaction will proceed via the S_N1 mechanism.

NITROSATION OF AMINES

In the examples considered to date it is carbon that has been undergoing nucleophilic attack but similar attack may also take place on nitrogen as, for example, in the nitrosation of amines where the amine acts as the nucleophile:

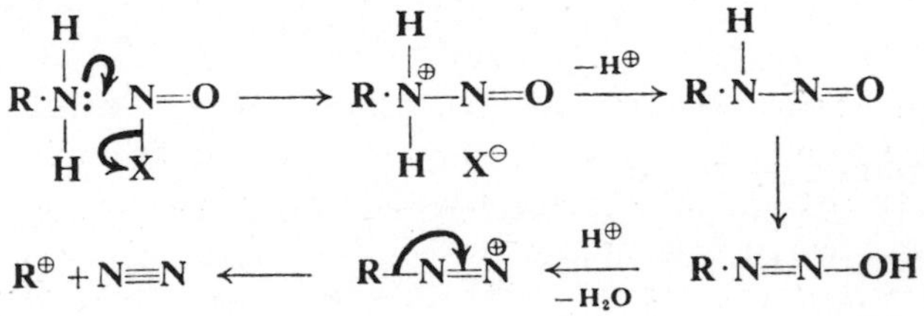

In the familiar reaction of primary amines with nitrites and acid, the species that is acting as the effective nitrosating agent has been shown to depend on the conditions though it is apparently never HNO_2 itself. Thus at low acidity $N_2O_3(X = ONO)$ obtained by

$$2HNO_2 \rightleftharpoons ONO—NO + H_2O$$

is thought to be the effective nitrosating agent while as the acidity increases it is first protonated nitrous acid, $H_2\overset{\oplus}{O}—NO(X = H_2O^{\oplus})$ and finally the nitrosonium ion $^{\oplus}NO$ (*cf.* p. 106), though nitrosyl halides, e.g. $NOCl$, also play a part in the presence of halogen acids. Though the latter are more powerful nitrosating agents than N_2O_3, the reaction with aliphatic amines is nevertheless inhibited by increasing acidity as the nucleophilic $R \cdot NH_2$ is a relatively strong base which is progressively converted into the unreactive cation, $R \cdot \overset{\oplus}{N}H_3$.

With aliphatic primary amines the carbonium ion obtained by breakdown of the highly unstable $R \cdot N_2^{\oplus}$ can lead to the formation of a wide range of ultimate products (*cf.* p. 85). The instability of the diazonium cation is due to the very great stability of the N_2 that may be obtained by its breakdown, but with aromatic primary amines some stabilisation of this cation is conferred by delocalisation via the π orbital system of the aromatic nucleus

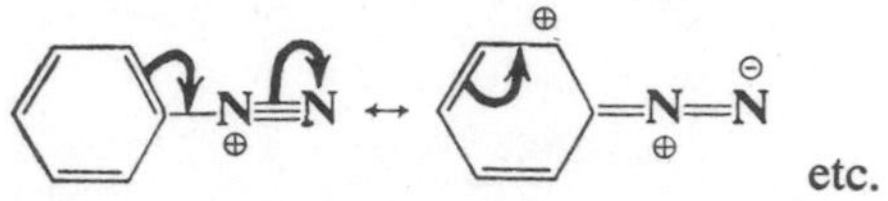

etc.

and diazonium salts may be obtained from such amines provided the conditions are mild. Such diazotisation must normally be carried out under conditions of fairly high acidity (*a*) to provide a powerful nitrosating agent, for primary aromatic amines are not very powerful nucleophiles (due to interaction of the electron pair on nitrogen with the π orbital system of the nucleus, p. 118) and (*b*) to reduce the $\rightleftharpoons$ concentration of $\mathbf{Ar \cdot NH_2}$ by converting it to $\mathbf{Ar \cdot \overset{\oplus}{N}H_3}$ ($\mathbf{Ar \cdot NH_2}$ is a very much weaker base than $\mathbf{R \cdot NH_2}$, p. 52) so as to avoid as yet undiazotised amine undergoing azo-coupling with the first formed $\mathbf{Ar \cdot \overset{\oplus}{N}_2}$ (*cf.* p. 115).

Reaction also takes place with the secondary amines but cannot proceed further than the N-nitroso compound, $\mathbf{R_2N{-}N{=}O}$, while with tertiary aliphatic amines the readily decomposed nitroso-trialkylammonium cation, $\mathbf{R_3\overset{\oplus}{N}{-}NO}$ is obtained. With aromatic tertiary amines such as N-dialkylanilines, however, attack can take place on the activated nucleus (*cf.* p. 106) to yield a **C**-nitroso compound:

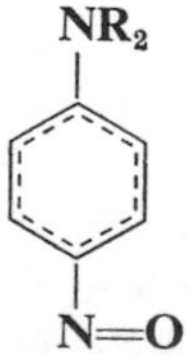

OTHER NUCLEOPHILIC DISPLACEMENT REACTIONS

In the discussion of nucleophilic substitution at a saturated carbon atom, the attack on halides by negatively charged ions, e.g. $\mathbf{HO^{\ominus}}$ and $\mathbf{EtO^{\ominus}}$, has been used almost exclusively to illustrate the mechanism of the reactions involved. In fact this type of reaction is extremely widespread in organic chemistry and embraces very many more types than those of which passing mention has been made. Thus other typical examples include:

(i) The formation of a tetralkylammonium salt

$$R_3N: + RBr \rightarrow R_3\overset{\oplus}{N}:R + Br^{\ominus}$$

where the unshared pair of electrons on nitrogen attack carbon with the expulsion of a bromide ion; and also the breakdown of such a salt

$$Br^{\ominus} + R:\overset{\oplus}{N}R_3 \rightarrow BrR + :NR_3$$

in which it is the bromide ion that acts as a nucleophile and $:NR_3$ that is expelled as the leaving group. An exactly similar situation is, of course, met with in the formation of sulphonium salts

$$R_2S: + RBr \rightarrow R_2\overset{\oplus}{S}:R + Br^{\ominus}$$

and in their breakdown.

(ii) The alkylation of reactive methylene groups etc. (*cf.* p. 221):

$$EtO^{\ominus} + CH_2(CO_2Et)_2 \rightarrow EtOH + \overset{\ominus}{C}H(CO_2Et)_2$$

$$(EtO_2C)_2HC^{\ominus} + RBr \rightarrow (EtO_2C)_2HC \cdot R + Br^{\ominus}$$

Here, and in the next two examples, a carbanion or a source of negative carbon is acting as the nucleophile.

(iii) Reactions of acetylene in the presence of strong base, e.g. $NaNH_2$ in liquid NH_3:

$$H_2N^{\ominus} + HC\equiv CH \rightarrow H_3N + \overset{\ominus}{C}\equiv CH$$

$$HC\equiv C^{\ominus} + RBr \rightarrow HC\equiv C \cdot R + Br^{\ominus}$$

(iv) Reaction of Grignard reagents:

$$\overset{\delta+}{BrMg} \cdot \overset{\delta-}{R} + R'Br \rightarrow Br_2Mg + R \cdot R'$$

(v) Decomposition of diazonium salts in water:

$$H_2O: + PhN_2{}^{\oplus} \rightarrow \underset{H}{H\overset{\oplus}{O}:Ph} + N_2$$

$$\underset{H}{H\overset{\oplus}{O}:Ph} \rightarrow HO:Ph + H^{\oplus}$$

(vi) The formation of alkyl halides:

$$\text{R} \cdot \overset{..}{\underset{..}{\text{O}}} \text{H} + \text{H}^{\oplus} \rightarrow \text{R} \cdot \overset{\oplus}{\underset{\text{H}}{\text{O}}} \text{H}$$

$$\text{Br}^{\ominus} + \text{R} \cdot \overset{\oplus}{\underset{\underset{\text{H}}{..}}{\text{O}}} \text{H} \rightarrow \text{BrR} + \text{H}_2\text{O}$$

(vii) The cleavage of ethers:

$$\text{Ph} \cdot \overset{..}{\underset{..}{\text{O}}} \cdot \text{R} + \text{H}^{\oplus} \rightarrow \text{Ph} \cdot \overset{\oplus}{\underset{\text{H}}{\text{O}}} \cdot \text{R}$$

$$\text{Ph} \cdot \overset{\oplus}{\underset{\text{H}}{\text{O}}} \cdot \text{R} + \text{I}^{\ominus} \rightarrow \text{Ph} \cdot \text{OH} + \text{RI}$$

(viii) The formation of esters:

$$\text{R}' \cdot \text{CO}_2^{\ominus} + \text{RBr} \rightarrow \text{R}' \cdot \text{CO}_2\text{R} + \text{Br}^{\ominus}$$

(ix) The formation of ethers:

$$\text{R} \cdot \text{O}^{\ominus} + \text{R}'\text{Br} \rightarrow \text{R} \cdot \text{O} \cdot \text{R}' + \text{Br}^{\ominus}$$

(x) LiAlH$_4$ reduction of halides:

$$\text{LiAlH}_4 + \text{RBr} \rightarrow \text{LiAlH}_3\text{Br} + \text{HR}$$

Here the complex hydride is, essentially, acting as a carrier for hydride ion, $\text{H}^{\ominus}$, which is the effective nucleophile.

(xi) Ring fission in epoxides:

$$\text{Cl}^{\ominus} \, \text{CH}_2 \!\!-\!\! \text{CH}_2 \rightarrow \text{Cl} \cdot \text{CH}_2 \cdot \text{CH}_2 \cdot \text{O}^{\ominus}$$

$$\text{Cl} \cdot \text{CH}_2 \cdot \text{CH}_2 \cdot \text{O}^{\ominus} + \text{H}_2\text{O} \rightarrow \text{Cl} \cdot \text{CH}_2 \cdot \text{CH}_2 \cdot \text{OH} + {}^{\ominus}\text{OH}$$

Here it is the relief of strain achieved on opening the three-membered ring that is responsible for the ready attack by a weak nucleophile.

This is only a very small selection: there are many more displacement reactions of preparative utility and synthetic importance.

It will be noticed from these examples that the attacking nucleophile need not of necessity be an anion with a full-blown negative charge (e.g. $HO^{\ominus}$, $Br^{\ominus}$, $(EtO_2C)_2HC^{\ominus}$) but it must at least have unshared electron pairs available (e.g. $R_3N:$, $R_2S:$) with which to attack a positive carbon or other atom. Equally the species that is attacked may be a cation with a full-blown positive charge (e.g. $R_3\overset{\oplus}{N}:R$), but more commonly it is a neutral molecule (e.g. RBr). It must, of course, also be remembered that what is a nucleophilic attack from the point of view of one participant will be an electrophilic attack from the point of view of the other. Our attitude, and hence normal classification of reactions, tends to be formed by somewhat arbitrary preconceptions about what constitutes a reagent as opposed to a substrate (*cf.* p. 27). Overall, the most common nucleophile of preparative significance is probably $HO^{\ominus}$ or, producing essentially the same result, H_2O, especially when the latter is the solvent and therefore present in extremely high concentration.

Hardly surprisingly, not all displacement reactions proceed so as to yield nothing but the desired product. Side reactions may take place yielding both unexpected and unwanted products, particularly elimination reactions to yield unsaturated compounds; the origin of these is discussed subsequently (p. 189).

4 CARBONIUM IONS, ELECTRON-DEFICIENT N AND O ATOMS AND THEIR REACTIONS

REFERENCE has already been made in the last chapter to the generation of carbonium ions as intermediates in displacement reactions at a saturated carbon atom, e.g. the hydrolysis of an alkyl halide that take place via the S_N1 mechanism. Carbonium ions are, however, fairly widespread in occurrence and although their existence is normally only transient, they are of considerable importance in a wide variety of chemical reactions.

METHODS OF FORMATION OF CARBONIUM IONS

(i) Direct ionisation

This has already been commented on in the last chapter, e.g.

$$Me_3CCl \rightarrow Me_3C^{\oplus} + Cl^{\ominus}$$
$$Ph \cdot CH_2Cl \rightarrow Ph \cdot CH_2^{\oplus} + Cl^{\ominus}$$
$$CH_2{=}CH \cdot CH_2Cl \rightarrow CH_2{=}CH \cdot CH_2^{\oplus} + Cl^{\ominus}$$
$$Me \cdot O \cdot CH_2Cl \rightarrow Me \cdot O \cdot CH_2^{\oplus} + Cl^{\ominus}$$

It should be emphasised however that a highly polar, ion-solvating medium is usually necessary and that it is *ionisation* (i.e. the formation of an ion pair) rather than *dissociation* that may actually be taking place.

The question of how the relative stability, and consequent ease of formation, of carbonium ions is influenced by their structure will be discussed below (p. 82).

(ii) Protonation

This may, for instance, occur directly by addition to an unsaturated linkage, e.g. in the acid-catalysed hydration of olefines (p. 143):

$$-CH{=}CH- \underset{}{\overset{H^{\oplus}}{\rightleftharpoons}} -CH_2-\overset{\oplus}{C}H- \underset{}{\overset{H_2O}{\rightleftharpoons}} -CH_2-\underset{\overset{|}{\oplus OH_2}}{CH} \underset{}{\overset{-H^{\oplus}}{\rightleftharpoons}} -CH_2-\underset{\overset{|}{OH}}{CH-}$$

This reaction is, of course, reversible and the reverse reaction, the acid-catalysed dehydration of alcohols, is probably more familiar. A proton may also add on to a carbon–oxygen double bond

$$>\!\!C\!\!=\!\!O \;\overset{H\oplus}{\rightleftharpoons}\; >\!\!\overset{\oplus}{C}\!\!-\!\!OH \;\overset{Y\ominus}{\rightleftharpoons}\; >\!\!C\!\!\overset{OH}{\underset{Y}{<}}$$

as in the acid-catalysed addition of some anions, $Y^{\ominus}$, to an aldehyde or ketone, the addition of proton to the $>\!\!C\!\!=\!\!O$ providing a highly positive carbon atom for attack by the anion. That such protonation does indeed take place is confirmed by the fact that many ketones showed double the theoretical freezing-point depression when dissolved in concentrated sulphuric acid due to:

$$>\!\!C\!\!=\!\!O + H_2SO_4 \;\rightleftharpoons\; >\!\!\overset{\oplus}{C}\!\!-\!\!OH + HSO_4^{\ominus}$$

That the ketones undergo no irreversible change in the process may be shown by subsequent dilution of the sulphuric acid solution with water when the ketone may be recovered unchanged.

A similar result may also be obtained by the use of other electron deficient species, i.e. Lewis acids:

$$>\!\!C\!\!=\!\!O + AlCl_3 \;\rightleftharpoons\; >\!\!\overset{\oplus}{C}\!\!-\!\!O\overset{\ominus}{A}lCl_3$$

Carbonium ions may also be generated where an atom containing unshared electrons is protonated, the actual carbonium ion being generated subsequently by the removal of this atom:

$$R\!\!-\!\!\underset{\cdot\cdot}{O}\!\!-\!\!H + H^{\oplus} \;\rightleftharpoons\; R\!\!-\!\!\overset{\oplus}{\underset{\overset{|}{H}}{O}}\!\!-\!\!H \;\rightleftharpoons\; R^{\oplus} + H_2O$$

This is, of course, one of the steps in the acid-catalysed dehydration of alcohols mentioned above. It may also be encountered in the acid-catalysed decomposition of ethers, esters, anhydrides, etc.:

$$R\!\cdot\!\underset{\cdot\cdot}{O}\!\cdot\!R + H^{\oplus} \;\rightleftharpoons\; R\!\cdot\!\overset{\oplus}{\underset{\overset{|}{H}}{O}}\!\cdot\!R \;\rightleftharpoons\; R^{\oplus} + HO\!\cdot\!R$$

$$R\!\cdot\!CO\!\cdot\!\underset{\cdot\cdot}{O}\!\cdot\!R' + H^{\oplus} \;\rightleftharpoons\; R\!\cdot\!CO\!\cdot\!\overset{\oplus}{\underset{\overset{|}{H}}{O}}\!\cdot\!R' \;\rightleftharpoons\; R\!\cdot\!\overset{\oplus}{C}O + HO\!\cdot\!R'$$

$$R\!\cdot\!CO\!\cdot\!\underset{\cdot\cdot}{O}\!\cdot\!CO\!\cdot\!R + H^{\oplus} \;\rightleftharpoons\; R\!\cdot\!CO\!\cdot\!\overset{\oplus}{\underset{\overset{|}{H}}{O}}\!\cdot\!CO\!\cdot\!R \;\rightleftharpoons\; R\!\cdot\!\overset{\oplus}{C}O + HO_2C\!\cdot\!R$$

D.

In the two latter cases it is an acyl carbonium ion that may be momentarily formed, in contrast to the alkyl ones that we have seen so far. This acyl carbonium ion reacts with water to yield the corresponding fatty acid and regenerates a proton:

$$R \cdot \overset{\oplus}{C}O + H_2O \;\rightleftharpoons\; R \cdot CO \cdot \underset{H}{\overset{\oplus}{O}H} \;\rightleftharpoons\; R \cdot CO_2H + H^{\oplus}$$

The reversal of this, and of the second reaction above, are involved in some examples of the acid-catalysed formation of an ester from the corresponding acid and alcohol (p. 187).

(iii) Decomposition

The most common example is the decomposition of a diazonium salt, $R \cdot N_2{}^{\oplus}$:

$$[R\!-\!\overset{\curvearrowright}{N}\!\!=\!\!\overset{\oplus}{N} \leftrightarrow R\!-\!\overset{\oplus}{N}\!\!\equiv\!\!N] \;\rightarrow\; R^{\oplus} + N_2$$

This may be observed with both aromatic and aliphatic diazonium compounds but, under suitable conditions, these may also undergo decomposition to yield free radicals (p. 255).

The catalysis of a number of nucleophilic displacement reactions of halides by $Ag^{\oplus}$ is due to 'electrophilic pull' on the halogen atom by the heavy metal cation:

$$Ag^{\oplus} + Br\!-\!R \;\rightarrow\; AgBr + R^{\oplus}$$

The presence of $Ag^{\oplus}$ may thus have the effect of inducing a shift in mechanistic type from S_N2 to S_N1 but the kinetic picture is often complicated by the fact that the precipitated silver halide may itself act as a heterogeneous catalyst for the displacement reaction.

It should be emphasised that the methods of formation of carbonium ions considered above are not intended to constitute a definitive list.

THE STABILITY OF CARBONIUM IONS

The major factor influencing the stability of carbonium ions is that the more the positive charge may be shared among nearby atoms the greater will be the stability of the ion. This is particularly marked where the charge-spreading may take place through the intervention of suitably placed π orbitals, e.g.

$$CH_2\!=\!CH\!-\!\overset{\oplus}{C}H_2 \leftrightarrow \overset{\oplus}{C}H_2\!-\!CH\!=\!CH_2$$

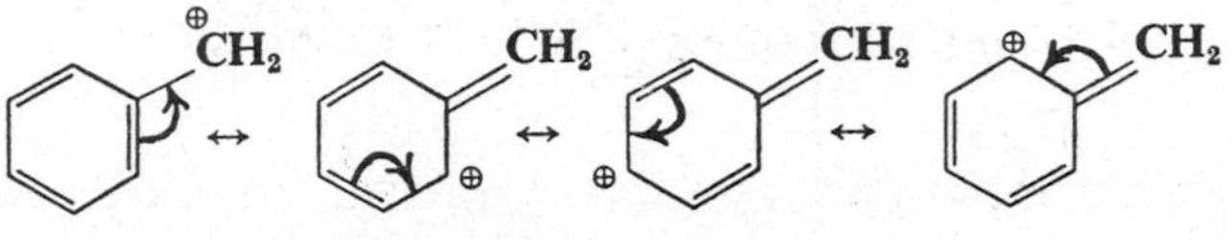

leading to carbonium ions characteristically stabilised by delocalisation.

An interesting example of a carbonium ion being more stable than might have been envisaged is the one that can arise from β-phenylethyl derivatives, $Ph \cdot CH_2 \cdot CH_2 \cdot Y$. The carbonium ion, $Ph \cdot CH_2 \cdot \overset{\oplus}{C}H_2$, supposedly involved, would not be markedly stabilised by the phenyl group on the β-carbon atom for this is too far away to exert any marked inductive effect and delocalisation via its π orbitals is prevented by the intervening saturated carbon atom. It has, therefore, been suggested on this and other evidence that the carbonium ion involved is actually a bridged structure, a *phenonium* ion

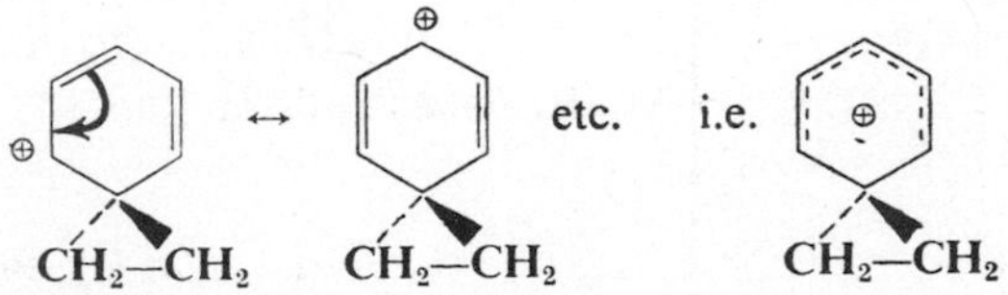

that *can* stabilise itself by delocalisation via the π orbitals of the aromatic nucleus.

The most stable carbonium ion of all is derived from cycloheptatrienyl (tropylium) bromide which ostensibly has the structure:

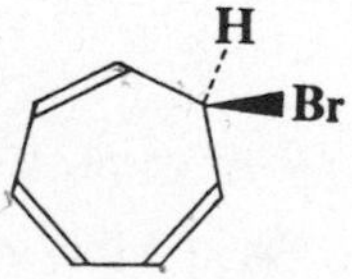

It is found, however, to be highly water-soluble, yielding bromide ions and the evidence is overwhelming that it produces, in solution, a carbonium ion that is so stable that its reaction with water, alcohols, etc., is quite slow. The reason for this quite outstanding stability is that in the tropylium cation, the seven-membered ring possesses six π electrons, which can spread themselves over the seven carbon atoms in delocalised orbitals (*cf.* benzene, p. 9), thereby conferring on the ion quasi-aromatic stability:

The simple alkyl carbonium ions have already been seen (p. 62) to follow the stability sequence

$$\overset{\oplus}{Me_3C} > \overset{\oplus}{Me_2CH} > \overset{\oplus}{MeCH_2} > \overset{\oplus}{CH_3}$$

due to the fact that increasing substitution of the carbonium ion carbon atom by methyl groups results in increasing delocalisation of the charge by both inductive and hyperconjugative effects. But stabilisation here and in other cases requires that the carbonium ion should be planar, for it is only in this state that effective delocalisation can occur. As planarity is departed from or its attainment inhibited, instability of the ion, with consequent difficulty in its initial formation, increases very rapidly. This has already been seen in the extreme inertness of 1-bromotriptycene, where inability to assume a planar state prevents formation of a carbonium ion with consequent inertness to S_N1 attack (p. 65).

This great preference for the planar state, if at all possible, effectively settles the question of the stereochemistry of simple carbonium ions.

TYPES OF REACTION UNDERGONE BY CARBONIUM IONS

Essentially, carbonium ions can undergo three main types of reaction:

(*a*) combination with a nucleophile,
(*b*) elimination of a proton,
(*c*) rearrangement of structure.

It should be noted that (*c*) will result in a further carbonium ion which may then undergo (*a*) or (*b*) before a stable product is obtained.

All these possibilities are nicely illustrated in the reaction of nitrous acid with n-propylamine:

$$Me \cdot CH_2 \cdot CH_2 \cdot \overset{\oplus}{N}_2 \xleftarrow[\text{NaNO}_2]{\text{HCl}} Me \cdot CH_2 \cdot CH_2 \cdot NH_2$$

$$Me \cdot CH_2 \cdot CH_2 \cdot OH + H^{\oplus}$$
(II)

$$(a) \; H_2O$$

$$N_2 + Me \cdot CH_2 \cdot \overset{\oplus}{CH_2} \xrightarrow{(b) -H^{\oplus}} Me \cdot CH{=}CH_2 \quad \text{(III)}$$
(I)

$$(c) \qquad (b) \quad -H^{\oplus}$$

$$Me \cdot \overset{\oplus}{CH} \cdot Me \xrightarrow[\text{H}_2\text{O}]{(a)} Me \cdot CH(OH) \cdot Me + H^{\oplus}$$
(IV) (V)

Thus reaction of the n-propyl cation (I) with water as nucleophile, i.e. (a), yields n-propanol (II), elimination of a proton from the adjacent carbon atom, (b), yields propylene (III), while rearrangement, (c), in this case migration of hydrogen, yields the isopropyl cation (IV), which can then undergo (b) or (a) to yield more propylene (III) or isopropanol (V), respectively. The products obtained in a typical experiment were n-propanol, 7 per cent, propylene, 28 per cent and isopropanol, 32 per cent; the greater stability of the iso-, rather than the n-, propyl cation being reflected in the much greater amount of the secondary alcohol produced.

This has not exhausted the possibilities however for reaction of either carbonium ion with other nucleophiles present in the system can obviously lead to further products. Thus $NO_2^{\ominus}$ from sodium nitrite may lead to the formation of $R \cdot NO_2$ and $R \cdot ONO$ (the latter may also arise from direct esterification of first formed $R \cdot OH$), $Cl^{\ominus}$ from the acid may lead to $R \cdot Cl$, first formed $R \cdot OH$ be converted to $R \cdot O \cdot R$ and as yet unchanged $R \cdot NH_2$ to $R \cdot NH \cdot R$. The mixture of products actually obtained is, hardly surprisingly, greatly influenced by the conditions under which the reaction is carried out but it will come as no surprise that this reaction is, in the aliphatic series, seldom a satisfactory preparative method for the conversion of $R \cdot NH_2 \rightarrow R \cdot OH$!

An analogous situation is observed in the Friedel-Crafts alkylation of benzene with n-propyl bromide in the presence of gallium bromide. Here the attacking species, if not an actual carbonium ion, is a highly polarised complex (p. 109) $\overset{\delta+ \; \delta-}{RGaBr_4}$, and the greater stability of the complex which carries its positive charge on a secondary, rather than a primary, carbon atom, i.e. $\overset{\delta+}{Me_2}CH\overset{\delta-}{GaBr_4}$ rather than $Me \cdot \overset{\delta+}{CH_2} \cdot \overset{\delta-}{CH_2}GaBr_4$, again results in a hydride shift so that the major product of the reaction is actually isopropylbenzene.

That such rearrangements need not always be quite as simple as they look, however, i.e. mere migration of hydrogen, is illustrated by the behaviour with $AlBr_3$ of propane in which a terminal carbon atom is labelled with ^{13}C, when partial transfer of the labelled carbon to the 2-position occurs. This is presumably due to

$$Me—CH_2—CH_3 + AlBr_3 \; \rightleftharpoons \; (Me)CH_2—\overset{\oplus}{C}H_2 \cdot H\overset{\ominus}{AlBr_3}$$

$$CH_3—CH_2—Me + AlBr_3 \; \rightleftharpoons \; \overset{\oplus}{C}H_2—CH_2—Me \cdot H\overset{\ominus}{AlBr_3}$$

which *may* happen in cases such as the above where it is only hydrogen that has *apparently* moved.

The elimination reactions of carbonium ions will be discussed further below (p. 191) when elimination reactions in general are dealt with, but their rearrangement merits further study.

THE REARRANGEMENT OF CARBONIUM IONS

Despite the apparent confusion introduced above by the isomerisation of propane, the rearrangement reactions of carbonium ions can be divided essentially into those in which a change of actual carbon skeleton does, or does not, take place; the former are the more important but the latter will be briefly mentioned first.

(i) Without change in carbon skeleton

(a) **Allylic rearrangements:** A classical example of this variety may occur where the carbonium ion formed is stabilised by delocalisation, e.g. in the S_N1 solvolysis of 3-chlorobut-1-ene, $Me \cdot CHCl \cdot CH{=}CH_2$, in ethanol. After formation of the carbonium ion

$$Me \cdot CHCl \cdot CH{=}CH_2 \rightleftharpoons Cl^{\ominus} + \begin{bmatrix} Me \cdot \overset{\oplus}{C}H{-}CH{=}CH_2 \\ \updownarrow \\ Me \cdot CH{=}CH{-}\overset{\oplus}{C}H_2 \end{bmatrix}$$

attack by **EtOH** can be at C_1 *or* C_3 and a mixture of the two possible ethers is indeed obtained:

$$
\left[
\begin{array}{c}
\text{Me} \cdot \overset{\oplus}{\text{CH}} \text{—CH} \overset{}{=} \text{CH}_2 \\
\updownarrow \\
\text{Me} \cdot \text{CH} \overset{}{=} \text{CH} \text{—} \overset{\oplus}{\text{CH}}_2
\end{array}
\right]
\underset{\text{EtOH}}{\rightleftharpoons}
\begin{array}{c}
\text{Me} \cdot \text{CH (OEt)} \cdot \text{CH} \overset{}{=} \text{CH}_2 \\
+ \\
\text{Me} \cdot \text{CH} \overset{}{=} \text{CH} \cdot \text{CH}_2 \cdot \text{OEt}
\end{array}
\quad + \text{H}^{\oplus}
$$

If, however, the reaction is carried out in ethanol with ethoxide ions present as powerful nucleophilic reagents, the reaction proceeds as a straightforward S_N2 displacement reaction, $^{\ominus}\text{OEt}$ displacing $\text{Cl}^{\ominus}$, and only the one product, $\text{Me} \cdot \text{CH(OEt)} \cdot \text{CH} = \text{CH}_2$, is obtained. Allylic rearrangements have been observed, however, in the course of displacement reactions that are undoubtedly proceeding by a bimolecular process. Such reactions are designated as S_N2' and are believed to proceed:

$$
\text{Y}^{\ominus}\text{CH}_2 \overset{}{=} \text{CH} \text{—CH—Cl} \rightarrow \text{Y—CH}_2\text{—CH} \overset{}{=} \overset{\overset{\text{R}}{|}}{\text{CH}} + \text{Cl}^{\ominus}
$$

S_N2' reactions tend to occur more particularly when there are bulky substituents on the α-carbon atom for these markedly reduce the rate of the competing, direct displacement reaction by the normal S_N2 mode. Allylic rearrangements, by whichever mechanism they may actually be proceeding, are relatively common.

(ii) With change in carbon skeleton

(a) **The neopentyl rearrangement:** A good example is the hydrolysis of neopentyl chloride (VI) under conditions favouring the S_N1 mechanism (it may be remembered that the S_N2 hydrolysis of these halides is highly hindered in any case, p. 65); this might be expected to yield neopentyl alcohol (VIII):

$$
\underset{\text{(VI)}}{\overset{\overset{\text{Me}}{|}}{\text{Me—C—CH}_2\text{Cl}}} \overset{S_N1}{\longrightarrow} \underset{\text{(VII)}}{\overset{\overset{\text{Me}}{|}}{\text{Me—C—}\overset{\oplus}{\text{CH}}_2}} \overset{\text{H}_2\text{O}}{\longrightarrow} \underset{\text{(VIII)}}{\overset{\overset{\text{Me}}{|}}{\text{Me—C—CH}_2 \cdot \text{OH}}} + \text{H}^{\oplus}
$$

In fact no neopentyl alcohol (VIII) is obtained, the only alcoholic product is found to be t-amyl alcohol (X); this is due to the initial carbonium ion (VII) rearranging to yield a second one (IX). It will be seen that the latter is a tertiary carbonium ion whereas the former is a primary one, and it is an interesting reflection that the tertiary ion is so much more stable than the primary as to make it energetically worthwhile for a carbon–carbon bond to be broken and for a methyl group to migrate:

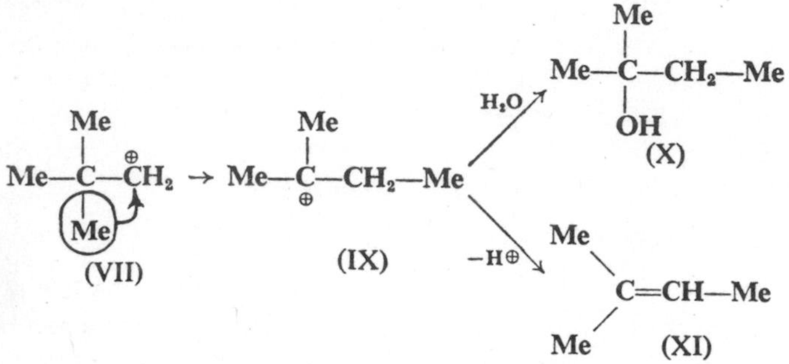

Such reactions in which a rearrangement of carbon skeleton takes place are known collectively as Wagner–Meerwein rearrangements. The rearranged carbonium ion (IX) is also able to eliminate $H^\oplus$ to yield an olefine and some 2-methylbut-2-ene (XI) is, in fact, obtained. The rearrangement, with its attendant consequences, can be avoided if the displacement is carried out under conditions to promote an S_N2 reaction path but, as has already been mentioned, the reaction is then very slow.

The possible occurrence of such rearrangements of a compound's carbon skeleton during the course of apparently unequivocal reactions is clearly of the utmost significance in interpreting the results of degradative and synthetic experiments aimed at structure elucidation. Some rearrangements of this type are highly complex, e.g. in the field of natural products such as the terpenes, and have often rendered the unambiguous assignment of structure extremely difficult.

It is interesting that if the halide $Me_3C \cdot CHCl \cdot Ph$ is hydrolysed under S_N1 conditions, no rearrangement like the above takes place for the first formed carbonium ion (XII) can stabilise itself by delocalisation via the π orbitals of the benzene nucleus, and rearrangement such as the above is thus no longer energetically advantageous:

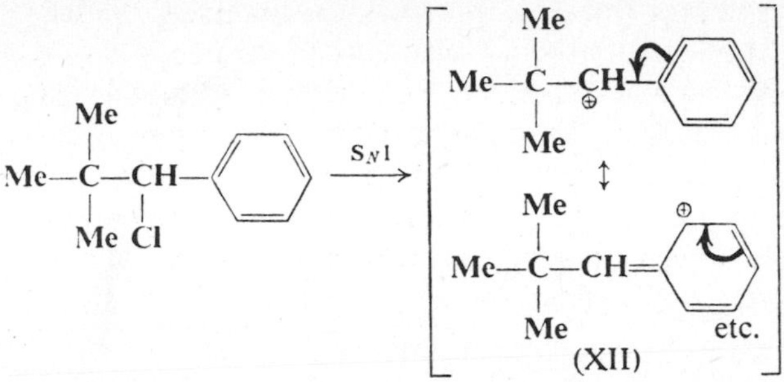

(XII)

(b) Rearrangement of hydrocarbons: Wagner-Meerwein type rearrangements are also encountered in the cracking of petroleum hydrocarbons where catalysts of a Lewis acid type are used. These generate carbonium ions from the straight-chain hydrocarbons (*cf.* the isomerisation of ^{13}C labelled propane above), which then tend to rearrange to yield branched-chain products. Fission also takes place, of course, but the branching is of importance as the branched hydrocarbons produced cause less knocking in the cylinders of internal combustion engines than do their straight-chain isomers. It should, however, be mentioned that cracking can also be brought about by catalysts that promote reaction via radical intermediates (p. 236).

Rearrangement of unsaturated hydrocarbons takes place readily in the presence of acids:

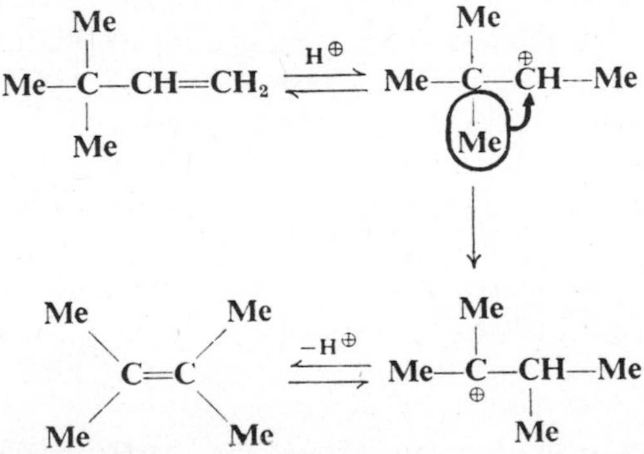

This tendency can be a nuisance when acid reagents, e.g. hydrogen halides, are being added preparatively to olefines: mixed products that are difficult to separate may result or, in unfavourable cases, practically none of the desired product may be obtained.

(c) **The pinacol/pinacolone rearrangement:** Another case of migration of an alkyl group to a carbonium ion carbon atom occurs in the acid-catalysed rearrangement of pinacol (*cf.* p. 168) to pinacolone, $Me_2C(OH) \cdot C(OH) \cdot Me_2 \rightarrow Me \cdot CO \cdot CMe_3$:

$$
\begin{array}{ccc}
\underset{\substack{| \\ OH\ \underset{\cdot\cdot}{OH}}}{\overset{Me}{\underset{|}{Me-C-CMe_2}}} & \underset{\xrightarrow{}}{\overset{+H^\oplus}{\rightleftharpoons}} & \underset{\substack{| \quad | \\ OH\ \underset{\underset{H}{\cdot\cdot}}{\overset{\oplus}{OH}}}}{\overset{Me}{\underset{|}{Me-C-CMe_2}}} \qquad \overset{-H_2O}{\rightleftharpoons} \qquad \underset{\substack{| \\ OH}}{\overset{\textcircled{Me}}{\underset{\oplus}{Me-C-CMe_2}}} \quad (XIII)
\end{array}
$$

$$
\underset{\overset{\|}{O}}{Me-C-CMe_3} \; \xrightleftharpoons{\; +^\oplus \;} \; \underset{\overset{|}{O^-H}}{\overset{\oplus}{Me-C-CMe_3}}
$$

It might be expected that an analogous reaction would take place with any other compounds that could yield the crucial carbonium ion (XIII) and this is, in fact, found to be the case; thus the corresponding bromohydrin (XIV) and hydroxyamine (XV) yield pinacolone when reacted with $Ag^\oplus$ and $NaNO_2/HCl$, respectively:

$$
\underset{\substack{| \quad | \\ OH\ Br \\ (XIV)}}{\overset{Me}{\underset{|}{Me-C-CMe_2}}} \quad \underset{\xrightarrow[\text{i.e.--AgBr}]{Ag^\oplus}}{} \quad \underset{\substack{| \quad | \\ OH \quad \oplus}}{\overset{Me}{\underset{|}{Me-C-CMe_2}}} \quad (XIII)
$$

$$
\downarrow -N_2
$$

$$
\underset{\substack{| \quad | \\ OH\ NH_2 \\ (XV)}}{\overset{Me}{\underset{|}{Me-C-CMe_2}}} \quad \underset{\xrightarrow[/HCl]{NaNO_2}}{} \quad \underset{\substack{| \quad | \\ OH\ \underset{\oplus}{N\equiv N}}}{\overset{Me}{\underset{|}{Me-C-CMe_2}}}
$$

It seems likely that the migration of the alkyl group follows extremely rapidly on the loss of H_2O, $Br^\ominus$ or N_2, or probably takes place simultaneously, for in a compound in which the carbonium ion carbon is asymmetric, the ion does not get time to become planar and so yield a racemic product, for the product obtained is found to have undergone inversion of configuration

$$Me-\underset{\substack{|\\OH}}{C}-\underset{\substack{\nwarrow\\N\equiv N\\\oplus}}{\overset{\nearrow R}{C}}\overset{R'}{} \rightarrow Me-\overset{\oplus}{C}-\underset{\substack{\downarrow\\O-H}}{\overset{\overset{\displaystyle Me}{\diagup}}{C}}\cdots R \rightarrow Me-\underset{\substack{\|\\O}}{C}-\overset{\overset{\displaystyle Me}{\diagup}}{C}\cdots R$$

attack taking place 'from the back' in an internal S_N2 type displacement reaction. That the migrating group prefers to move in from the side opposite to that of the leaving group may be demonstrated in cyclic systems where there is restricted rotation about the $C_1—C_2$ bond; it is then found that compounds in which migrating and leaving groups are *trans* to each other rearrange very much more readily than do those in which the groups are *cis*. It is noteworthy that the migrating alkyl group in this and other cases is migrating with its bonding electrons and so can obviously act as a powerfully nucleophilic reagent. Where the migrating group is asymmetric, it has in certain other cases, though not in this particular one, been shown to retain its configuration as it migrates, indicating that it never actually becomes wholly free from the rest of the molecule; other evidence is also against the migrating group ever becoming free, e.g. no 'crossed product' when two different but very similar pinacols (that undergo rearrangement at approximately the same rate) are rearranged in the same solution: thus the reaction is said to be a typical *intra*molecular, as opposed to *inter*molecular, rearrangement. Indeed, it is probable that the migrating group begins to be attached to the carbonium ion carbon before becoming separated from the carbon atom that it is leaving. A state such as

$$\overset{\displaystyle R^{\oplus}}{\underset{\diagdown C—C\diagdown}{\diagup\diagup}}$$

probably intervenes between the initial and the rearranged carbonium ions (*cf.* bromonium ion structures encountered in the addition of bromine to olefines, p. 138).

As the migrating group migrates with its electron pair i.e. as a nucleophile, it might be expected that where the groups on the noncarbonium ion carbon are different, it would be the more nucleophilic of them, i.e. the more powerful electron donor, that would actually migrate. Thus in the example it is the p-MeO·C_6H_4 that migrates in preference to C_6H_5 owing to the electron-donating effect of the MeO group in the p-position.

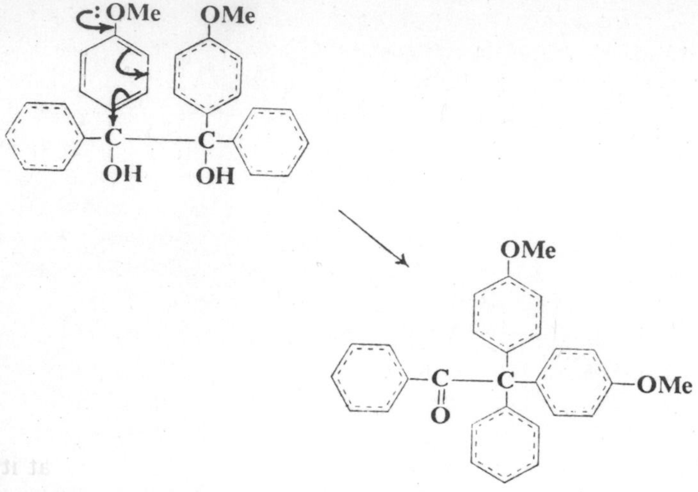

Steric factors also play a part, however, and it is found that o-MeO·C_6H_4 migrates more than a thousand times less readily than the corresponding p-substituted group—less readily indeed than phenyl itself—due to its interference in the transition state with the non-migrating groups.

In pinacols of the form

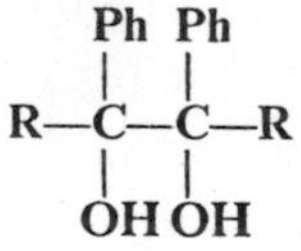

Ph will migrate in preference to **R** because of the greater stabilisation it can, by delocalisation, confer on the intervening bridged intermediate (*cf.* p. 83).

(d) The Wolff rearrangement: This involves the loss of nitrogen from α-diazoketones (XVI) and their rearrangement to highly reactive ketenes (XVII):

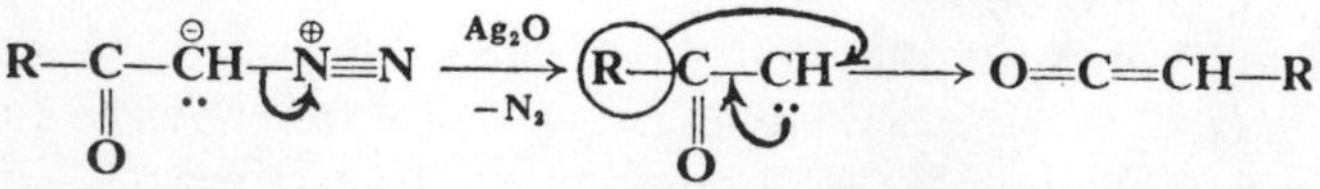

92

The intermediate (XVIII) is not a carbonium ion but it is nevertheless an *electron-deficient* species, known as a *carbene*, so the R group migrates with its electron complement complete as in the cases we have already considered. The diazoketone may be obtained by the reaction of diazomethane, CH_2N_2, on the acid chloride and the Wolff rearrangement is of importance because it constitutes part of the Arndt-Eistert procedure by which an acid may be converted into its homologue:

$$
\underset{\substack{\| \\ R \cdot C - OH}}{O} \xrightarrow{SOCl_2} \underset{\substack{\| \\ R \cdot C - Cl}}{O} \xrightarrow{CH_2N_2} \underset{\substack{\| \\ R \cdot C - CHN_2}}{O}
$$

$$
\underset{\substack{\| \\ R \cdot CH_2 \cdot C - OH}}{O} \xleftarrow{H_2O} R \cdot CH = C = O \quad \big\downarrow Ag_2O \;\; -N_2
$$

In aqueous solution, the acid is obtained directly by addition of water to the ketene but if the reaction is carried out in ammonia or an alcohol the corresponding amide or ester, respectively, may be obtained directly.

MIGRATION TO ELECTRON-DEFICIENT NITROGEN ATOMS

The reactions involving rearrangement of structure that we have already considered all have one feature in common: the migration of an alkyl or aryl group with its electron pair to a carbon atom which, whether a carbonium ion or not, is electron-deficient. Another atom that can similarly become electron-deficient is nitrogen in, e.g., $R_2\overset{..}{N}{}^{\oplus}$ or $R\overset{..}{N}$, and it might be expected that the nitrogen atoms in such species should be able to induce migration to themselves as is observed with $R_3C^{\oplus}$ or $R_2\overset{..}{C}$. This is indeed found to be the case.

(i) The Hofmann, Curtius and Lossen reactions

A typical example is the conversion of an amide to an amine containing one carbon less by the action of alkaline hypobromite, the Hofmann reaction (see p. 94).

It will be noticed that the species (XXI) has an electron-deficient nitrogen atom corresponding exactly to the electron-deficient carbon atom in the carbene (XVIII) from the Wolff rearrangement, and that the isocyanate (XXII) obtained by the former's rearrangement

93

$$R-\overset{\overset{O}{\|}}{C}-NH_2 \xrightarrow{BrO^{\ominus}} R-\overset{\overset{O}{\|}}{C}-NH\cdot Br \xrightarrow{\ominus OH} R-\overset{\overset{O}{\|}}{C}-N\overset{\ominus}{\underset{}{}}Br$$

$$(XIX) \qquad\qquad (XX)$$

$$O=C=N-R \longleftarrow O=\overset{\oplus}{C}-\overset{\ominus}{N}-R \longleftarrow \left(R-\overset{\overset{O}{\|}}{C}-\overset{\cdot\cdot}{N}\right)$$

$$(XXII) \qquad\qquad\qquad\qquad\qquad\qquad (XXI)$$

$$\downarrow H_2O$$

$$HO_2C-NH-R \longrightarrow O_2C + H_2NR$$
$$(XXIII)$$

corresponds closely to the ketene (XVII) obtained from the latter. The reaction is completed by hydration of the isocyanate to yield the carbamic acid (XXIII) which undergoes spontaneous decarboxylation to the amine. The N-bromamide (XIX), its anion (XX) and the isocyanate (XXII) postulated as intermediates can all be isolated under suitable conditions.

The rate-determining step of the reaction is the loss of $Br^{\ominus}$ from the ion (XX) but it is probable that the loss of $Br^{\ominus}$ and the migration of R take place simultaneously, i.e. effectively internal S_N2 once again. It might be expected that the more electron-releasing R is, the more rapid would be the reaction: this has been confirmed by a study of the rates of decomposition of benzamides substituted in the nucleus by electron-donating substituents.

There are two reactions very closely related to that of Hofmann, namely the Curtius degradation of acid azides (XXIV) and the Lossen decomposition of hydroxamic acids (XXV), both of which also yield amines; all three reactions proceed via the isocyanate as a common intermediate (see p. 95).

The Lossen reaction is, in practice, normally carried out not on the free hydroxamic acids but on their O-acyl derivatives which tend to give higher yields; the principle is, however, exactly analogous except that now $R'\cdot CO\cdot O^{\ominus}$ instead of $HO^{\ominus}$ is expelled from the anion. In the Curtius reaction, the azide is generated as required by the action of sodium nitrite and acid on the hydrazide; if the reaction is carried out in solution in an alcohol instead of in water (nitrous acid being

$$R-\overset{\overset{\displaystyle O}{\|}}{C}-NH\cdot OH \;\xleftarrow{\;H_2N\cdot OH\;}\; R-\overset{\overset{\displaystyle O}{\|}}{C}-OEt \;\xrightarrow{\;H_2N\cdot NH_2\;}\; R-\overset{\overset{\displaystyle O}{\|}}{C}-NH\cdot NH_2$$

(XXV)

$\Big\downarrow \ominus OH$ $NaNO_2 \Big/ \Big| \; HCl$

$$R-\overset{\overset{\displaystyle O}{\|}}{\underset{\displaystyle ..}{C}}-\overset{\ominus}{\underset{\displaystyle ..}{N}}-OH \;\xrightarrow{\;-OH^{\ominus}\;}\; \bigg(R-\overset{\overset{\displaystyle O}{\|}}{C}-\overset{..}{N}\bigg) \;\underset{-N_2}{\overset{heat}{\longleftarrow}}\; R-\overset{\overset{\displaystyle O}{\|}}{C}-\overset{\ominus}{\underset{\displaystyle ..}{N}}-\overset{\oplus}{N}\!\!\equiv\!\!N$$

(XXIV)

$$\Big\downarrow$$

$$O{=}C{=}N{-}R$$

derived from amyl nitrite and hydrogen chloride), the urethane is obtained:

$$R-\overset{\overset{\displaystyle O}{\|}}{C}-N_3 \;\longrightarrow\; R-\overset{\overset{\displaystyle O}{\|}}{C}-\overset{..}{\underset{\displaystyle ..}{N}} \;\longrightarrow\; R-N{=}C{=}O \;\xrightarrow{\;R'OH\;}\; R-NH\cdot CO_2R'$$

In all these cases, the **R** group that migrates conserves its configuration as in the carbon → carbon rearrangements already discussed and, as with them, no mixed products are formed when two different, but very similar, compounds are rearranged in the same solution, showing that the **R** groups never became free in the solution when migrating, i.e. these too are *intra*molecular rearrangements.

(ii) The Beckmann rearrangement

The most famous of the rearrangements in which **R** migrates from carbon to nitrogen is undoubtedly the conversion of ketoximes to N-substituted amides, the Beckmann transformation:

$$RR'C{=}N\cdot OH \;\rightarrow\; R'\cdot CO\cdot NHR \quad \text{or} \quad R\cdot CO\cdot NHR'$$

The reaction is catalysed by a wide variety of acidic reagents, e.g. H_2SO_4, P_2O_5, SO_3, $SOCl_2$, BF_3, PCl_5, etc., and takes place not only with the oximes themselves but also with their **O**-esters. Only a very few aldoximes rearrange under these conditions but more can be made to do so by use of polyphosphoric acid as a catalyst. The most interesting feature of the change is, that unlike the reactions we have already considered, it is not the *nature*, e.g. relative electron-releasing ability, but the *stereochemical arrangement* of the **R, R′** groups that determines which of them in fact migrates. Thus it is found, in practice, to be always the *anti*-R group that rearranges:

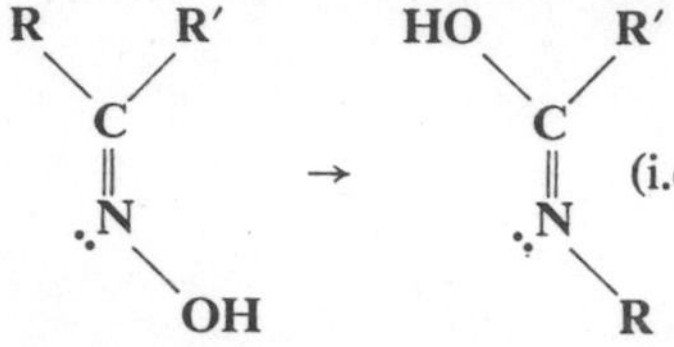

$$
\begin{array}{ccc}
R \quad R' & & HO \quad R' \\
\diagdown \diagup & & \diagdown \diagup \\
C & & C \\
\parallel & \rightarrow & \parallel \qquad \text{(i.e. } R' \cdot CO \cdot NHR) \text{ } only \\
:N & & :N \\
\diagdown & & \diagdown \\
OH & & R
\end{array}
$$

Confirmation of this fact requires an initial, unambiguous assignment of configuration to a pair of oximes. This was effected as follows: working with the pair of oximes (XXVI) and (XXVII), it was shown that one of them was converted into the cyclic isoxazole (XXVIII) on treatment with alkali even in the cold, while the other was but little attacked even under very much more vigorous conditions. The oxime undergoing ready cyclisation was, on this basis, assigned the configuration (XXVI) in which the oxime **OH** group and the nuclear bromine atom are close together and the one resisting cyclisation, the configuration (XXVII), in which these groups are far apart and correspondingly unlikely to interact with each other:

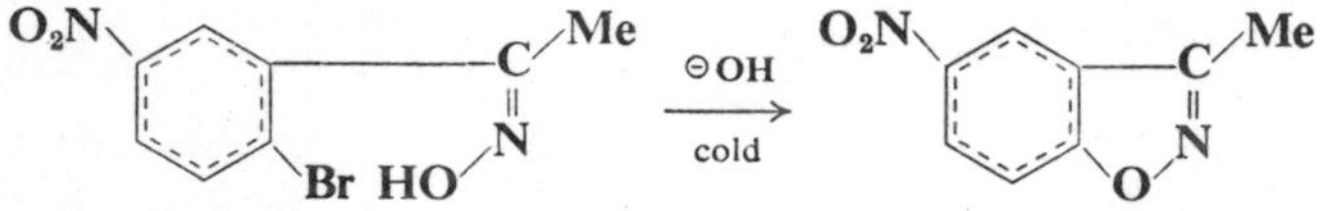

(XXVI)   (XXVIII)

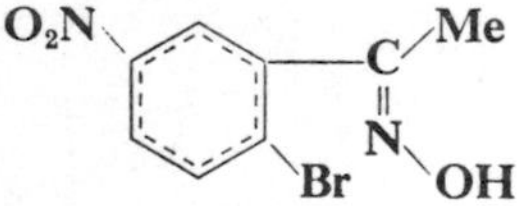

(XXVII)

Subsequently, configuration may be assigned to other pairs of ketoximes by correlation of their physical constants with those of pairs of oximes whose configuration has already been established. Once it had been clearly demonstrated that it was *always* the *anti*-R group that migrated in the Beckmann reaction, however, the product obtained by such transformation of a given oxime has normally been used to establish the configuration of that oxime. Thus, as expected, (XXVI) is found to yield only a substituted N-methylbenzamide, while (XXVII) yields only a substituted acetanilide.

That a mere, direct interchange of **R** and **OH** has not taken place has been shown by rearrangement of benzophenone oxime to benzanilide in $H_2{}^{18}O$:

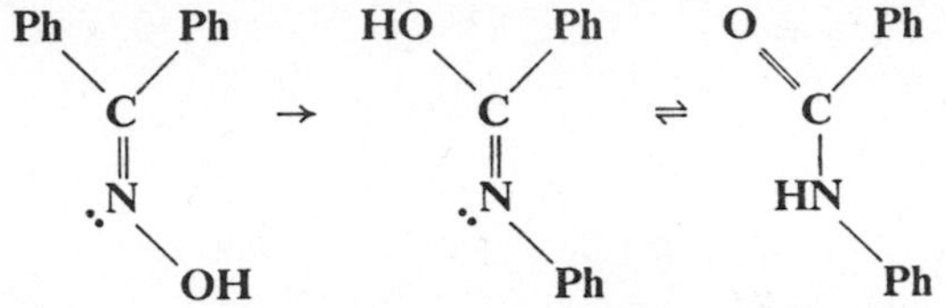

Provided that neither the initial oxime nor the anilide produced will exchange their oxygen for ^{18}O when dissolved in $H_2{}^{18}O$ (as has been confirmed), a mere intramolecular exchange of **Ph** and **OH** cannot result in the incorporation of any ^{18}O in the rearranged product. In fact, however, the benzanilide is found to contain the same proportion of ^{18}O as did the original water so that the rearrangement must involve loss of the **OH** group and the subsequent replacement of oxygen by reaction with water.

The rearrangement is believed to take place as follows:

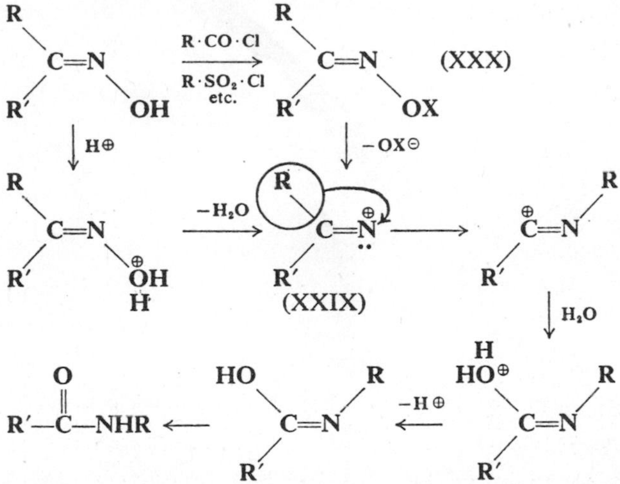

In fairly strong acid, the rearrangement proceeds by protonation of the oxime, followed by loss of water to yield the species (XXIX) having an electron-deficient nitrogen atom; while with acid chlorides, etc., the ester (XXX) is obtained which loses an anion, $^{\ominus}OX$, to yield the same intermediate. Support for the latter interpretation is provided by the fact that such **O**-esters may be prepared separately and shown to undergo the subsequent rearrangement in neutral solvents in the absence of added catalysts. Also, the stronger the acid **XOH**, i.e. the more stable the anion $^{\ominus}OX$, the more readily $^{\ominus}OX$ should be lost to yield (XXIX) and the more rapid the reaction should be. This is borne out by the fact that the rate of reaction increases in the series where $XO^{\ominus}$ is $CH_3 \cdot CO_2{}^{\ominus} < ClCH_2 \cdot CO_2{}^{\ominus} < Ph \cdot SO_3{}^{\ominus}$. That such ionisation is the rate-determining step in the reaction is also suggested by the observed increase in the rate of reaction as the solvent is made more polar.

It is not certain, in either case, whether the fission of the **N—O** bond and migration of **R** are actually simultaneous but, if not, the rearrangement follows extremely rapidly after the fission for it has been demonstrated that the migrating group attacks the *back* of the nitrogen atom, i.e. the side remote from the leaving group, and that if **R** is asymmetric it migrates without undergoing any change of configuration. In addition, no cross-migration of **R** groups has been observed when two different, but similar, oximes are rearranged simultaneously in the same solution, i.e. this is another intramolecular rearrangement in which **R** never becomes wholly detached from the molecule.

After migration of **R**, the rearrangement is completed by attack of water on the positive carbon (it is, of course, at this stage that ^{18}O is introduced in the rearrangement of benzophenone oxime referred to above), followed by loss of proton to yield the enol of the amide which then reverts to the amide proper.

The stereochemical use of the Beckmann rearrangement in assigning configuration to ketoximes has already been referred to and one large-scale application is in the synthesis of the textile polymer, perlon:

$$\left(-\underset{\underset{O}{\parallel}}{C}-NH(CH_2)_5- \right)_n$$

Perlon

MIGRATION TO ELECTRON-DEFICIENT OXYGEN ATOMS

It might reasonably be expected that similar reactions could occur in which the migration terminus is an electron-deficient oxygen atom: such rearrangements are indeed known.

(i) The Baeyer-Villiger oxidation of ketones

Treatment of ketones with hydrogen peroxide or organic peracids,

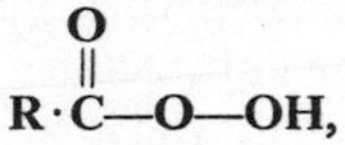

$$\underset{\displaystyle R \cdot C - O - OH,}{\overset{\displaystyle O \atop \displaystyle \|}{}}$$

results in their conversion to esters:

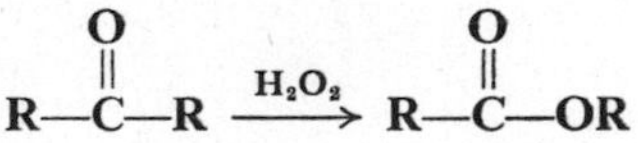

$$\underset{\displaystyle R - C - R}{\overset{\displaystyle O \atop \displaystyle \|}{}} \xrightarrow{H_2O_2} \underset{\displaystyle R - C - OR}{\overset{\displaystyle O \atop \displaystyle \|}{}}$$

The rate-determining step has been shown to be the acid-catalysed addition of the peracid to the ketone and the reaction is believed to follow the course:

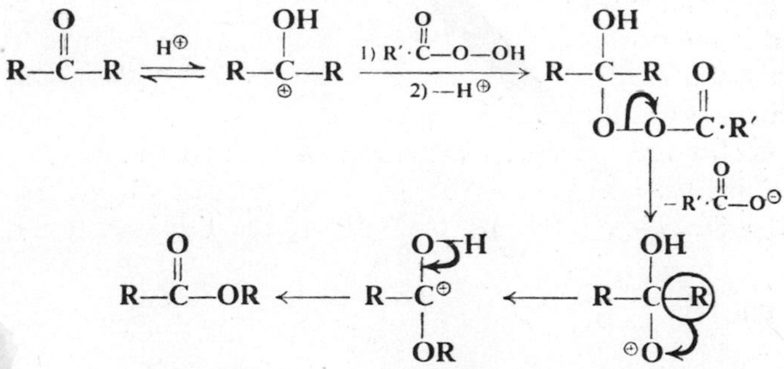

The initial adduct (XXXI) undergoes ready loss of an anion and migration of one of the **R** groups with its electron pair to yield a protonated form (XXXIII) of the final ester (XXXIV). In support of the above mechanism it has been shown by using ^{18}O labelled oxygen that the carbonyl oxygen in the original ketone becomes the carbonyl oxygen in the final ester. The **R** group has been shown to migrate with retention of configuration and bearing in mind that a cation of the $RO^{\oplus}$ type, such as (XXXII), is likely to be extremely unstable, it

99

seems probable that the rearrangement occurs simultaneously with loss of the anion as a concerted process reminiscent of the Hofmann reaction (p. 94). When an unsymmetrical ketone is oxidised it is usually the more nucleophilic group that migrates, as in the pinacol/pinacolone rearrangement (p. 91), but as in the latter reaction steric effects may also be involved and can have the effect of markedly changing the expected order of relative migratory aptitude of a series of groups based on their electron-releasing abilities alone.

(ii) Rearrangements of peroxides

A rather similar rearrangement is observed during the acid-catalysed decomposition of a number of peroxides. Thus the hydroperoxide (XXXV) obtained by the air oxidation (*cf.* p. 252) of isopropylbenzene (cumene) is used on the commercial scale for the production of phenol + acetone by treatment with acid:

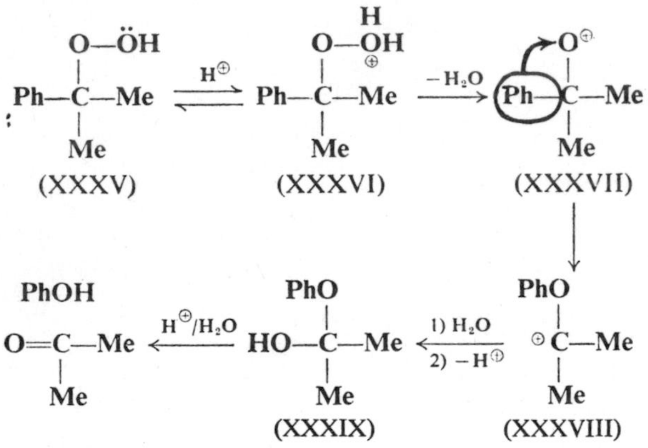

Here again it seems likely that the species (XXXVII) has no separate existence and that loss of H_2O from (XXXVI) and migration of the phenyl group with its electron pair occur as a concerted process to yield the acetone hemiketal (XXXIX), which then undergoes ready hydrolysis to yield the end-products, phenol and acetone.

In these examples we have been considering the heterolytic fission of peroxide linkages, $-O:O- \rightarrow -O^{\oplus} + :O^{\ominus}-$, and though this takes place in more polar solvents, the linkage may also undergo homolytic fission to yield free radicals, $-O:O- \rightarrow -O \cdot + \cdot O-$, as we shall see below (p. 240).

5 ELECTROPHILIC AND NUCLEOPHILIC SUBSTITUTION IN AROMATIC SYSTEMS

REFERENCE has already been made to the structure of benzene and, in particular, to its delocalised π orbitals (p. 9); the concentration of negative charge above and below the plane of the ring-carbon atoms is thus benzene's most accessible feature:

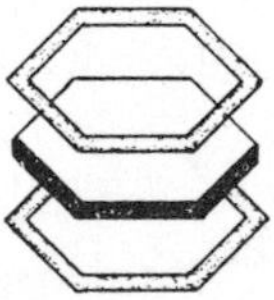

This concentration of charge might be expected to shield the ring-carbon atoms from the attack of nucleophilic reagents and, by contrast, to promote attack by cations, $X^{\oplus}$, or electron-deficient species, i.e. by electrophilic reagents; this is indeed found to be the case.

ELECTROPHILIC ATTACK ON BENZENE

(i) π and σ complexes

It might be expected that the first phase of reaction would be interaction between the approaching electrophile and the delocalised π orbitals and, in fact, so-called π *complexes* such as (I) are formed:

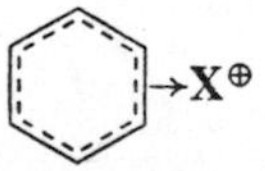

$$\longrightarrow X^{\oplus}$$

(I)

Thus toluene forms a 1:1 complex with hydrogen chloride at $-78°$, the reaction being readily reversible. That no actual bond is formed between a ring-carbon atom and the proton from HCl is confirmed by repeating the reaction with DCl; this also yields a π complex, but

101

its formation and decomposition does not lead to the exchange of deuterium with any of the hydrogen atoms of the nucleus, showing that no **C—D** bond has been formed in the complex.

In the presence of a compound having an electron-deficient orbital, e.g. a Lewis acid such as $AlCl_3$, a different complex is formed, however. If **DCl** is now employed in place of **HCl**, rapid exchange of deuterium with the hydrogen atoms of the nucleus is found to take place indicating the formation of a σ *complex* (II) in which $H^{\oplus}$ or $D^{\oplus}$, as the case may be, has actually become bonded to a ring-carbon atom. The positive charge is shared over the remaining five carbon atoms of the nucleus via the π orbitals and the deuterium and hydrogen atoms are in a plane at right angles to that of the ring:

(II)

That the π and σ complexes with, e.g. toluene and **HCl**, really are different from each other is confirmed by their differing behaviour. Thus formation of the former leads to no colour change and but little difference in absorption spectrum, indicating that there has been practically no disturbance in the electron distribution in toluene; while if $AlCl_3$ is present the solution becomes green, will conduct electricity and the absorption spectrum of toluene is modified, indicating the formation of a complex such as (II) as there is no evidence that aluminium chloride forms complexes of the type, $H^{\oplus}AlCl_4^{\ominus}$.

The reaction may be completed by $AlCl_4^{\ominus}$ removing a proton from the σ complex (II) → (IV). This can lead only to exchange of hydrogen atoms when **HCl** is employed but to some substitution of hydrogen by deuterium with **DCl**, i.e. the overall process is electrophilic *substitution*. In theory, (II) could, as an alternative, react by removing $Cl^{\ominus}$ from $AlCl_4^{\ominus}$ resulting in an overall electrophilic *addition* reaction (II) → (III) as happens with the π orbital of a simple carbon–carbon double bond (p. 141); but this would result in loss of the stabilisation conferred on the molecule by the presence of delocalised π orbitals involving all six carbon atoms of the nucleus, so that the product, an addition compound, would no longer be aromatic with all that that implies. By expelling $H^{\oplus}$, i.e. by undergoing substitution rather than addition, the complete delocalised π orbitals are regained in the product (IV) and characteristic aromatic stability recovered:

(III)   (II)   (IV)

Addition   *Substitution*

The gain in stabilisation in going from (II) → (IV) helps to provide the energy required to break the strong C—H bond that expulsion of $H^{\oplus}$ necessitates; in the reaction of, for example, HCl with alkenes (p. 141) there is no such factor promoting substitution and addition reactions are therefore the rule.

In the face of the concentration of negative charge presented to an attacking reagent it might be expected that the substitution of benzene by the common electrophiles (i.e. halogenation, nitration, sulphonation and the Friedel-Crafts reaction) would be extremely easy. Though the electrophilic substitution of benzene is not difficult, that it is not easier than it is, is due to the energy barrier to be surmounted in converting the very readily formed π complex to a σ complex in which actual bonding of the reagent to a ring-carbon atom has taken place. For in the π complex, the aromatic nature of the nucleus (i.e. the delocalised π orbitals) is largely undisturbed, while in the σ complex some of the characteristic stabilisation has been lost as the orbitals now only involve five carbon atoms. The loss of stabilisation involved is greater than might be expected as the π orbitals are now no longer symmetrical; it is the symmetry of the orbitals in the intact aromatic nucleus that underlies its characteristic stability and relative unwillingness to undergo change. The regaining of this symmetry (or near symmetry, for the orbitals will be deformed to a certain extent by the introduction of any substituent other than hydrogen into the nucleus) is responsible for the ease with which the relatively strong C—H bond undergoes fission in order to allow the conversion of (II) → (IV).

How this basic theory is borne out in the common electrophilic substitution reactions of benzene will now be considered.

NITRATION

The aromatic substitution reaction that has received by far the closest study is nitration and, as a result, it is the one that probably provides the most detailed mechanistic picture. Preparative nitration is most frequently carried out with a mixture of concentrated nitric and sulphuric acids, the so-called 'nitrating mixture'. The classical explanation for the presence of the sulphuric acid is that it absorbs the water formed in the nitration proper

$$C_6H_6 + HNO_3 \rightarrow C_6H_5 \cdot NO_2 + H_2O$$

and so prevents the reverse reaction from proceeding. This explanation is unsatisfactory in a number of respects, not least that nitrobenzene, once formed, appears not to be attacked by water under the conditions of the reaction! What is certain is that nitration is slow in the absence of sulphuric acid, yet sulphuric acid by itself has virtually no effect on benzene under the conditions normally employed. It would thus appear that the sulphuric acid is acting on the nitric acid rather than the benzene in the system. This is borne out by the fact that solutions of nitric acid in concentrated sulphuric acid show a four-fold molecular freezing-point depression, which has been interpreted as being due to formation of the four ions:

$$HNO_3 + 2H_2SO_4 \rightleftharpoons {}^{\oplus}NO_2 + H_3O^{\oplus} + 2HSO_4^{\ominus}$$

i.e.

$$HO\!\!-\!\!NO_2 \xrightarrow{\ H_2SO_4\ } HSO_4^{\ominus} + HO^{\oplus}\!\!\!\!\!\underset{H}{\overset{}{\Big|}}\!\!\!\!NO_2 \xrightarrow{\ H_2SO_4\ } H_3O^{\oplus} + HSO_4^{\ominus} + {}^{\oplus}NO_2$$

The presence of ${}^{\oplus}NO_2$, the *nitronium ion*, in this solution and also in a number of salts has now been confirmed spectroscopically, and some of the salts, e.g. ${}^{\oplus}NO_2\, ClO_4^{\ominus}$, have actually been isolated. Nitric acid itself is converted in concentrated sulphuric acid virtually entirely into ${}^{\oplus}NO_2$, and there can be little doubt left that this is the effective electrophile in nitration under these conditions. If the purpose of the sulphuric acid is merely to function as a highly acid medium in which ${}^{\oplus}NO_2$ can be released from $HO\!\!-\!\!NO_2$, it would be expected that other strong acids, e.g. $HClO_4$, would also promote nitration. This is indeed found to be the case, HF and BF$_3$ also being effective. The poor performance of nitric acid by itself in the nitration of benzene is thus explained for it contains but little $^{\oplus}NO_2$; the small amount that is present is obtained by the two-stage process

$$HO{-}NO_2 + HNO_3 \xrightleftharpoons{\text{fast}} NO_3{}^{\ominus} + HO\overset{\oplus}{-}NO_2$$
$$\phantom{HO{-}NO_2 + HNO_3 \xrightleftharpoons{\text{fast}} NO_3{}^{\ominus} + HO}H$$

$$\overset{\oplus}{HO}{-}NO_2 + HNO_3 \xrightleftharpoons{\text{slow}} H_3O^{\oplus} + NO_3{}^{\ominus} + {}^{\oplus}NO_2$$
$$H$$

in which nitric acid is first converted rapidly into its conjugate acid and that then more slowly into nitronium ion.

The kinetics of nitration are not easy to follow under normal preparative conditions for the solubility of, e.g., benzene in nitrating mixture is sufficiently low for the rate of nitration to be governed by the rate at which the immiscible hydrocarbon dissolves in the mixture. This apart, the rate-determining step is, however, almost certainly the initial attack by $^{\oplus}NO_2$

(V)

rather than the subsequent removal of proton by $HSO_4{}^{\ominus}$ or other anion. That the latter step cannot be rate-determining has been confirmed by studying the nitration of nitrobenzene in which the hydrogen atoms have been replaced by deuterium. Nitrobenzene is chosen rather than benzene itself as the former is more soluble in nitrating mixture so that the overall rate of the reaction is no longer controlled by the rate at which it dissolves. Studies of the relative rates of fission of C—H and C—D in general would lead us to expect an approximately ten-fold drop in nitration rate on going $C_6H_5 \cdot NO_2 \rightarrow C_6D_5 \cdot NO_2$. In fact there is no detectable difference in rate, indicating that the fission of the C—H or C—D bond is not involved in the rate-determining stage of nitration. The species (V) is thought to enjoy an actual existence—albeit an extremely transient one—in solution and is thus looked upon as a real intermediate, though a metastable one (*cf.* p. 33), rather than merely as a transition state. An added significance of the existence of

105

(V) is that the energy that becomes available from the formation of the $C—NO_2$ linkage may be used to assist in the subsequent fission of the strong $C—H$ bond, which would otherwise be a relatively difficult undertaking.

A further point of preparative significance still requires explanation, however. Highly reactive aromatic compounds, such as phenol, are found to undergo ready nitration even in dilute nitric acid and at a far more rapid rate than can be explained on the basis of the concentration of $^{\oplus}NO_2$ that is present in the mixture. This has been shown to be due to the presence of nitrous acid in the system which nitrosates the reactive nucleus via the *nitrosonium ion*, $^{\oplus}NO$:

$$HNO_2 + 2HNO_3 \rightleftharpoons H_3O^{\oplus} + 2NO_3^{\ominus} + {}^{\oplus}NO$$

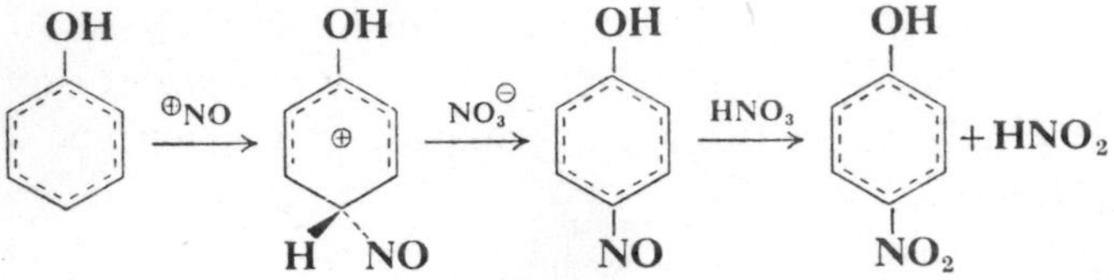

The nitroso-phenol (VII) so obtained is known to be oxidised very rapidly by nitric acid to yield the nitrophenol (VIII) and nitrous acid; thus more nitrous acid is produced and the process is progressively speeded up. No nitrous acid need be present initially in the nitric acid for a little of the latter attacks phenol oxidatively to yield HNO_2. The rate-determining step is again believed to be the formation of the intermediate (VI). Some direct nitration of such reactive aromatic compounds by $^{\oplus}NO_2$ also takes place simultaneously, the relative amount by the two routes depending on the conditions.

HALOGENATION

Halogenation, e.g. bromination, with the halogen itself only takes place in the presence of a catalyst such as $ZnCl_2$, $FeBr_3$, $AlBr_3$, etc. The nature of the catalyst is usually that of a Lewis acid and it acts by inducing some degree of polarisation in the halogen molecule, thereby increasing its electrophilic character, so that its now more positive end attacks the π electrons of the nucleus:

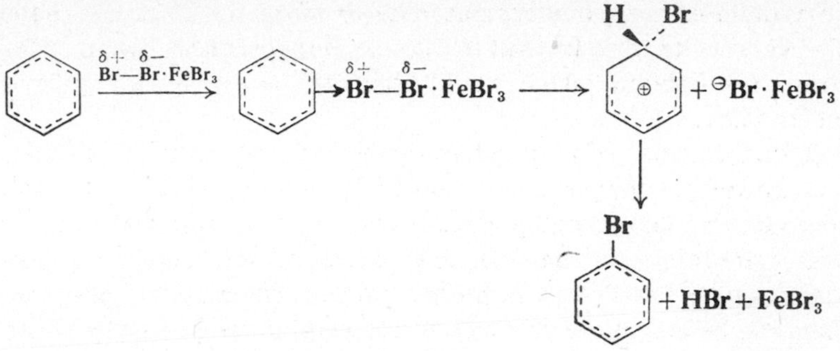

After fission of the bromine–bromine bond in forming the σ complex with benzene, the anionic complex, $^{\ominus}\mathbf{Br}\cdot\mathbf{FeBr_3}$, so obtained then removes the proton to yield bromobenzene.

Halogenation may also be carried out with the aqueous hypohalous acid, $\mathbf{HO}\cdot\mathbf{Hal}$, provided that a strong acid is also present. Here the evidence is very strong that in, for example, chlorination, the chlorinating agent is actually $\mathbf{Cl}^{\oplus}$, produced as follows:

$$\mathbf{HO{-}Cl} \xrightarrow[\text{fast}]{\mathbf{H}\,\oplus} \overset{\oplus}{\underset{\mathbf{H}}{\mathbf{HO}}}{-}\mathbf{Cl} \xrightarrow{\text{slow}} \mathbf{H_2O} + \mathbf{Cl}^{\oplus}$$

The further attack on benzene is then exactly analogous to nitration by $^{\oplus}\mathbf{NO_2}$. A further similarity between the two is provided by the fact that $\mathbf{HOCl}$ alone has, like $\mathbf{HNO_3}$, very little action on benzene; the presence of a further entity, i.e. strong acid, is necessary in either case to release the highly electrophilic species, $\mathbf{Cl}^{\oplus}$ or $^{\oplus}\mathbf{NO_2}$ by protonation of their 'carrier molecules':

$$\overset{\oplus}{\underset{\mathbf{H}}{\mathbf{HO}}}{\perp}\mathbf{Cl} \text{ and } \overset{\oplus}{\underset{\mathbf{H}}{\mathbf{HO}}}{\perp}\mathbf{NO_2}$$

Further support for the idea that a halonium ion or a positively polarised halogen-containing complex is the effective substituting agent is provided by a study of the reactions of interhalogen compounds with aromatic substances. Thus $\mathbf{Br}\cdot\mathbf{Cl}$ leads only to bromination and $\mathbf{I}\cdot\mathbf{Cl}$ only to iodination, i.e. it is the *less* electronegative halogen that is introduced, due to:

$$\overset{\delta+}{\mathbf{Br}}{\rightarrow}{-}\overset{\delta-}{\mathbf{Cl}}, \text{ etc.}$$

In the absence of a catalyst and in the presence of light, chlorine will add on to benzene; this proceeds by a radical mechanism and will be discussed subsequently (p. 244).

SULPHONATION

The intimate details of sulphonation are less well known than those of nitration and there has been a good deal of debate about whether the effective electrophilic agent is the bisulphonium ion, $^{\oplus}SO_3H$, or free SO_3. The weight of evidence for sulphonation under normal conditions, however, resides with the latter produced in the following way:

$$2H_2SO_4 \rightleftharpoons SO_3 + H_3O^{\oplus} + HSO_4^{\ominus}$$

The sulphur atom of the trioxide is highly electron-deficient

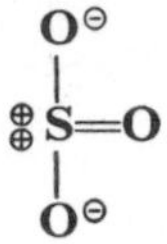

$$\overset{\displaystyle O^{\ominus}}{\underset{\displaystyle O^{\ominus}}{\overset{\displaystyle |}{\underset{\displaystyle |}{\oplus S{=}O}}}}$$

and it is this atom, therefore, that becomes bonded to a ring carbon atom. Two features of sulphonation that distinguish it from nitration are that it is reversible and that it is slowed down when the hydrogen atoms of an aromatic nucleus are replaced by the heavier, radioactive isotope tritium, ^3H. The latter observation indicates, of course, that the removal of proton from the σ complex of benzene and sulphur trioxide (IX) must, by contrast to nitration, be the rate-determining step of the reaction, the formation of (IX) being fast and non rate-determining:

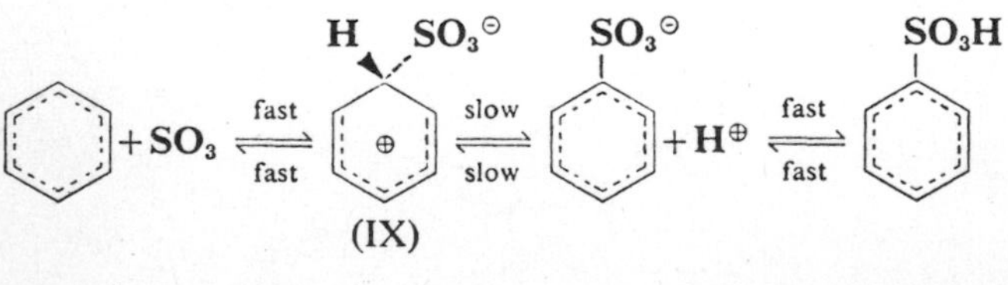

(IX)

Practical use is made of the reversibility of the reaction in the replacement of SO_3H by H on treating sulphonic acids with steam. Partly because of low miscibility, the reaction of hot concentrated sulphuric acid with benzene is slow and fuming sulphuric acid in the cold is generally used instead; the more rapid reaction is, of course, due to the concentration of free SO_3 that this acid contains.

FRIEDEL-CRAFTS REACTION

This can be conveniently divided into alkylation and acylation.

(i) Alkylation

The reaction of primary alkyl halides, e.g. **MeCl**, with aromatic compounds in the presence of Lewis acids—such as aluminium halides, **BF₃**, etc.—closely resembles the mechanism of catalysed halogenation that has already been discussed:

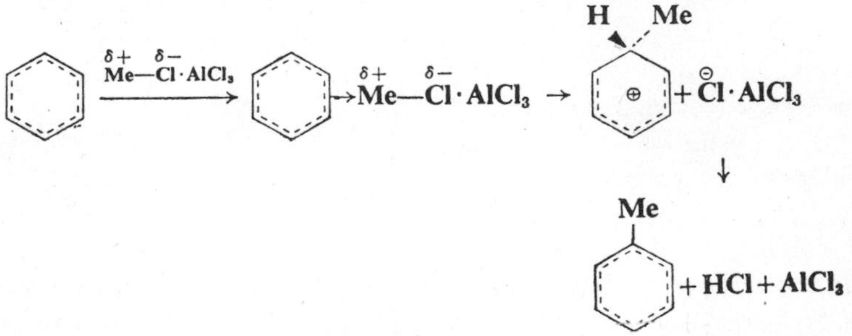

That such polarised complexes between the halide and the aluminium halide are undoubtedly formed is shown by the fact that the halogen of isotopically-labelled aluminium halides is found to exchange with that of the alkyl halide. With secondary and tertiary halides, however, the carbon atom carrying the halogen is increasingly more able to accommodate positive charge (i.e. it will form a more stable carbonium ion, *cf.* p. 84), and there is thus an increasing tendency towards ionisation of the complex to yield $R^{\oplus}$, in an ion pair (*cf.* p. 80), as the effective electrophilic species. No clear distinction can be made between primary and other halides in the extent to which they form actual carbonium ions, however, as the nature of the catalyst used and of the halogen in the halide also play a part. Thus with the halide $Me_3C \cdot CH_2Cl$ in the presence of **AlCl₃**, benzene yields almost wholly $Ph \cdot CMe_2 \cdot CH_2 \cdot Me$, due to isomerisation of the first-formed primary carbonium ion, $Me_3C \cdot CH_2{}^{\oplus}$, to the tertiary carbonium ion, $Me_2\overset{\oplus}{C} \cdot CH_2 \cdot Me$ (*cf.*

p. 88) *before* it reacts with benzene. In the presence of $FeCl_3$ as catalyst, however, the major product is $Me_3C \cdot CH_2 \cdot Ph$ from the unrearranged ion, indicating that it never became fully-formed in the complex. Similarly n-propyl bromide in the presence of gallium bromide, $GaBr_3$, yields isopropylbenzene as the major product (p. 85), whereas n-propyl chloride with aluminium chloride yields very largely n-propylbenzene.

Alkenes can also be used in place of alkyl halides for alkylating benzene, the presence of an acid being required to generate a carbonium ion; BF_3 is then often used as the Lewis acid catalyst:

$$Me—CH{=}CH_2 \xrightarrow{H\oplus} Me—\overset{\oplus}{C}H—Me \xrightarrow[BF_3]{C_6H_6} Ph \cdot CHMe_2$$

Several of the usual catalysts, especially $AlCl_3$, also bring about ready dealkylation: i.e. the reaction is reversible. Thus heating of *p*-xylene (X) with hydrogen chloride and $AlCl_3$ results in the conversion of a major part of it to the thermodynamically more stable *m*-xylene (XI). This is normally explained as taking place by alkylation (the $MeCl$ necessary to start the process being derived by a little initial dealkylation) followed by dealkylation:

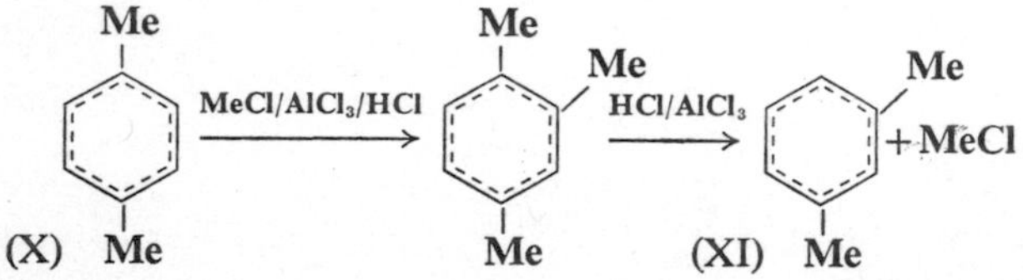

The presence of hydrogen chloride is, however, essential for the isomerisation to take place and it has therefore been suggested that an alkyl group may also migrate directly by a Wagner-Meerwein type rearrangement (p. 88):

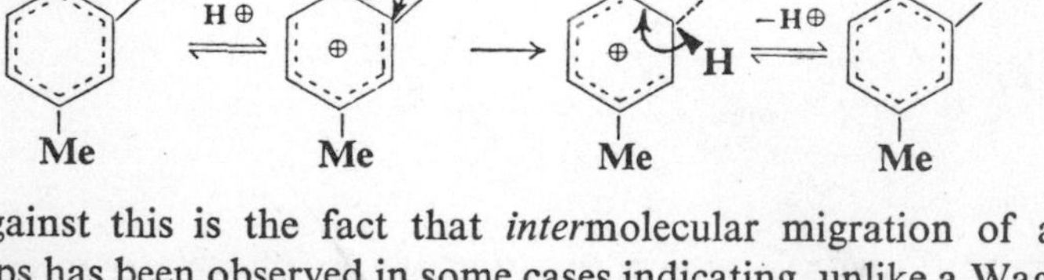

Against this is the fact that *inter*molecular migration of alkyl groups has been observed in some cases indicating, unlike a Wagner-Meerwein rearrangement, that the alkyl group actually becomes free.

The main drawback in the preparative use of the Friedel-Crafts reaction is polyalkylation, however (p. 118).

(ii) Acylation

Acid chlorides or anhydrides in the presence of Lewis acids yield an *acylium ion*, $R \cdot \overset{\oplus}{C}{=}O$, which acts as the effective electrophile to form a ketone (XII):

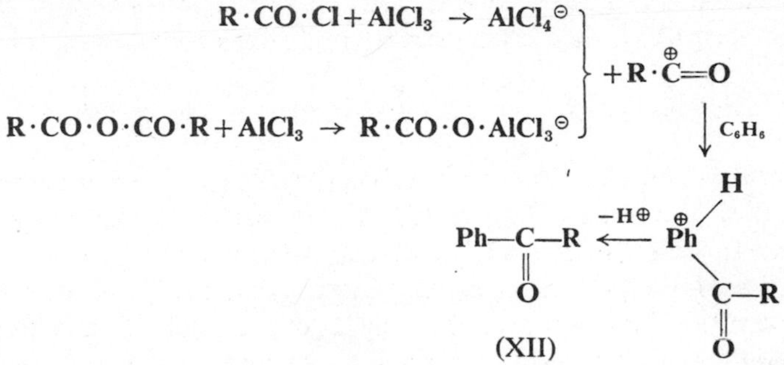

$$R \cdot CO \cdot Cl + AlCl_3 \rightarrow AlCl_4^{\ominus}$$

$$R \cdot CO \cdot O \cdot CO \cdot R + AlCl_3 \rightarrow R \cdot CO \cdot O \cdot AlCl_3^{\ominus}$$

$$\left. \right\} + R \cdot \overset{\oplus}{C}{=}O$$

$$\downarrow C_6H_6$$

$$Ph{-}\underset{\underset{O}{\|}}{C}{-}R \xleftarrow{-H^{\oplus}} \overset{\oplus}{Ph}\overset{\displaystyle H}{\diagup} \underset{\underset{O}{\|}}{\diagdown}{C}{-}R$$

$$(XII)$$

The ketone, once formed, complexes with aluminium chloride

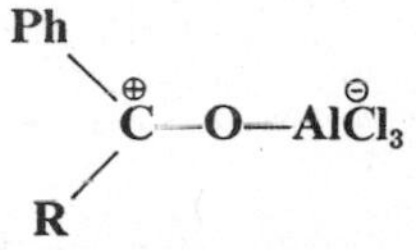

$$\underset{R}{\overset{Ph}{\diagdown}}\overset{\oplus}{C}{-}O{-}\overset{\ominus}{A}lCl_3$$

removing it from the sphere of reaction. Thus rather more than one equivalent of the catalyst must be employed, unlike alkylation where only small amounts are necessary. There is however some evidence that such AlCl₃ complexing of the ketone is an essential rather than merely a nuisance feature of the reaction as otherwise the ketone forms a complex with the acylium ion

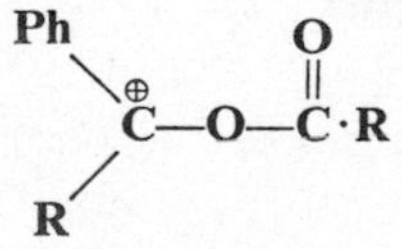

$$\underset{R}{\overset{Ph}{\diagdown}}\overset{\oplus}{C}{-}O{-}\overset{\overset{O}{\|}}{C}{\cdot}R$$

and thus prevents the latter from attacking its proper substrate, in this case C_6H_6.

111

Rearrangement of **R** does not take place as with alkylation, but if it is highly branched loss of **CO** can occur leading ultimately to alkylation rather than the expected acylation:

$$Me_3C\text{—}\overset{+}{C}\text{=O} \longrightarrow CO + Me_3\overset{\oplus}{C} \xrightarrow{C_6H_6} Ph \cdot CMe_3$$

A useful synthetic application of Friedel-Crafts acylation is the use of cyclic anhydrides in a two-stage process to build a second ring on to an aromatic nucleus:

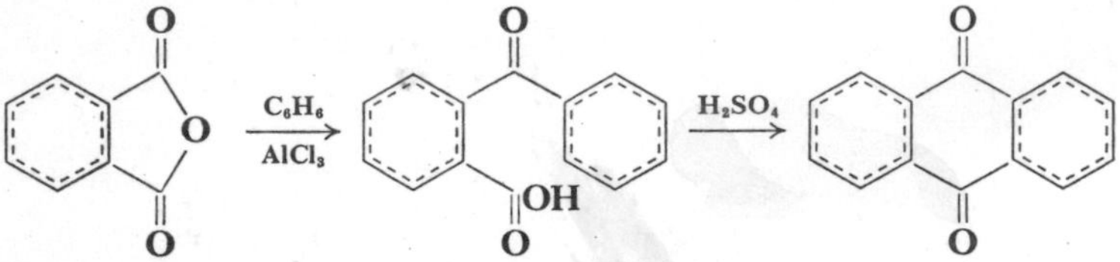

HCOCl is very unstable but formylation may be accomplished by protonating carbon monoxide to yield $H\overset{\oplus}{C}\text{=O}$, i.e. by use of **CO**, **HCl** and **AlCl₃** (the Gattermann-Koch reaction):

$$C_6H_6 + H\overset{\oplus}{C}\text{=O} \xrightarrow{AlCl_3} Ph \cdot CHO + H^\oplus$$

DIAZO COUPLING

Another classical electrophilic aromatic substitution is diazo coupling, in which the effective electrophile has been shown to be the diazonium cation:

$$Ph \cdot \overset{\oplus}{N}\text{=}N \leftrightarrow Ph \cdot N\text{=}\overset{\oplus}{N}$$

This is, however, a weak electrophile compared with species such as $^\oplus NO_2$ and will normally only attack highly reactive aromatic compounds such as phenols and amines; it is thus without effect on the otherwise highly reactive **Ph·OMe**. Introduction of electron-withdrawing groups into the *o*- or *p*-positions of the diazonium cation enhance its electrophilic character, however, by increasing the positive charge on the diazo group:

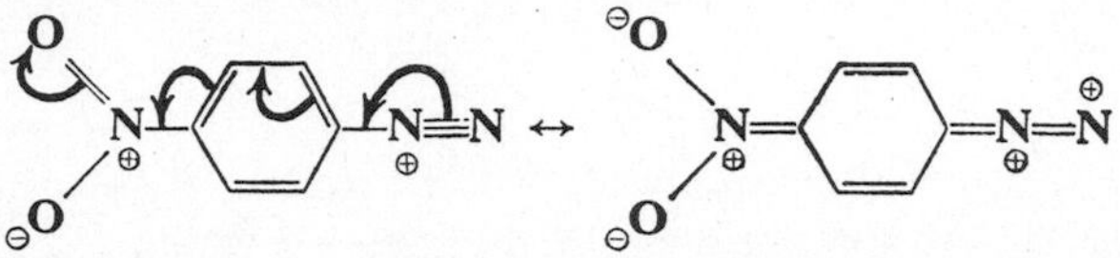

Thus the 2,4-dinitrophenyldiazonium cation will couple with **Ph·OMe** and the 2,4,6-compound with the hydrocarbon mesitylene. Diazonium cations exist in acid and slightly alkaline solution (in more strongly alkaline solution they are converted into diazohydroxides, **Ph·N=N—OH** and further into diazotate anions, **Ph·N=N– O$^\ominus$**) and coupling reactions are therefore carried out under these conditions, the optimum **pH** depending on the species being attacked. With phenols this is at a slightly alkaline **pH** as phenoxide ion is very much more rapidly attacked than phenol itself because of the considerably greater electron-density available to the electrophile:

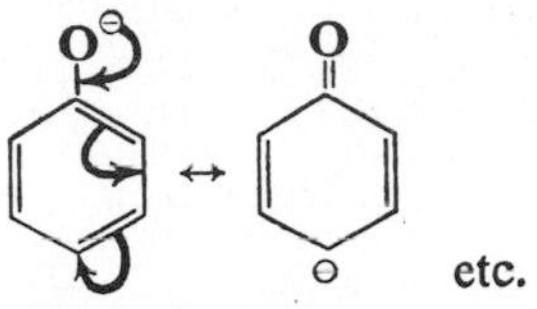

Coupling could take place on either oxygen or carbon and though relative electron-density might be expected to favour the former, the strength of the bond formed is also of significance and as with electrophilic attack on phenols in general it is a C-substituted product that normally results:

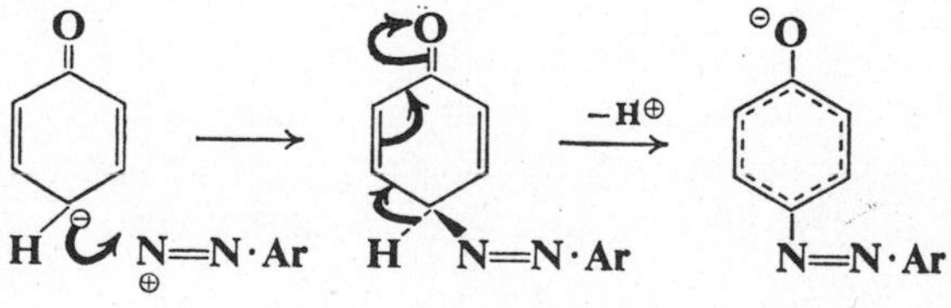

The proton is removed by one or other of the basic species present in solution.

Aromatic amines are in general somewhat less readily attacked than phenols and coupling is often carried out in slightly acid solution, thus ensuring a high $[PhN_2^{\oplus}]$ without markedly converting the amine, $Ar\overset{..}{N}H_2$, into the unreactive, protonated cation, $Ar\overset{\oplus}{N}H_3$—such aromatic amines are very weak bases (*cf.* p. 52). The initial diazotisation of aromatic primary amines is carried out in strongly acid media to ensure that as yet unreacted amine *is* converted to the cation and so prevented from coupling with the diazonium salt as it is formed.

With aromatic amines there is the possibility of attack on either nitrogen or carbon, and, by contrast with phenols, attack takes place largely on nitrogen in primary and secondary amines (i.e. N-alkylanilines) to yield *diazo-amino* compounds:

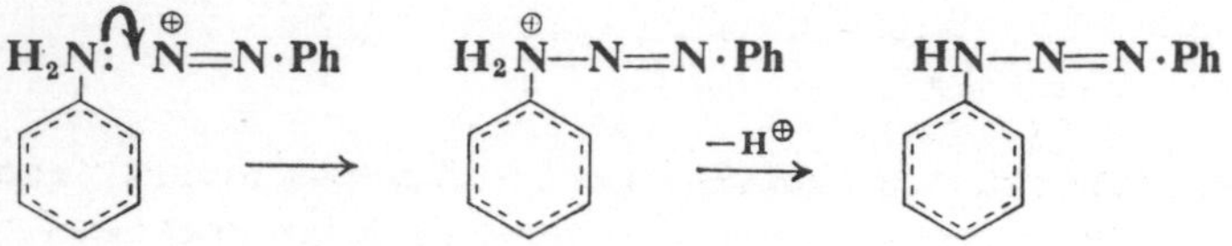

With most primary amines this is virtually the sole product, with N-alkylated anilines some coupling may also take place on the benzene nucleus while with tertiary amines (N-dialkylanilines) only the product coupled on carbon is obtained:

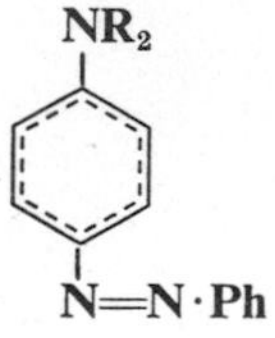

This difference in position of attack with primary and secondary aromatic amines, compared with phenols, probably reflects the relative electron-density of the various positions in the former compounds exerting the controlling influence for, in contrast to a number of other aromatic electrophilic substitution reactions, diazo coupling is sensitive to relatively small differences in electron density (reflecting the rather low ability as an electrophile of $PhN_2^{\oplus}$). Similar differences in electron-density do of course occur in phenols but here control over the position of attack is exerted more by the relative strengths of the bonds formed in the two products: in the two alternative coupled products derivable from amines, this latter difference is much less marked.

The formation of diazoamino compounds by coupling with primary amines does not constitute a preparative bar to obtaining the products coupled on the benzene nucleus for the diazoamino compound may be rearranged to the corresponding *amino-azo* compound by warming in acid:

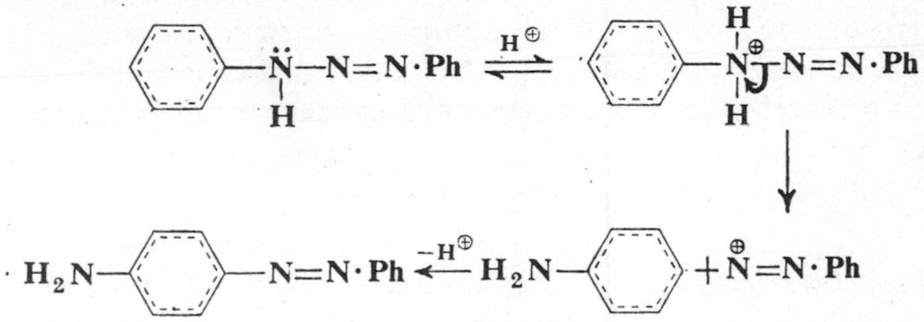

The rearrangement has been shown under these conditions to be an *inter*molecular process, i.e. that the diazonium cation becomes free, for the latter may be transferred to phenols, aromatic amines or other suitable species added to the solution. It is indeed found that the rearrangement proceeds most readily with an acid catalyst plus an excess of the amine that initially underwent coupling to yield the diazoamino compound, it may then be that this amine attacks the protonated diazoamino compound directly with expulsion of $Ph \cdot NH_2$ and loss of a proton:

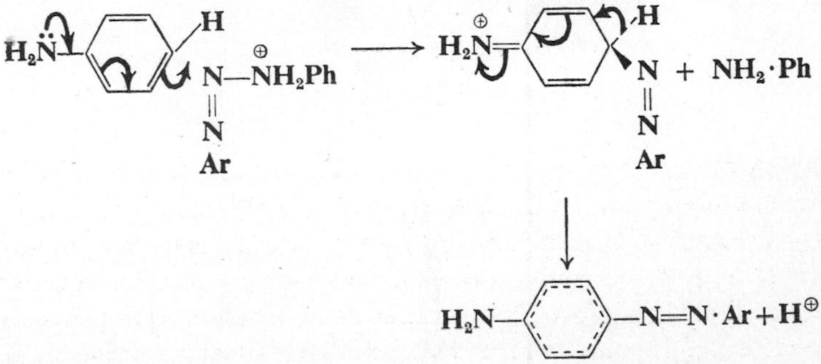

It should perhaps be mentioned that aromatic electrophilic substitution of atoms or groups other than hydrogen is also known. An example is

$$Ph \cdot I + HI \rightarrow Ph \cdot H + I_2$$

which shows all the characteristics (in the way of effect of substituents, etc.) of a typical electrophilic substitution reaction, but such displacements are not common and are usually of little preparative importance.

In the face of the wholly polar viewpoint of aromatic substitution that has so far been adopted, it should be emphasised that examples of homolytic aromatic substitution by free radicals are also known (p. 250).

THE EFFECT OF A SUBSTITUENT ALREADY PRESENT

The effect of a substituent already present in a benzene nucleus in governing not only the reactivity of the nucleus towards further electrophilic attack, but also in determining what position the incoming substituent shall enter, is well known. A number of empirical rules have been devised to account for these effects but they can be better explained on the basis of the electron-donating or -attracting powers of the initial substituent.

(i) Inductive effect of substituents

Alkyl groups are electron-donating and so will increase electron-availability over the nucleus. The effect in toluene

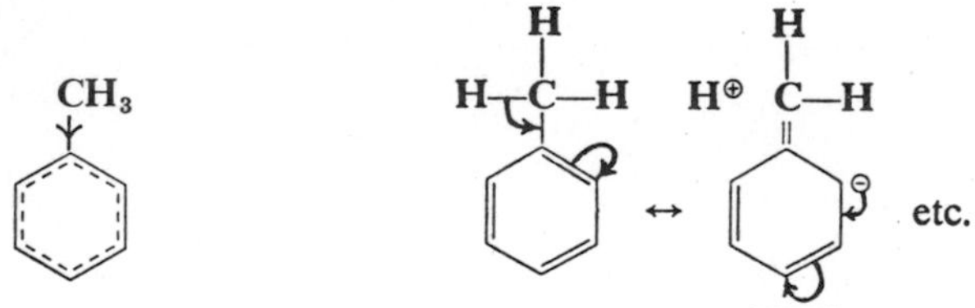

(XIII)

probably arises in part from a contribution to the hybrid by forms such as (XIII), i.e. by hyperconjugation (p. 20). The inductive effect of most other substituents, e.g. halogens, $OH, OMe, NH_2, SO_3H, NO_2$ etc. will be in the opposite direction as the atom next to the nucleus is more electronegative than the carbon to which it is attached, e.g.:

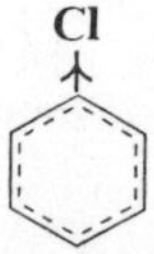

116

But this is not the only way in which a substituent can affect electron-availability in the nucleus.

(ii) Mesomeric effect of substituents

A number of common substituents have unshared electron pairs on the atom attached to the nucleus and these can interact with its delocalised π orbitals

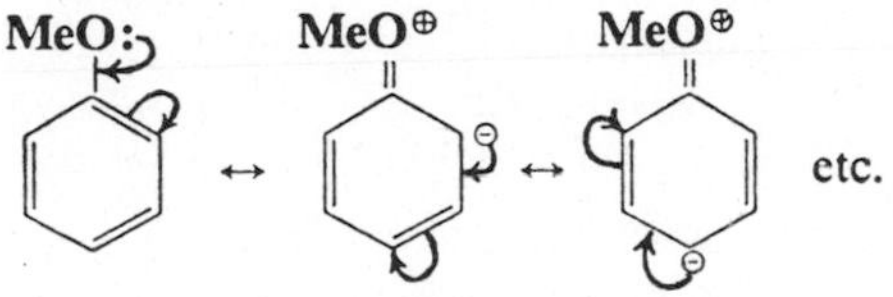

and the same consideration clearly applies to **OH, SH, NH$_2$,** halogens, etc.

It will be noticed that electron-availability over the nucleus is thereby increased. An effect in the opposite direction can take place if the substituent atom attached to the nucleus itself carries a more electronegative atom to which it is multiply bonded, i.e. this atom is then conjugated with the nucleus and can interact with its delocalised π orbitals:

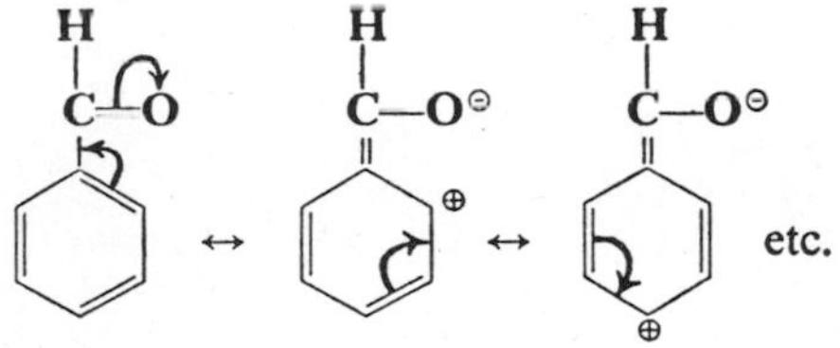

The same consideration clearly applies to **CO·R, CO$_2$H, SO$_3$H, NO$_2$, CN,** etc. Here it will be seen that electron-availability over the nucleus is thereby decreased.

(iii) The overall effect

Clearly any group that, overall, is electron-donating is going to lead to more rapid substitution by an electrophilic reagent than in benzene itself, for the electron-density on the ring carbon atoms is now higher; correspondingly, any group that is, overall, electron-withdrawing is going to lead to less rapid substitution. This is reflected in the relative ease of attack of oxidising agents, which are, of course, electrophilic reagents (e.g. $KMnO_4$), on phenol, benzene and nitrobenzene; phenol is extremely readily attacked with destruction of the aromatic nucleus, while benzene is resistant to attack and nitrobenzene even more so.

It is also reflected in the Friedel-Crafts reaction. Alkylation of benzene leads to an initial product, **Ph·R**, which is more readily attacked than benzene itself due to the electron-donating substituent **R**. It is thus extremely difficult to stop the reaction at the mono-alkylated stage and polyalkylation is the rule (p. 111). In acylation, however, the initial product, **Ph·CO·R**, is less readily attacked than is benzene itself and the reaction can readily be stopped at this stage. It is indeed often preferable to synthesise a mono-alkyl benzene by acylation followed by Clemmensen or other reduction, rather than by direct alkylation, because of difficulties introduced during the latter by polyalkylation and possible rearrangement of **R**. The presence of an electron-withdrawing substituent is generally sufficient to inhibit the Friedel-Crafts reaction and, for example, nitrobenzene is often used as a solvent as it readily dissolves $AlCl_3$.

The overall electron-withdrawing effect is clear-cut with, for example, NO_2, for here inductive and mesomeric effects reinforce each other, but with, e.g. NH_2, these effects are in opposite directions

and it is not possible to say, *a priori*, whether the overall effect on the nucleus will be activation or de-activation. Here the direction and magnitude of the dipole moment of **Ph·Y** can be some guide (see p.119).

The overall electron-donating effect of **OH** and NH_2, as compared with the overall electron-withdrawing effect of **Cl**, reflects the considerably greater ease with which oxygen and nitrogen will release their electron pairs as compared with chlorine; this is more than sufficient to outweigh the inductive effect in the two former cases but not in the latter. It should, however, be remembered that the moments of a number of the composite groups, e.g. **OH**, are not collinear with

Y	μ	Direction in 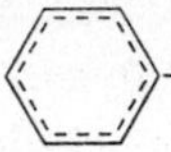 ⬡—Y
OH NH$_2$ OMe Me	1·6 1·5 1·2 0·3	←+
H	0·0	
Cl CHO SO$_3$H NO$_2$	1·6 2·8 3·8 3·9	+→

the axis of the benzene ring and hence the component of the moment actually affecting the bond to the ring may thus be different from the observed moment of the molecule as a whole:

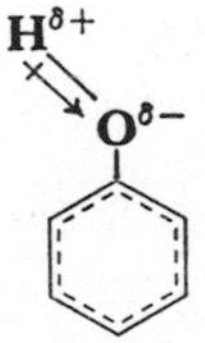

The relation between electron-availability and ease of electrophilic substitution may, however, be seen by comparing the direction and magnitude of dipole moments (p. 119) with the following relative rates of attack by $^{\oplus}$NO$_2$:

PhOH	PhMe	PhH	PhCl	PhNO$_2$
10^3	2·5	1	3×10^{-2}	$< 10^{-4}$

(iv) The position of substitution

Which position, *o*-, *m*- or *p*- is actually entered by the incoming group will depend on which leads to the most readily formed transition state.

As the transition state usually resembles the related metastable intermediate or σ complex reasonably closely energetically (p. 32), it may be assumed that it also resembles it in structure. Thus structural features that stabilise a particular σ complex might be expected to stabilise the related transition state in a similar way. Thus considering the three possibilities for nitration when the initial substituent is **OMe** (i.e. with anisole),

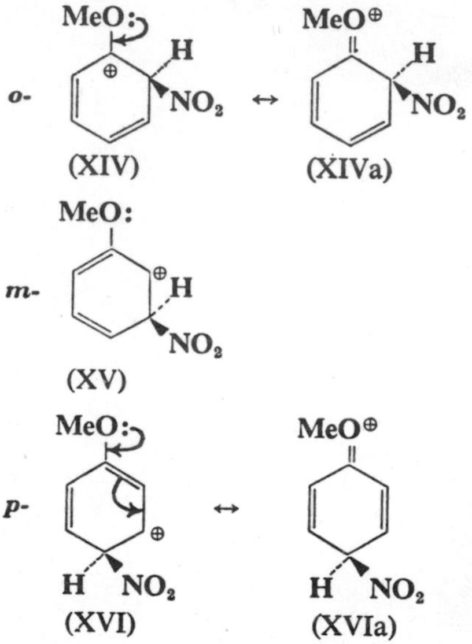

o-

(XIV)   (XIVa)

m-

(XV)

p-

(XVI)   (XVIa)

clearly **OMe**, being an electron-donating group, is able to stabilise the intermediate by assisting in the delocalisation of its charge when the incoming group has entered the *o-* or *p-*, (XIV*a* and XVI*a*), but *not* the *m*-position, (XV). It should be noted that additional structures (two in each case), in which the positive charge is delocalised merely within the benzene nucleus (*cf.* nitrobenzene below), have, for convenience, been omitted as their contribution will be essentially the same whether the incoming substituent has entered the *o-*, *m-* or *p*-position. The effect of stabilising a transition state (*cf.* related σ complex) is to lower the activation energy of the reaction leading to its formation, and preferential *o*/*p*-substitution thus takes place. With nitrobenzene, however,

(XVII) (XVII*a*) (XVII*b*)

(XVIII) (XVIII*a*) (XVIII*b*)

(XIX) (XIX*a*) (XIX*b*)

the group already present has a positively charged nitrogen atom adjacent to the nucleus so it will clearly not function in helping to delocalise the positive charge that is introduced on to the nucleus by nitration. The three possible intermediates can thus only stabilise themselves by delocalisation of the charge over the nucleus itself. This will, however, clearly be less effective if substitution takes place in the *o*- and *p*-positions, for in each case one of the contributing structures (XVII*b* and XIX*a*) would have to carry a positive charge on a carbon atom which is already bonded to a positively charged nitrogen atom, a far from stable juxtaposition. With the intermediate arising from *m*-substitution (XVIII) there is no such limitation; this intermediate is thus more stable than those that would be obtained by *o*- or *p*-substitution and preferential *m*-substitution thus takes place.

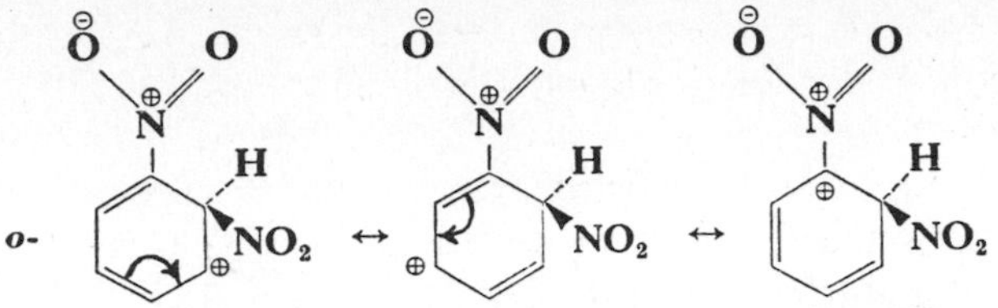

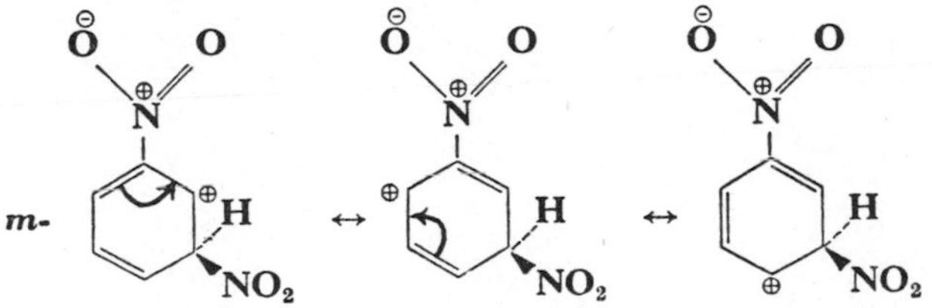

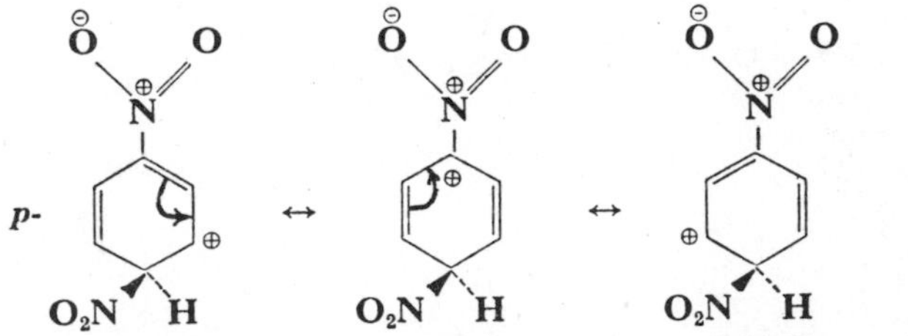

It should be remembered, however, that whatever the nature of the substituent already present what we are actually considering are the *relative* rates of attack on *o*-, *m*- and *p*-positions and though either *o/p*- or *m*-substitution is usually preponderant, neither alternative is of necessity exclusive. Thus nitration of toluene has been found to lead to ≈ 3 per cent of *m*-nitrotoluene and of *t*-butylbenzene to ≈ 9 per cent of the *m*-nitro derivative.

A somewhat less satisfactory explanation of a substituent being predominantly *either o/p*- or *m*-directing is provided by

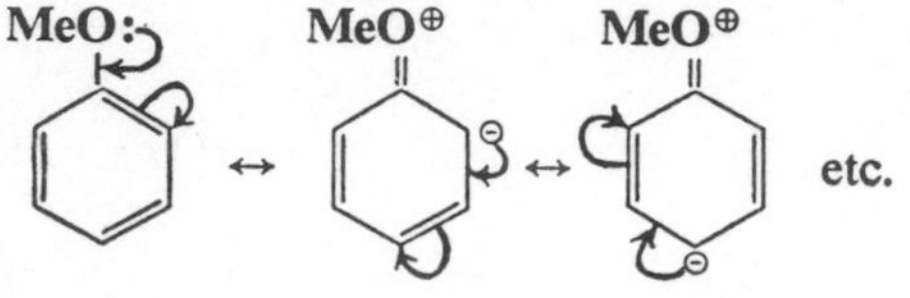

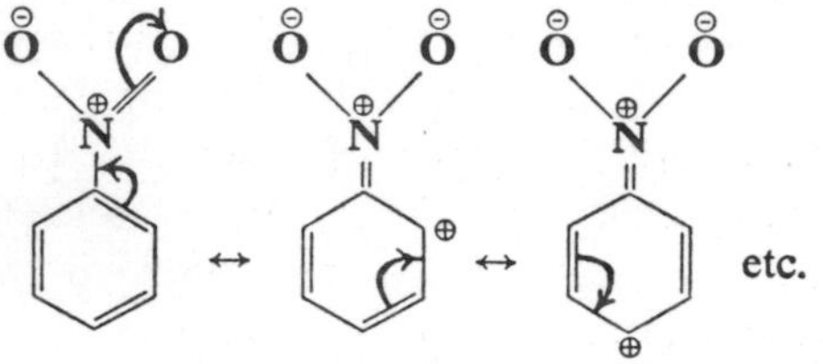

OMe activating the *o*- and *p*-positions preferentially leading, there-fore, to *o/p*-substitution and **NO₂** deactivating the *o*- and *p*-positions preferentially leading, therefore, to *m*-substitution by *default* as this is the *least* deactivated position. This, however, is considering the state of affairs in the starting material, the substrate, whereas the previous argument compared the several alternative metastable inter-mediates or σ complexes. As the formation of the transition state is the determining step in the reaction, a consideration of the factors that influence the stability of the related σ complex is likely to prove the more reliable guide as the σ complex resembles the transition state more closely than does the substrate.

This is readily seen with styrene which, considering the substrate only, might be expected to substitute *m*- due to electron-withdrawal (XX):

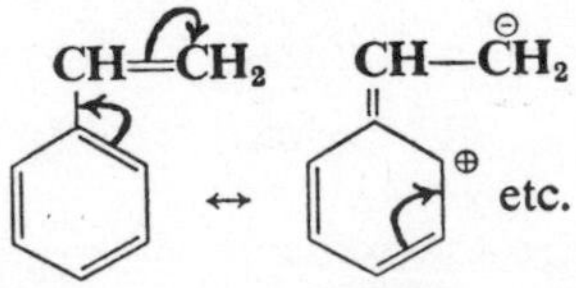

(XX)

In practice, however, it substitutes *o/p*- (it also undergoes substitution on the CH_2 of the vinyl group) owing to the fact that the metastable intermediates or σ complexes arising from *o*- and *p*-substitution are stabilised, by delocalisation due to the vinyl group, in a way that the intermediate arising from *m*-substitution cannot be (*cf.* anisole above):

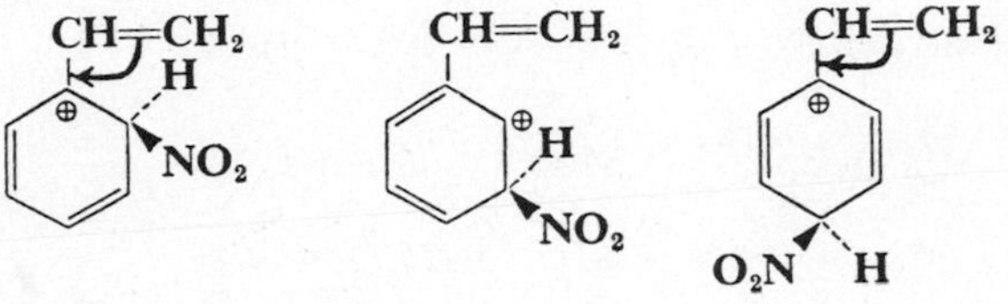

| *o*- | *m*- | *p*- |

The behaviour of chlorobenzene is interesting for although Cl is, overall, electron-withdrawing and the nucleus is therefore more difficult to nitrate than is benzene itself (a circumstance normally associated with *m*-directive groups) it does nevertheless substitute *o/p*-. This is due to the electron pairs on chlorine being able to assist in the stabilisation by delocalisation of the intermediates for *o*- and *p*- but not for *m*-substitution (*cf.* anisole, p. 120):

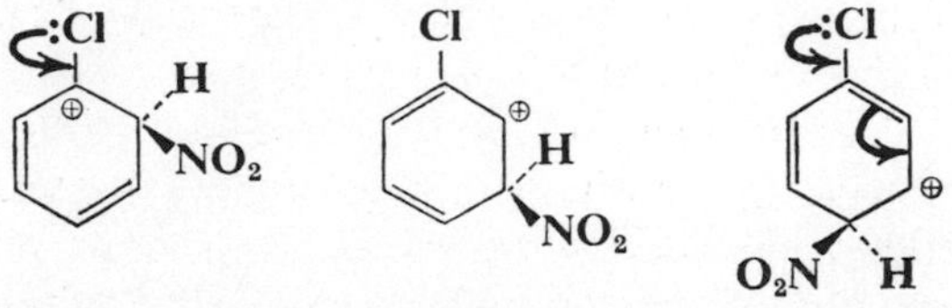

| *o*- | *m*- | *p*- |

These electron pairs are somewhat more loth than those on oxygen or nitrogen to interact with the π orbital system of the nucleus (p. 119), but such interaction is enhanced by a temporary polarisation, sometimes called the *electromeric effect*, superimposed on the permanent polarisation of the molecule at the close approach of the attacking electrophile $^{\oplus}NO_2$:

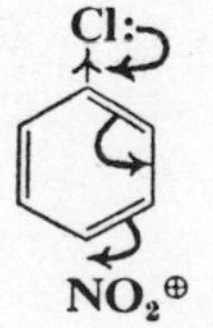

123

The rate of reaction will remain slower than in benzene itself, however, due to the overall deactivation of the nucleus by chlorine's inductive effect in the opposite direction. A very similar situation is encountered in the addition of unsymmetrical adducts to vinyl halides, e.g. $CH_2{=}CHBr$, where the inductive effect controls the *rate*, but mesomeric stabilisation of the carbonium ion intermediate governs the *orientation*, of addition (p. 142).

(v) Conditions of reaction

The conditions under which an electrophilic substitution reaction is carried out can modify or even alter completely the directing effect of a group. Thus phenol is even more powerfully *o/p*-directing in alkaline than in neutral or acid solution, for the species undergoing substitution is then the phenoxide ion (XXI), in which the inductive effect is now reversed compared with phenol itself and, more important, a full blown negative charge is available for interaction with the π orbital system of the nucleus; the electron density over the nucleus is thus notably increased:

(XXI)

Conversely aniline, normally *o/p*-directing, becomes in part at least *m*-directing in strongly acid solution, due to protonation to form the anilinium cation:

$$H{:}\overset{\oplus}{N}H_2$$

This is due to the fact that there can no longer be any interaction of the unshared electron pair on nitrogen with the delocalised π orbitals of the nucleus, for the former are now involved in bond formation with the proton that has been taken up and the inductive effect, drawing electrons away from the nucleus, is now enormously enhanced by the positive charge on nitrogen. The reason that any *o*- and *p*-nitroanilines are obtained at all under ordinary conditions with nitrating mixture is due to the small, residual concentration of free aniline, a very weak base (*cf.* p. 52), that is still in equilibrium with the anilinium cation in the acid medium. The free base, having an activated nucleus, undergoes *o/p*-substitution very, very much faster than the deactivated cation suffers attack at the *m*-position. The difference in rate is so marked that the presence of less than one part per million of free base will still lead to more than 50 per cent *o/p*-substitution, but the proportion of *m*-nitroaniline obtained does increase as the acid concentration of the medium increases, as would be expected.

As soon as more than one saturated atom is interposed between a positive charge and the nucleus, however, its inductive effect falls off very sharply (*cf.* strengths of acids, p. 43) and so does the percentage of the *m*-isomer produced, as seen in the nitration of:

Compound	Percentage *m*-
$Ph \cdot \overset{\oplus}{N}Me_3$	100
$Ph \cdot CH_2 \cdot \overset{\oplus}{N}Me_3$	88
$Ph \cdot CH_2 \cdot CH_2 \cdot \overset{\oplus}{N}Me_3$	19
$Ph \cdot CH_2 \cdot CH_2 \cdot CH_2 \cdot \overset{\oplus}{N}Me_3$	5

(vi) o/p-ratios

It might, at first sight, be expected that the relative proportions of *o*- and *p*-isomers obtained during substitution of a nucleus containing an *o/p*-directive substituent would be 67 per cent *o*- and 33 per cent *p*-, as there are two *o*-positions to be substituted for every one *p*-. Apart from the fact that a little *m*-product is often obtained (the extent to which a position is substituted is merely a matter of *relative* rates of attack, after all), the above ratio is virtually never realised and more often than not more *p*- than *o*-product is obtained. This may be due to the substituent already present hindering attack at the *o*-positions adjacent to it by its very bulk, an interference to which the more distant *p*-position is not susceptible. In support of this it is found that as the initial substituent increases in size from $CH_3 \rightarrow Me_3C$, the proportion of the *o*-isomer obtained drops markedly (57 per cent → 12 per cent) while that of the *p*- increases (40 per cent → 80 per cent). Increase in size of the attacking agent has the same effect; thus substitution of chlorobenzene leads to:

Group introduced	Cl	NO$_2$	Br	SO$_3$H
Percentage *o*-	39	30	11	0
Percentage *p*-	55	70	87	100

That a steric factor is not the only one at work, however, is seen in the nitration of fluoro-, chloro-, bromo- and iodobenzenes where the percentage of *o*-isomer obtained *increases* as we go along the series, despite the *increase* in size of the substituent. This is due to the fact that the electron-withdrawing inductive effect influences the adjacent *o*-positions much more powerfully than the more distant *p*-position. The inductive effect decreases considerably on going from fluoro- to iodobenzene (the biggest change being seen in going from fluoro- to chlorobenzene) resulting in easier attack at the *o*-positions *despite* the increasing size of the group already present.

With *o/p*-directive groups having unshared electrons, e.g. **OMe**, the metastable intermediate leading to *p*-substitution has a contribution from a quasi *p*-quinonoid structure (XVI*a*, p. 120), as compared with the intermediate leading to *o*-substitution which has a contribution from a quasi *o*-quinonoid structure (XIV*a*, p. 120); as with the corresponding quinones themselves, the former is likely to be more stable than the latter thus leading to preferential *p*-substitution.

The *o/p*-ratio is also a good deal influenced by the actual conditions, e.g. temperature, under which substitution is carried out, and there are a number of anomalies that have not yet been adequately explained.

COMPETITION BETWEEN SUBSTITUENTS

If two substituents are already present in a benzene nucleus, the position of entry of a third can, in a number of cases, be forecast with fair accuracy. Thus if an *o/p*- and a *m*-directive substituent are present, as in *m*-nitrotoluene (XXII), we should expect nitration to take place at the positions indicated by arrows:

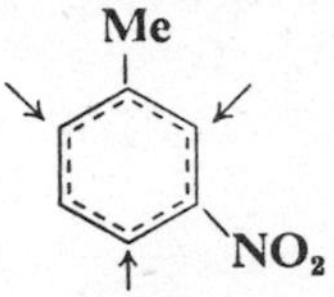

Me

NO$_2$

(XXII)

That is *o*- and *p*- to the activating substituent, **Me**, but not *m*- to the deactivating substituent, **NO$_2$**. This is borne out in practice, i.e. where an *o/p*- and a *m*-directive substituent are in competition the latter can often be looked upon as merely occupying a position in the nucleus; though any possible steric effects it may exert must also be taken into account in deciding which positions, out of several alternatives, are likely to be most readily attacked. With two suitably situated *o/p*-directive substituents, however, actual competition does take place. It is not always possible accurately to forecast the outcome, but normally those groups that exert their effects via unshared electron pairs are more potent than those operating via inductive or hyperconjugative effects, possibly due to the added electromeric effect (p. 123) exerted on approach of the electrophile. Thus nitration of acet-*p*-toluidide (XXIII) leads to

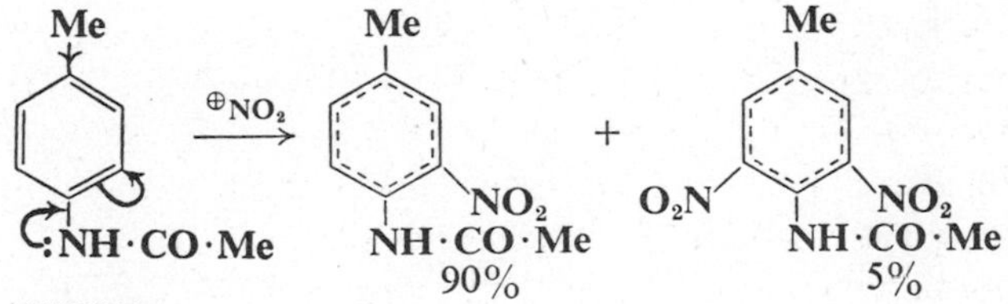

Me   Me   Me

$\oplus$NO$_2$ →   +

:NH·CO·Me   NH·CO·Me   O$_2$N   NH·CO·Me
                    NO$_2$ NO$_2$
(XXIII)   90%   5%

virtually no attack at all taking place *o*- to **Me**.

ELECTROPHILIC SUBSTITUTION OF OTHER AROMATIC SPECIES

With naphthalene, electrophilic substitution, e.g. nitration, takes place preferentially at the α- rather than the β-position. This can be accounted for by the fact that more effective stabilisation by delocalisation can take place in the metastable intermediate or transition state from α-substitution than that from β- attack (*cf.* benzene with an *o/p*-directive substituent):

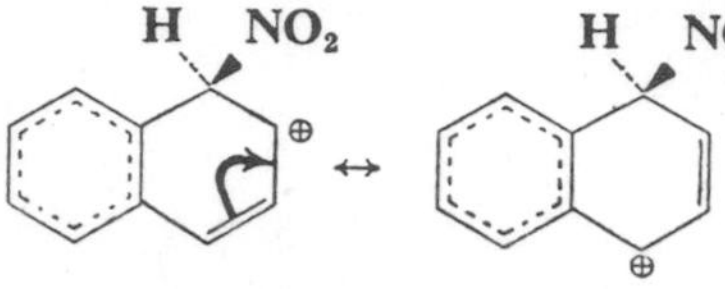

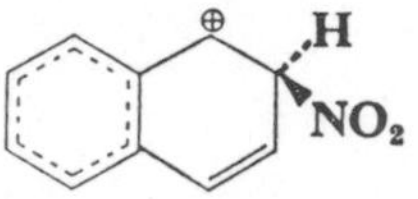

More forms can also be written in each case in which the positive charge is now delocalised over the other ring, leading to a total of seven forms for the α-intermediate as against six for the β-, but the above, in which the second ring retains intact, fully delocalised π orbitals, are probably the most important and the contrast, between two contributing forms in the one case and one in the other, correspondingly more marked.

The sulphonation of naphthalene is found to lead to almost complete α-substitution at 80° but to approximately 85 per cent β-substitution at 160°. This is due to the fact that the rate of β-substitution is essentially negligible below *ca.* 110° but α-substitution, although very rapid, is reversible and as the β-sulphonic acid is thermodynamically more stable than the α- (primarily due to the large SO_3H group occupying a less hindered position in the former), *kinetic* or *rate* control of product (→α-) at low temperatures gives place to *thermodynamic* control of product (→β-) at higher temperatures (*cf.* p. 220). That this is the real explanation is confirmed by heating the α-sulphonic acid with H_2SO_4 when an ⇌ mixture containing largely the β-acid is obtained, the detailed evidence being against a mere *intra*molecular rearrangement having taken place.

The possibility of the charge becoming more widely delocalised in the naphthalene intermediate, as compared with benzene, would lead us to expect more ready electrophilic attack on naphthalene which is indeed observed.

Pyridine (XXIV), like benzene, has six π electrons (one being supplied by nitrogen) in delocalised π orbitals but, unlike benzene, the orbitals will be deformed by being attracted towards the nitrogen atom because of the latter's being more electronegative than carbon. This is reflected in the observed dipole moment of pyridine

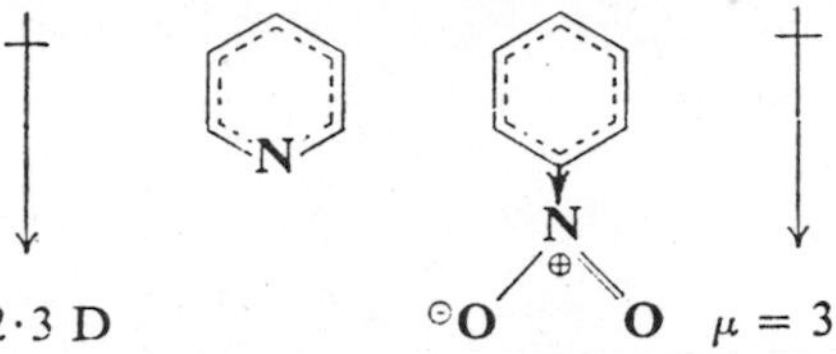

$\mu = 2\cdot3$ D

(XXIV)

$^{\ominus}O \quad O \quad \mu = 3\cdot9$ D

(XXV)

and the compound would therefore be expected to have a deactivated nucleus towards electrophilic substitution (*cf.* nitrobenzene (XXV)). The deactivation of the nucleus is considerably increased on electrophilic attack, for the positive charge introduced on nitrogen by protonation, or by direct attack on it of the substituting electrophile, withdraws electrons much more strongly:

In fact electrophilic substitution is extremely difficult, sulphonation, for example, requiring twenty-four hours heating with oleum at 230°. Substitution takes place at the β-position (*m*- to the electron-withdrawing centre), the explanation being similar to that already discussed for nitrobenzene (p. 121).

Pyrrole (XXVI) also has delocalised π orbitals but nitrogen has here had to contribute *two* electrons so becoming virtually non-basic (p. 56) and the dipole moment is found to be in the opposite direction to that of pyridine:

$\mu = 1\cdot8$ D

(XXVI)

It is thus referred to as a π *excessive* heterocycle as compared with pyridine which is a π *deficient* one. It behaves like a reactive benzene derivative, e.g. aniline, and electrophilic substitution is very easy.

129

Substitution is complicated, however, by the fact that if protonation is forced on pyrrole in strongly acid solution (this probably takes place on an α-carbon atom rather than on nitrogen, XXVII, *cf.* p. 56), the aromatic character is lost, the compound behaves like a conjugated diene and undergoes extremely rapid polymerisation:

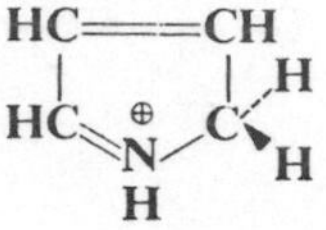

$$HC\!\!=\!\!=\!\!CH$$

(XXVII)

Electrophilic substitution can, however, be carried out under highly specialised conditions leading to preferential attack at the α-position, reflecting the greater delocalisation, and hence stabilisation, possible in the metastable intermediate leading to α-, as compared with β-, substitution:

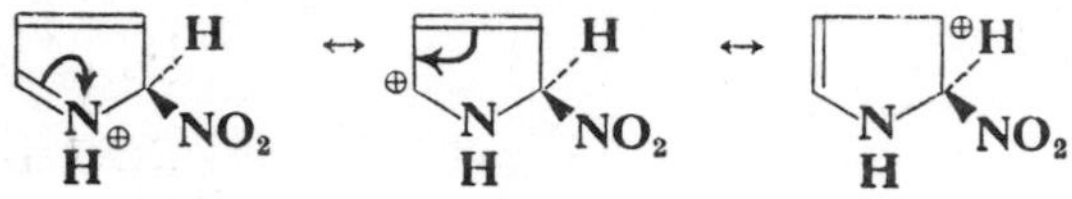

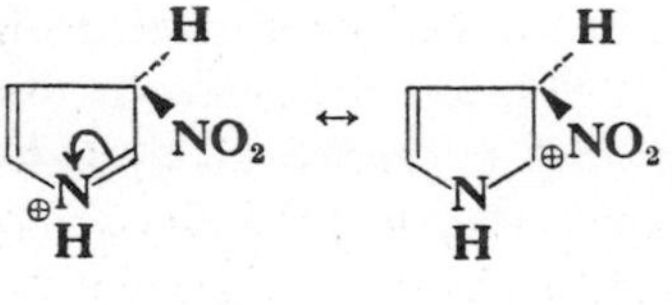

The difference in stability between the two is not very strongly marked, however, reflecting the highly activated state of the nucleus, and ready attack will take place at the β-position if the α- is already substituted.

NUCLEOPHILIC ATTACK ON AROMATIC SPECIES

(i) Substitution of hydrogen

As it is the π electrons that are initially responsible for the normal substitution of benzene being an electrophilic process, the presence of a strongly electron-withdrawing substituent might be expected to render attack by a nucleophile possible provided electron-withdrawal

from the nucleus was sufficiently great (*cf.* the addition of nucleophiles to alkenes carrying electron-withdrawing substituents, p. 153).
In fact, nitrobenzene can be fused with potash, in the presence of air,
to yield *o*-nitrophenol (XXVIII):

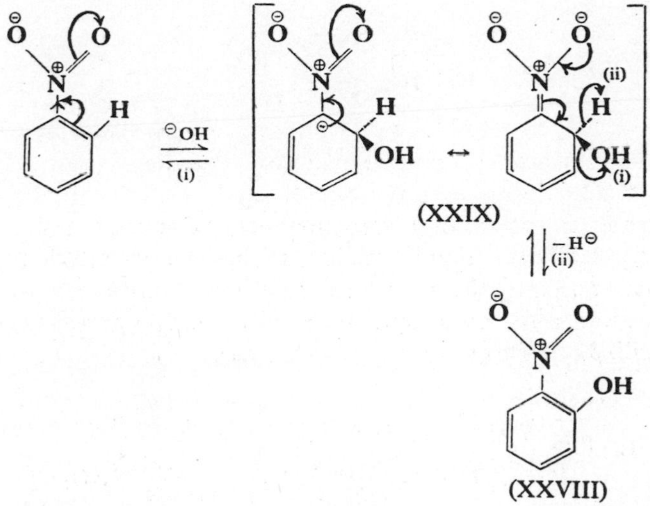

(XXIX)

(XXVIII)

The nitro-group is able to stabilise the anionic intermediate (XXIX)
by delocalising its charge if $^\ominus$OH enters the *o*- or *p*-positions but not
if it goes into the *m*-position. The *o*-attack is likely to be preferred,
despite the size of the adjacent NO_2, as the inductive effect of the
nitro-group, acting over a shorter distance, will make the *o*-position
more electron-deficient than the *p*-. The overall reaction is exactly
what we should expect, namely that a substituent promoting attack
on the *m*-position by an electrophile would promote *o*/*p*-attack by a
nucleophile.

Once (XXIX) has been formed, it can eliminate $^\ominus$OH (i) and so be
reconverted to nitrobenzene as readily as it can eliminate $H^\ominus$ (ii) to
yield the product (XXVIII). To drive the reaction over to the right an
oxidising agent must be present to encourage the elimination of
hydride ion and to destroy it as formed. Thus the fusion is either
carried out in the air, or an oxidising agent such as potassium
nitrate or ferricyanide is added.

Pyridine behaves in an exactly analogous manner undergoing
attack by sodamide (i.e. $^\ominus NH_2$, the Tschitschibabin reaction), to

yield α-aminopyridine (XXX), a compound of value in the synthesis of sulphapyridine:

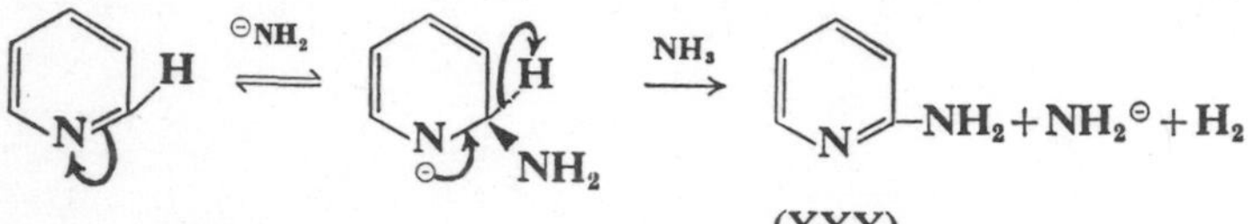

(XXX)

These are analogous to S_N2 reactions but with attack taking place from the side rather than from the back of the carbon atom undergoing nucleophilic attack; they differ also in that this atom never becomes bonded to more than four other atoms at once (*cf.* p. 58). This mechanism is probably sufficiently different from the normal S_N2 for it to be designated specifically as S_N2 (*aromatic*).

(ii) Substitution of atoms other than hydrogen

Aromatic nucleophilic substitution more commonly refers to the replacement of atoms other than hydrogen and both S_N1 and S_N2 (*aromatic*) mechanisms are encountered. The only important examples proceeding via the S_N1 mechanism are the replacement reactions of diazonium salts

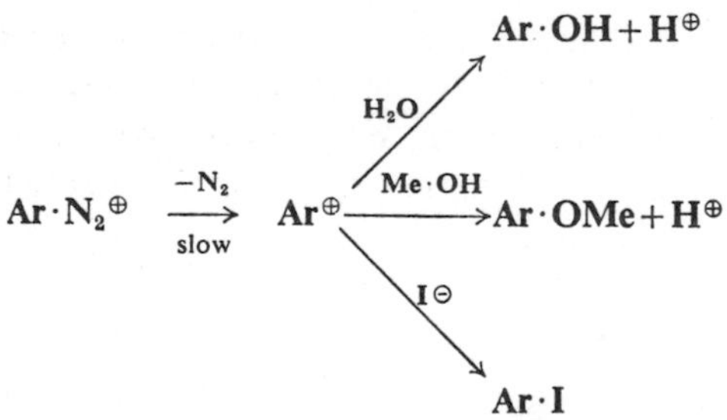

in which the rate-determining step is the elimination of nitrogen from the diazonium cation followed by rapid reaction of the aryl cation with a nucleophile, the rates being first order in $ArN_2^{\oplus}$ and independent of the concentration of the nucleophile. A number of the reactions of diazonium salts, particularly in less polar solvents, proceed by a radical mechanism, however (p. 255).

The most common example of an S_N2 (*aromatic*) reaction is the replacement of an activated halogen atom,

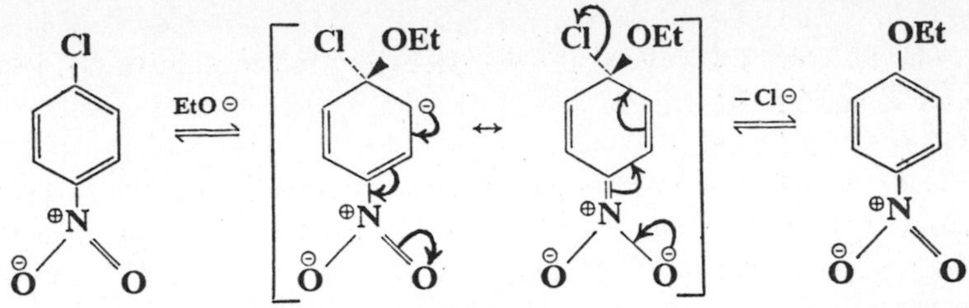

(XXXI)

kinetic studies in a number of examples supporting the bimolecularity of the reaction. That an actual intermediate such as (XXXI) is formed, unlike aliphatic bimolecular nucleophilic substitution where the bond to the leaving group is being broken as that to the entering group is being formed, is shown by the fact that chlorides and bromides react in a number of cases at essentially the same rate. The breakage of the carbon–halogen bond can thus not be involved in the rate-determining step for a **C—Cl** bond is more difficult to break than an analogous **C—Br** one and the chloride would, *a priori*, be expected to react more slowly than the bromide.

Confirmation of the formation of such an intermediate is provided by the actual isolation of the same species (XXXII) from the action of $^\ominus$OEt on 2,4,6-trinitroanisole (XXXIII) and $^\ominus$OMe on 2,4,6-trinitrophenetole (XXXIV):

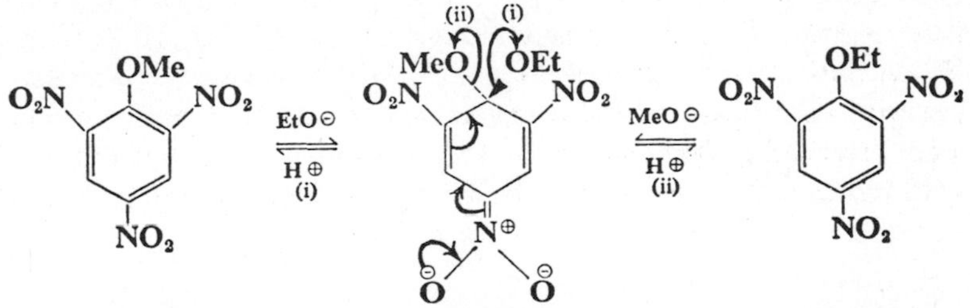

(XXXIII)   (XXXII)   (XXXIV)

It is also found that acidification of the reaction mixture obtained from *either* substrate yields exactly the same proportion of (XXXIII) and (XXXIV).

We have thus now encountered nucleophilic displacement reactions in which the bond to the leaving group is broken (*a*) *before* that to the

133

attacking nucleophile has been formed (S_N1), (*b*) *simultaneously* with the formation of the bond to the attacking nucleophile (S_N2), and (*c*) *after* the bond to the attacking nucleophile has been formed (S_N2 (*aromatic*)).

The reason for the activating effect of electron-withdrawing groups, especially NO_2, on nuclear halogen atoms is their ability to stabilise intermediates such as (XXXI) by delocalisation; it would therefore be expected that nitro-groups would be most effective when *o*- and *p*-to the substituent to be replaced, for in the *m*-position they can only assist in spreading the charge via their inductive effects. The presence of nitro-groups in the 2-, 4- and 6-positions in picryl chloride, $(O_2N)_3 \cdot C_6H_2 \cdot Cl$, thus confers almost acid chloride reactivity on the halogen, their effect is so pronounced. 2- and 4-, but not 3-, halogeno-pyridines also undergo ready replacement reactions for exactly the same reasons (the electron-withdrawing group here being the heterocyclic nitrogen atom); they do, indeed, resemble the corresponding *o*- and *p*-nitrohalogenobenzenes though the activation of the halogen is slightly less than in the latter.

If nitro-groups are to stabilise, and so assist in the formation of, intermediates such as (XXXI) the *p* orbitals on the nitrogen atom of the NO_2 group must be able to become parallel to those on the adjacent nuclear carbon atom. For this to happen the oxygen atoms attached to nitrogen must also lie in or near the plane of the nucleus. If such atoms are forced out of this plane by steric factors, the NO_2 group becomes a much less effective activator as only its inductive effect can then operate. Thus the bromine in (XXXV) is replaced much more slowly than in *p*-nitrobromobenzene (XXXVI) because the *o*-methyl groups in the former prevent the oxygen atoms of the nitro-group from becoming coplanar with the nucleus and so inhibit the withdrawal of electrons from it by the mesomeric effect (*cf.* p. 23):

(XXXV)   (XXXVI)

(iii) Replacement of halogen in an unactivated nucleus

The chlorine in chlorobenzene only undergoes replacement by $^\ominus$OH under extreme conditions due to the fact that the expected S_N2 (*aromatic*) intermediate (XXXVII), not being stabilised like the examples already considered, is reluctant to form:

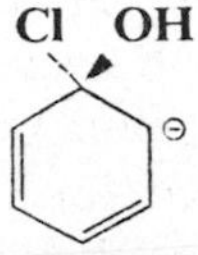

(XXXVII)

Nevertheless aryl halides having no activating groups are found to undergo ready conversion to amines with sodamide, but this reaction has been shown to proceed via an entirely different mechanism to that already considered. It has been shown not to be a direct replacement, but to involve elimination of hydrogen halide followed by addition of ammonia:

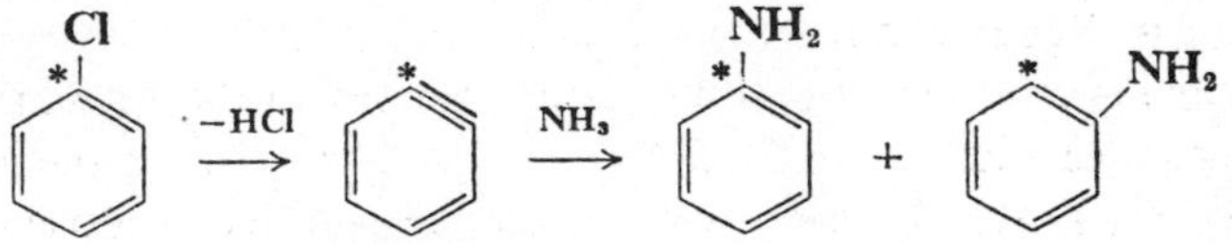

(XXXVIII)

The *benzyne* intermediate (XXXVIII) proposed seems inherently unlikely but the evidence in its favour is extremely strong. Thus when chlorobenzene, in which chlorine is attached to an isotopically-labelled carbon atom, reacts with sodamide the intervention of a benzyne intermediate should lead to equal quantities of two amines; in one of which the amino-group is attached directly to the labelled carbon and in the other in the *o*-position to it. This has, indeed, been confirmed experimentally. Similarly in the reaction of α–halogeno-naphthalenes with R_2NH, two isomeric compounds should be obtained

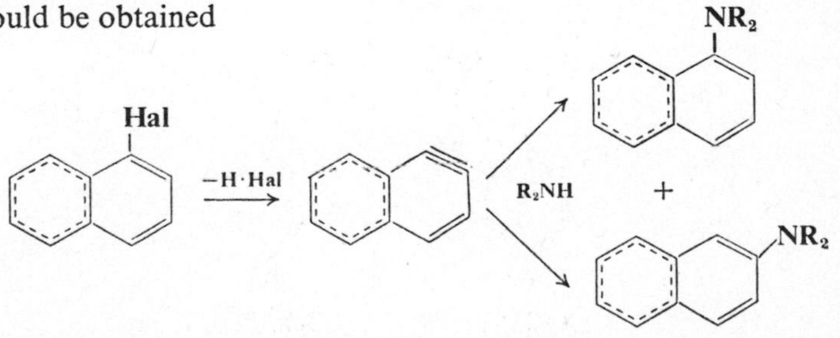

135

and the proportion of them in the product should be independent of the nature of the original halogen; this, too, has been confirmed experimentally. Support for the intervention of benzyne intermediates is also provided by the fact that aryl halides having no hydrogen in the *o*-positions, and so unable to eliminate **H·Hal**, are extremely resistant to amination. But, perhaps most conclusive of all, it has proved possible to 'trap' benzyne intermediates by reacting them with dienes to produce recognisable addition products in the Diels-Alder reaction (p. 151).

It has been shown using isotopically-labelled chlorobenzene that its conversion to phenol proceeds both via a benzyne intermediate and by an S_N2 (*aromatic*) reaction simultaneously. A strong base is always required for a replacement to proceed via a benzyne intermediate for the initial removal of a proton from the aromatic nucleus is far from easy:

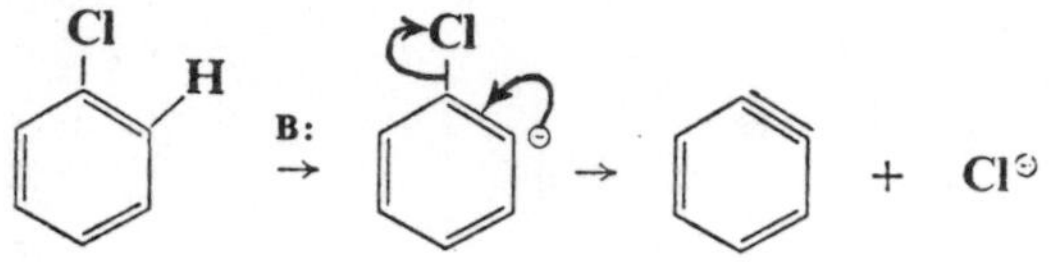

6 ADDITION TO CARBON–CARBON DOUBLE BONDS

As we have already seen (p. 6), a carbon–carbon double bond consists of a strong σ bond plus a weaker π bond, in a different position (I):

$$
\underset{(I)}{\overset{\text{H}\cdots\text{H}}{\underset{\text{H}\quad\text{H}}{\text{C}-\text{C}}}}
\qquad
\underset{(II)}{\overset{\text{H}\quad\text{H}}{\underset{\text{H}\quad\text{H}}{\overset{\oplus}{\text{C}}-\overset{\ominus}{\text{C}}}}}
\;\leftarrow\;
\underset{(\;)}{\overset{\text{H}\quad\text{H}}{\underset{\text{H}\quad\text{H}}{\text{C}=\text{C}}}}
\;\rightarrow\;
\underset{(III)}{\overset{\text{H}\quad\text{H}}{\underset{\text{H}\quad\text{H}}{\dot{\text{C}}-\dot{\text{C}}}}}
$$

The pair of electrons in the π orbital are less firmly held between the carbon nuclei and so more readily polarisable than those of the σ bond, leading to the characteristic reactivity of such unsaturated compounds. Addition to such compounds can proceed through ionic (II) or free radical (III) mechanisms, depending on the way in which the π electrons become polarised either by the approaching reagent or other causes. Thus the former tends to predominate in polar solvents, the latter in non-polar solvents, especially in the presence of other radicals or of light. Free radical addition reactions are discussed subsequently (p. 242) and attention will here be confined to the ionic mechanism.

As the π electrons are the most readily accessible feature of a carbon–carbon double bond, we should expect them to shield the molecule from attack by nucleophilic reagents. Thus the characteristic reactions of such a system should be with cations, $X^\oplus$, or electron-deficient species, i.e. with electrophilic reagents, and this is indeed found to be the case.

ADDITION OF BROMINE

The addition of halogens, e.g. bromine, is envisaged as taking place not as a one-stage process, in which both bromine atoms become attached simultaneously, but as a stepwise addition which is initiated by a species containing positively polarised bromine: in this case the bromine molecule which becomes polarised on its close approach to the π electron layer of the olefine. The bromine first interacts with the π electrons to form a so-called π complex (IV) and then breaks through to form a σ bond with carbon, yielding the carbonium ion (V):

$$\begin{array}{ccccc}
\underset{\underset{\underset{\text{Br}}{|}}{\overset{|}{\text{Br}}}}{\text{C}=\text{C}} & \rightleftharpoons & \underset{\underset{\text{(IV)}}{\overset{\overset{\delta+}{\text{Br}}}{\underset{\text{Br}^{\delta-}}{|}}}}{\text{C}=\text{C}} & \rightarrow & \underset{\underset{\text{(V)}}{\overset{\oplus}{\text{C}}-\text{C}}}{\underset{\overset{|}{\text{Br}}}{\underset{\text{Br}^{\ominus}}{}}} & \xrightarrow{\text{Br}^{\ominus}} & \underset{\underset{\text{(VI)}}{\overset{\overset{\text{Br}}{|}}{\text{C}-\text{C}}}}{\overset{|}{\text{Br}}}
\end{array}$$

The addition is then completed by $Br^{\ominus}$ attack to yield the dibromide (VI); the evidence suggests that the formation of (V) is the rate-determining step of the reaction. If an intermediate such as (V) is indeed formed then mixed products should result if the addition of bromine is carried out in the presence of other anions, for once (V) has been formed, $Br^{\ominus}$ will not then be in any specially privileged position for attacking it to complete the addition. It is, in fact, found that the presence of $Cl^{\ominus}$, $NO_3{}^{\ominus}$, etc., during bromination leads to the formation of, for example, $ClCH_2 \cdot CH_2Br$ and $O_3N \cdot CH_2 \cdot CH_2Br$ in addition to (VI). That these products are not formed merely by subsequent attack of $Cl^{\ominus}$ and $NO_3{}^{\ominus}$ on (VI) is confirmed by the fact that their formation proceeds much faster than do these substitution reactions.

An alternative intermediate has also been suggested, namely the *bromonium ion* (VII), which differs from (V) only in the distribution of its electrons (it could indeed be derived by the attack of one of the bromine atom's unshared electron pairs on the nearby carbonium ion carbon atom):

$$\begin{array}{ccc}
\underset{\underset{\text{(V)}}{\overset{\oplus}{\text{C}}-\text{C}}}{\underset{:\text{Br}}{\diagdown\diagup}} & \leftrightarrow & \underset{\underset{\text{(VII)}}{\underset{\overset{\text{Br}}{\oplus}}{\diagdown\diagup}}}{\text{C}-\text{C}}
\end{array}$$

The participation of such an intermediate would be expected to have stereochemical implications.

STEREOCHEMISTRY OF ADDITION

An intermediate such as (VII) would involve 'attack from the back' by $Br^{\ominus}$ as access from that side would be sterically so much readier than from the front where the bulky bromine atom would get in the way.

The overall addition should thus be *trans*, one bromine atom becoming attached from the front of the molecule and the other from the back. Thus if we consider the addition of bromine to maleic acid (VIII) to yield the dibromo-analogue of tartaric acid (IX):

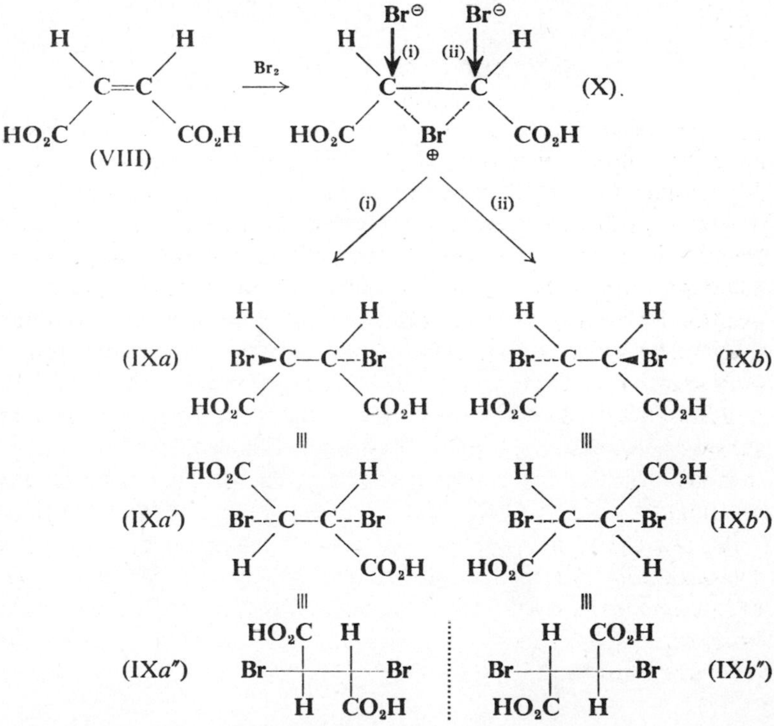

The first-formed bromonium ion (X) could be attacked 'from the back' on either carbon atom, with equal facility as these are identically situated, to yield equal quantities of the dibromides (IX*a*) and (IX*b*). Before these can be written in the more usual plane-projection formulae, they must be rotated about the carbon–carbon single bond so that the two bromine atoms are on the same side of the molecule,

(IX*a'*) and (IX*b'*); on projection these then yield the formulae (IX*a''*) and (IX*b''*). It will be seen that these are mirror images, and as equal quantities are produced, the end result would be DL-maleic acid dibromide (1,2-dibromosuccinic acid). This product is, in practice, obtained and, exactly analogously, fumaric acid (XI) is found to yield *meso*-1,2-dibromosuccinic acid (XII); attack by $Br^\ominus$ on either carbon of the cyclic bromonium intermediate here yielding the same product:

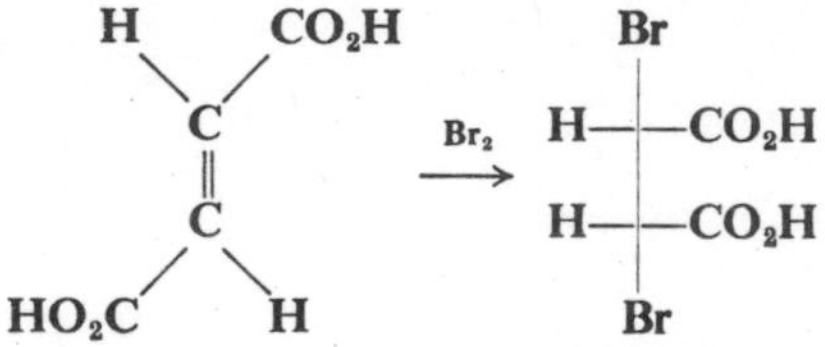

$$
\begin{array}{c}
\overset{H}{\diagdown} \quad \overset{CO_2H}{\diagup} \\
C \\
\| \\
C \\
\overset{HO_2C}{\diagup} \quad \overset{H}{\diagdown} \\
(XI)
\end{array}
\xrightarrow{Br_2}
\begin{array}{c}
Br \\
H-\!\!\!\!-CO_2H \\
H-\!\!\!\!-CO_2H \\
Br \\
(XII)
\end{array}
$$

Halogens are, in fact, found uniformly to add on by an overall *trans* mechanism. While this is good evidence in favour of the bromonium ion intermediate, it does not constitute actual confirmation; for provided attack by $Br^\ominus$ were rapid enough, a carbonium ion intermediate, e.g. (V), could also undergo preferential attack from the back before any significant rotation about the carbon–carbon single bond had taken place, thus also leading to stereospecific *trans* addition. Acetylenes also add on one molecule of halogen to yield a *trans* product; thus acetylene dicarboxylic acid, $HO_2C \cdot C \equiv C \cdot CO_2H$, yields the *trans* compound, dibromofumaric acid:

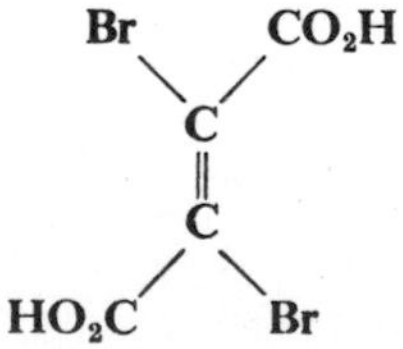

$$
\begin{array}{c}
\overset{Br}{\diagdown} \quad \overset{CO_2H}{\diagup} \\
C \\
\| \\
C \\
\overset{HO_2C}{\diagup} \quad \overset{Br}{\diagdown}
\end{array}
$$

EFFECT OF SUBSTITUENTS ON RATE OF ADDITION

If attack by incipient $Br^\oplus$ to form a cation, whether (V) or (VII), is the rate-determining step of the reaction, it would be expected that addition would be facilitated by the presence of electron-donating

substituents on the double-bond carbon atoms; the following relative
rates are observed:

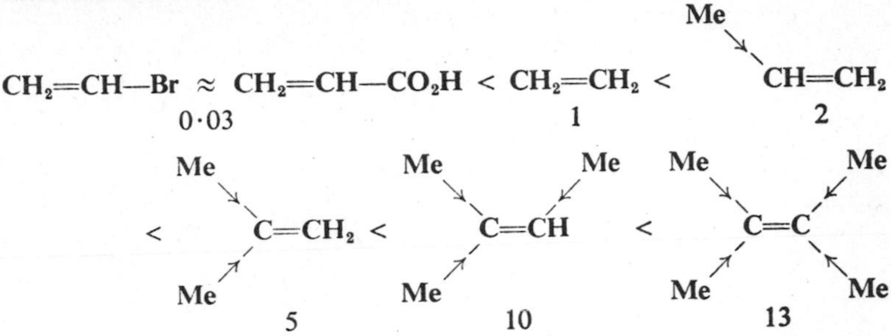

$$CH_2=CH-Br \approx CH_2=CH-CO_2H < CH_2=CH_2 < \underset{Me}{\overset{Me}{\diagdown}}CH=CH_2$$

$$0\cdot03 \qquad\qquad\qquad 1 \qquad\qquad 2$$

$$< \underset{Me}{\overset{Me}{\diagdown}}C=CH_2 < \underset{Me}{\overset{Me}{\diagdown}}C=CH < \underset{Me}{\overset{Me}{\diagdown}}C=C\overset{Me}{\underset{Me}{\diagup}}$$

$$5 \qquad\qquad 10 \qquad\qquad 13$$

The rate of addition increases with successive introductions of methyl
despite access to the double bond becoming progressively more
hindered sterically. By contrast, the presence of electron-withdrawing
substituents markedly slows down the rate of addition. The presence
of a benzene nucleus also speeds up reaction very markedly because
of the stability, and consequent ease of formation, of the carbonium
ion intermediate (XIII):

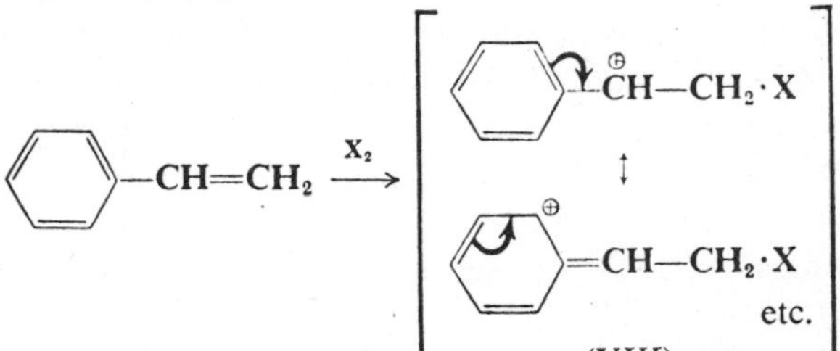

$$(XIII)$$

ORIENTATION OF ADDITION

With hydrogen halide, addition of $H^\oplus$ is the rate-determining step
via an initially formed π complex, the addition being completed by
subsequent attack of $Hal^\ominus$. In support of this, it is found that ease of
addition increases on going $HF \rightarrow HCl \rightarrow HBr \rightarrow HI$, i.e. in order of
increasing acid strength. The series not only implies relative ease of
proton donation, of course, but also increase of nucleophilicity in the
anion, $Hal^\ominus$, that completes the attack; but this second stage is not
involved in the rate-determining step of the overall addition. When
the olefine is unsymmetrical, e.g. propylene, hydrogen bromide can
add to form two possible products, $Me\cdot CHBr\cdot Me$ and $Me\cdot CH_2\cdot
CH_2Br$. In practice, however, we should only expect to get the former,

exemplifying the greater tendency to form a secondary rather than a primary carbonium ion (*cf.* p. 109):

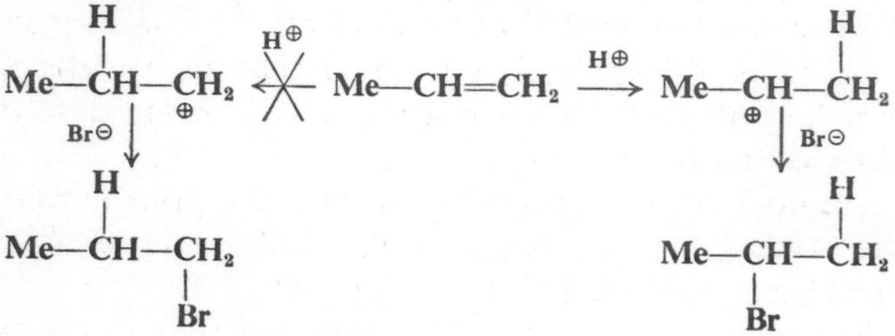

This is found to be the case and is the theoretical justification for the empirical generalisation of Markownikov: 'In the addition of unsymmetrical adducts to unsymmetrical olefines halogen, or the more negative group, becomes attached to the more highly substituted of the unsaturated carbon atoms.'

The study of the addition of hydrogen halides to olefines presents a number of experimental difficulties. In solution in water or hydroxylic solvents, acid-catalysed hydration, etc. (see below) constitutes a competing reaction, while in less polar solvents radical formation is encouraged and the mechanism changes, resulting with **HBr** in *anti*-Markownikov addition to yield $Me \cdot CH_2 \cdot CH_2Br$ via the preferentially formed intermediate, $Me \cdot \overset{\bullet}{C}H \cdot CH_2Br$. The radical mechanism of addition and the reasons for its occurrence are discussed subsequently (p. 244).

Addition of **HBr** to vinyl bromide, $CH_2{=}CHBr$, is also of some interest. Under polar conditions, $CH_3 \cdot CHBr_2$, rather than $CH_2Br \cdot CH_2Br$, is obtained reflecting the greater stability of the carbonium ion intermediate (XIV*a*) rather than (XIV*b*):

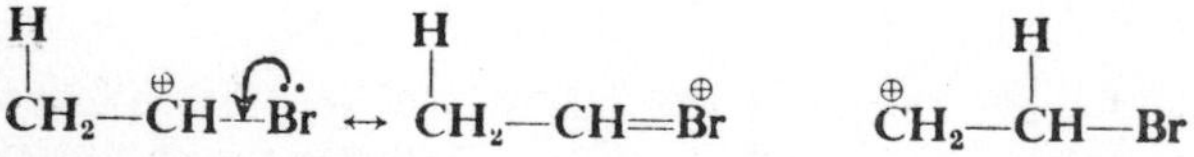

Nevertheless the *rate* of addition is, as described above, about thirty times slower than with ethylene, indicating the inductive effect of the bromine atom in reducing overall electron availability at the double bond:

$$CH_2{=}CH{\rightarrow}Br$$

This very closely resembles the electrophilic substitution of chlorobenzene which, as we have seen (p. 123), is *o/p*-directive (preferential stabilisation of the transition states for *o*- and *p*-substitution by interaction of the unshared electron pairs on chlorine with the π orbital system of the nucleus), yet slower than in benzene itself (large inductive effect of chlorine resulting in overall deactivation of the nucleus to electrophilic attack).

The rearrangements of structure that can take place during the addition of acids to olefines, due to alkyl migrations in the carbonium ion intermediates, have already been referred to (p. 89).

With hypochlorous acid, etc., the adduct polarises in the sense $\overset{\delta-}{HO}\!\!-\!\!\overset{\delta+}{Cl}$, thus yielding with propylene

$$Me\!-\!CH\!=\!CH_2 \xrightarrow{\overset{\delta-}{HO}-\overset{\delta+}{Cl}} Me\!-\!\overset{\oplus}{CH}\!-\!\underset{\underset{Cl}{|}}{CH_2} \xrightarrow[\text{or } H_2O]{\ominus OH} Me\!-\!\underset{\underset{Cl}{|}}{\overset{\overset{OH}{|}}{CH}}\!-\!CH_2$$

this being in accordance with the Markownikov rule as **OH** is a more negative group than **Cl**. That such additions are also *trans* (i.e. initial attack by $X^{\oplus}$ to yield a cationic intermediate) is shown by the conversion of cyclopentene to the *trans* chlorohydrin:

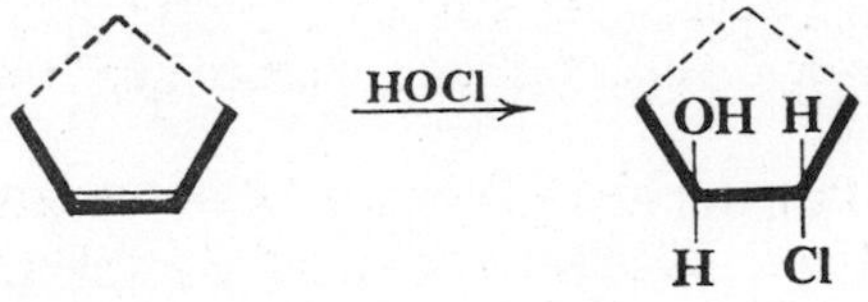

OTHER ADDITION REACTIONS

(i) Hydration

Hydration of a carbon–carbon double bond is, of course, the reversal of the acid-catalysed dehydration of alcohols to olefines (p. 192):

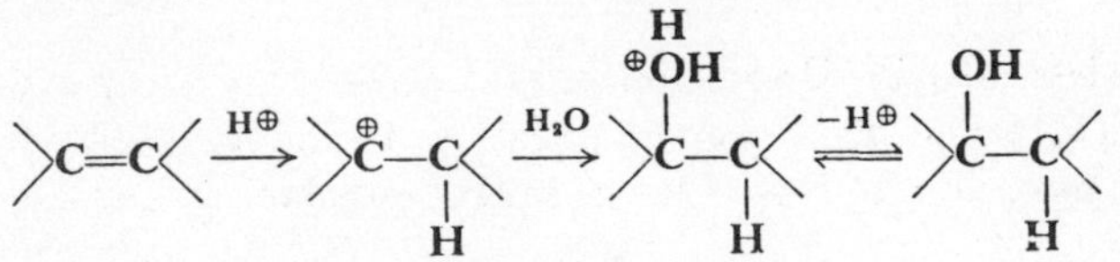

$$\underset{(XV)}{}$$

The formation of the carbonium ion (XV) is the rate-determining step in the reaction but whether this takes place directly or via the rapid, reversible formation of a π complex (XVI), followed by the slow, rate-determining conversion of the latter to the carbonium ion (XV)

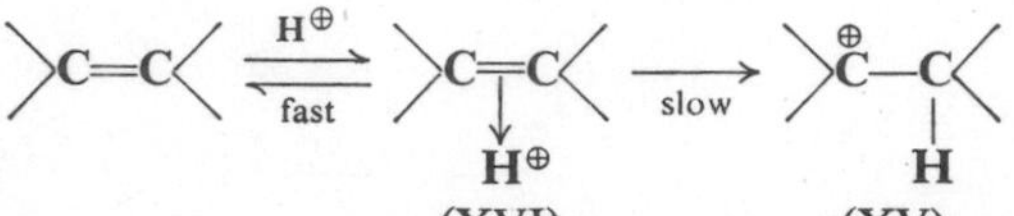

$$\rangle C = C \langle \underset{\text{fast}}{\overset{H^{\oplus}}{\rightleftharpoons}} \rangle \underset{\underset{\overset{|}{H^{\oplus}}}{\overset{\|}{C}}}{C} = C \langle \underset{\text{slow}}{\longrightarrow} \rangle \overset{\oplus}{C} - \underset{H}{\overset{|}{C}} \langle$$

$$\text{(XVI)} \qquad\qquad \text{(XV)}$$

is not wholly certain. Hydrogen halides are not normally used as sources of proton because of their tendency to add on themselves, but the $HSO_4^{\ominus}$ ions produced with sulphuric acid are only very weakly nucleophilic and, even if they should add on, the alkyl hydrogen sulphates (XVII) so produced are very readily hydrolysed by water:

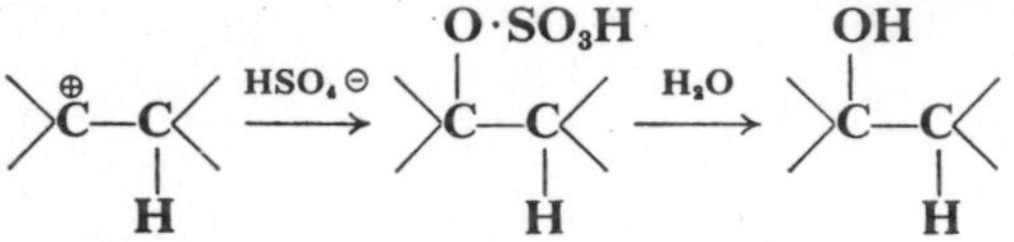

$$\rangle \overset{\oplus}{C} - \underset{H}{\overset{|}{C}} \langle \overset{HSO_4^{\ominus}}{\longrightarrow} \rangle \underset{H}{\overset{\overset{O \cdot SO_3H}{|}}{C}} - \underset{H}{\overset{|}{C}} \langle \overset{H_2O}{\longrightarrow} \rangle \underset{H}{\overset{\overset{OH}{|}}{C}} - \underset{H}{\overset{|}{C}} \langle$$

$$\text{(XV)} \qquad\qquad \text{(XVII)}$$

The reaction is of importance for converting petroleum fractions into alcohols and is sometimes brought about by dissolving the alkenes in concentrated sulphuric acid and then diluting the solution with water. The orientation of addition, being proton-initiated, follows the conventions already discussed and proceeds *trans*.

(ii) Carbonium ion addition

The carbonium ion intermediate that may result from initial protonation of the double bond in several of the above reactions can itself, of course, act as an electrophile towards a second molecule of alkene. Thus with isobutene (XVIII)

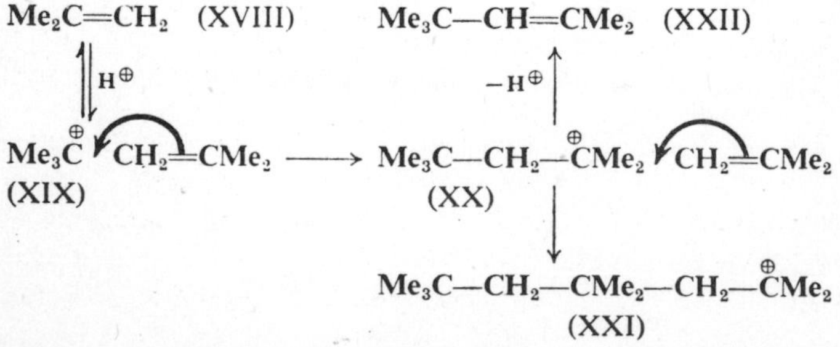

$$Me_2C = CH_2 \quad \text{(XVIII)} \qquad Me_3C - CH = CMe_2 \quad \text{(XXII)}$$

$$\Big\Updownarrow H^{\oplus} \qquad\qquad\qquad -H^{\oplus}\Big\uparrow$$

$$\underset{\text{(XIX)}}{Me_3\overset{\oplus}{C}} \,\overset{\frown}{CH_2} = CMe_2 \longrightarrow \underset{\text{(XX)}}{Me_3C - CH_2 - \overset{\oplus}{C}Me_2} \,\overset{\frown}{CH_2} = CMe_2$$

$$\Big\downarrow$$

$$Me_3C - CH_2 - CMe_2 - CH_2 - \overset{\oplus}{C}Me_2$$
$$\text{(XXI)}$$

the first formed carbonium ion (XIX) can add to the double bond of a second molecule to form a second carbonium ion (XX). This in its turn can add on to the double bond of a third molecule to yield (XXI) or, alternatively, lose a proton to yield the alkene (XXII). Such successive additions can lead to unwanted by-products in, for example, the simple addition of hydrogen halides, but they may be specifically promoted to yield polymers by the presence of Lewis acids, e.g. $AlCl_3$, $SnCl_4$, BF_3, as catalysts. Many polymerisations of olefines are radical-induced however (p. 247).

(iii) Hydroxylation

Investigation of the action of osmium tetroxide on alkenes has led to the isolation of cyclic osmic esters (XXIII) which undergo ready hydrolysis to yield the 1,2-diol:

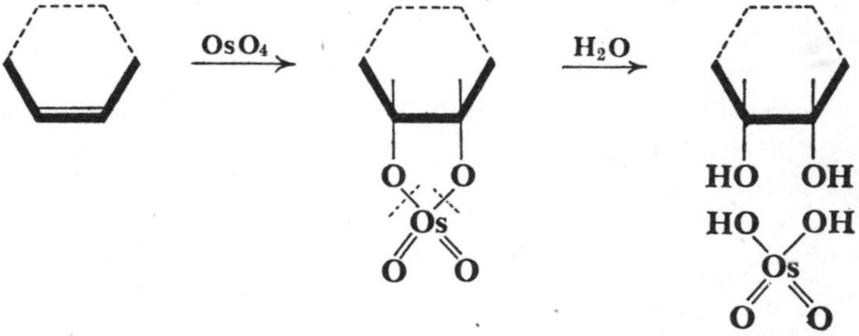

(XXIII)   (XXIV)

As the hydrolysis results in the splitting of the osmium–oxygen and not the oxygen–carbon bonds in (XXIII), no inversion of configuration can take place at the carbon atoms and the glycol produced must, like the cyclic osmic ester itself, be *cis*, i.e. this is a stereospecific *cis* addition. The expense and toxicity of osmium tetroxide preclude its large scale use but it can be employed in catalytic amounts in the presence of hydrogen peroxide which reoxidises osmic acid (XXIV) to the tetroxide.

The *cis* glycol is also obtained with permanganate, the classical reagent for the hydroxylation of double bonds, and though no cyclic permanganic esters have been isolated it is not unreasonable to suppose that the reaction follows a similar course. This is supported by the fact that use of ^{18}O labelled $MnO_4^{\ominus}$ results in *both* oxygen

F

atoms in the resultant glycol becoming labelled, i.e. both are derived from the permanganate and neither from the solvent.

If alkenes are oxidised by peracids, $R-\overset{\overset{\displaystyle O}{\|}}{C}-O-OH$, the result is an alkylene oxide or epoxide (XXV):

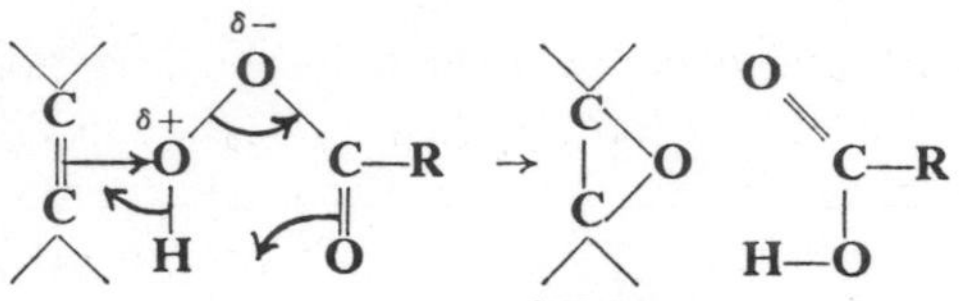

(XXV)

It is possible, however, that in polar solvents the reaction may be initiated by addition of $^{\oplus}OH$ obtained by breakdown of the peracid. The epoxides may be isolated (*cf.* p. 70) and then undergo acid or base-catalysed hydrolysis (a nucleophilic reaction) to yield the 1,2-diol. As attack must be 'from the back' on the cyclic epoxide, inversion of configuration will take place at the carbon atom attacked so that the *overall* addition reaction to yield the 1,2-diol will be *trans*:

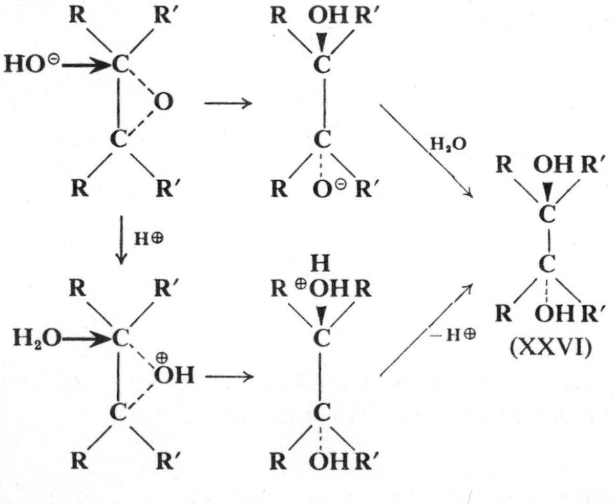

(XXVI)

Attack on only one carbon atom has been shown above, but equally easy attack on the other will lead to the mirror image of

(XXVI), i.e. the DL-glycol will result from the original *cis* olefine, confirming an overall *trans* hydroxylation (*cf.* addition of bromine to maleic acid, p. 139).

Thus by suitable choice of reagent, the hydroxylation of olefines can be stereospecifically controlled to proceed *cis* or *trans* at will.

(iv) Hydrogenation

The addition of hydrogen to alkenes in the presence of metallic catalysts, e.g. **Ni, Pt, Pd,** etc., is usually a *cis* addition. This comes about because reduction takes place when the alkene is adsorbed at the metallic surface; approach of active hydrogen occurs from one side of the alkene only, i.e. from the interior of the metal where the hydrogen is readily adsorbed, probably as reactive free atoms, in reasonable concentration: metals that are effective hydrogenation catalysts have the capacity of adsorbing quite large amounts of hydrogen. The alkene is probably bound to the metal surface by an interaction involving its π electrons for, after reduction has taken place, the reduced product becomes desorbed very readily and so leaves the catalysts surface free for adsorption of more alkene. For similar reasons, the partial hydrogenation of an acetylene would be expected to lead to a *cis* alkene. Thus 1,2-dimethylcyclohexene (XXVII) yields the *cis* cyclohexane derivative (XXVIII) and dimethyl-acetylene (XXIX), the *cis* 2-butene (XXX):

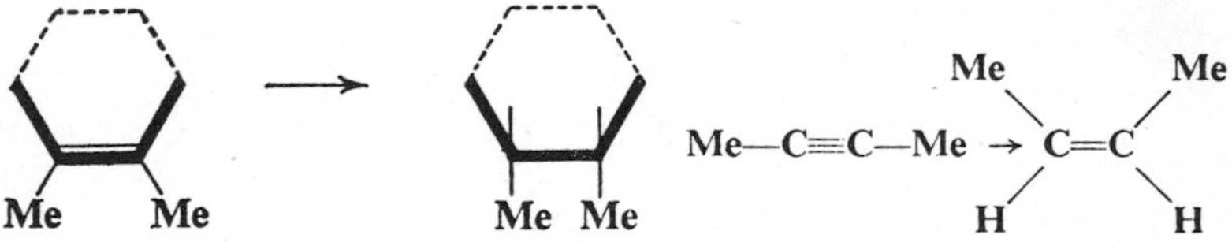

$$Me—C{\equiv}C—Me \rightarrow$$

(XXVII)   (XXVIII)   (XXIX)   (XXX)

Stereospecific *cis* hydrogenation has been of very great use in confirming molecular structures by synthetic methods.

(v) Ozonolysis

The addition of ozone to alkenes can also be looked upon essentially as an electrophilic addition and, in support of this view, it is found that the addition is catalysed by Lewis acids such as **BF₃**. The primary addition product (mol-ozonide) probably has the structure shown above, but it enjoys only a transient existence and is found to dissociate readily into two fragments:

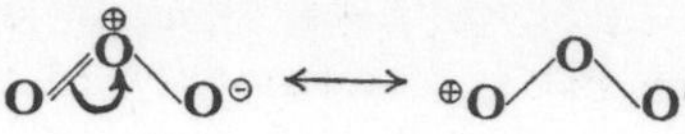

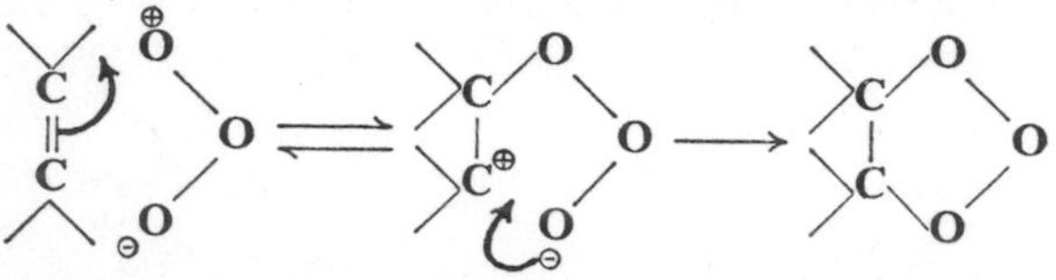

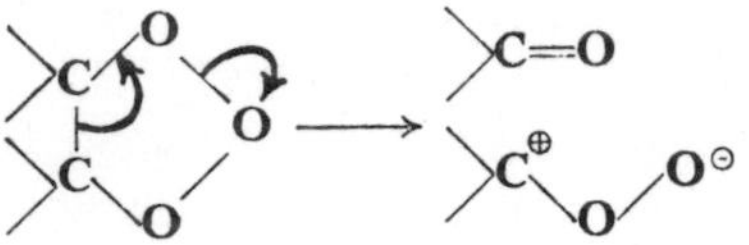

(XXXI)

These fragments may recombine to form the normal end-product (XXXII) of the reaction, generally called the iso-ozonide

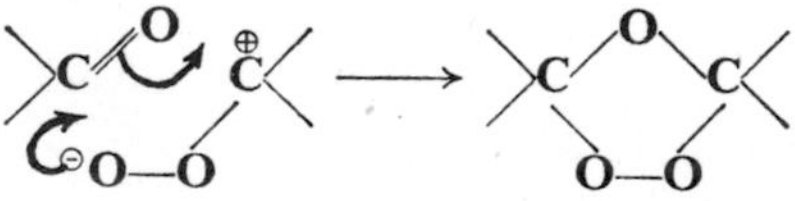

(XXXII)

but the peroxy zwitterion (XXXI) may also undergo alternative reactions, e.g. self-addition to yield a dimer:

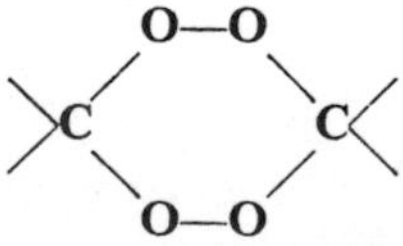

When ozonisation is carried out, either preparatively or diag-nostically, in order to cleave a carbon–carbon double bond the actual addition of ozone is usually followed by reductive cleavage of the products with **Pd/H$_2$**. This ensures that the carbonyl compounds, especially aldehydes, do not undergo further oxidation as tends to happen on simple hydrolytic cleavage due to the hydroperoxides (*cf.* p. 252) that are then formed. This is important as one of the advantages of ozonolysis as a preparative or a diagnostic method is the ease of isolation and characterisation of the carbonyl compounds that it yields as end-products.

ADDITION TO CONJUGATED DIENES

The presence of delocalised π orbitals in conjugated dienes, and their effect in transmitting reactivity over the whole of the system, has already been referred to (p. 8). Conjugated dienes are somewhat more stable than otherwise similar dienes in which the double bonds are not conjugated, as is revealed by a study of their respective heats of hydrogenation (*cf.* p. 11), the delocalisation energy consequent on the extended π orbital system probably being of the order of 6 kcal/mole. Conjugated dienes tend nevertheless to undergo addition reactions somewhat more readily than non-conjugated dienes because the transition state in such reactions, whether the addition is proceeding by a polar or a radical mechanism, is allylic in nature and thus more readily formed (*cf.* pp. 83, 234) than that from an isolated double bond:

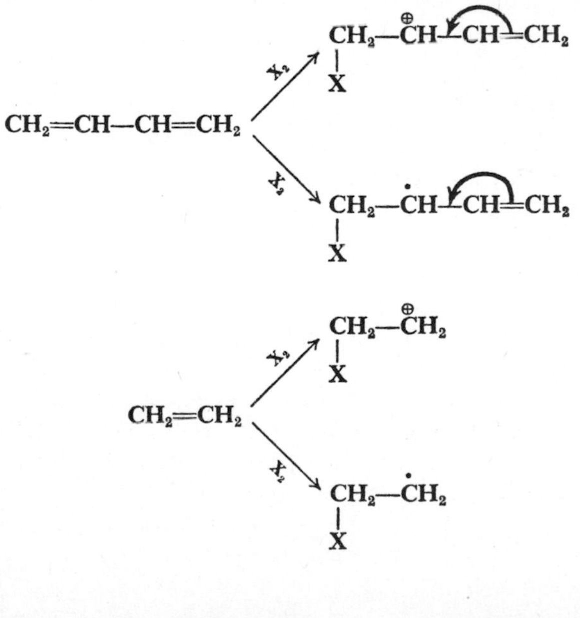

Thus conjugated dienes are reduced to dihydro-derivatives by sodium and alcohol whereas non-conjugated dienes or simple alkenes are unaffected.

It might be expected that in the addition of, for example, chlorine to butadiene, reaction could proceed through a cyclic chloronium ion

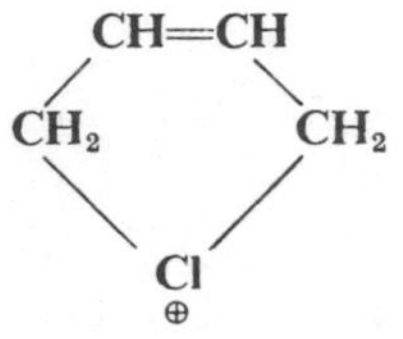

$$
\begin{array}{ccc}
 & CH{=}CH & \\
CH_2 & & CH_2 \\
 & Cl & \\
 & \oplus &
\end{array}
$$

that would be largely unstrained. That this is *not* formed, however, is shown by the fact that the above addition results in the formation of the *trans* compound

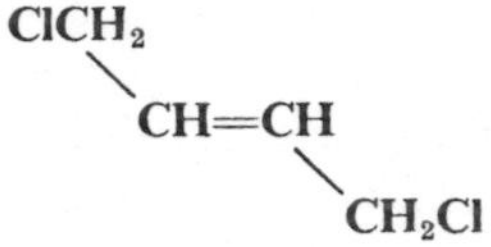

$$
\begin{array}{c}
ClCH_2 \\
CH{=}CH \\
CH_2Cl
\end{array}
$$

and not the corresponding *cis* compound that would have been obtained by the attack of $Cl^{\ominus}$ on the cyclic chloronium ion. Addition thus probably proceeds through a delocalised carbonium ion, *cf.* the addition of hydrogen halide below.

(i) Hydrogen halide

With butadiene itself a proton may initially form a π complex and then a σ complex with hydrogen on a terminal carbon atom (XXXIV). Protonation takes place at C_1 rather than C_2 as the former yields a secondary carbonium ion that is stabilised by delocalisation, whereas the latter would yield a primary carbonium ion (XXXIII) that is not. The resulting allylic cation (XXXIV) can take up $Br^{\ominus}$ at either C_2 or C_4 leading to 1:2 and 1:4 overall addition, i.e. (XXXVa) and (XXXVb), respectively (see p. 151).

The presence of conjugation does not make 1:4-addition obligatory: it merely makes it possible, and whether this or 1:2-addition actually takes place is governed by the relative rates of conversion of the cation (XXXIV) to the alternative products and also by the relative stability of these products. By and large, 1:2-addition tends

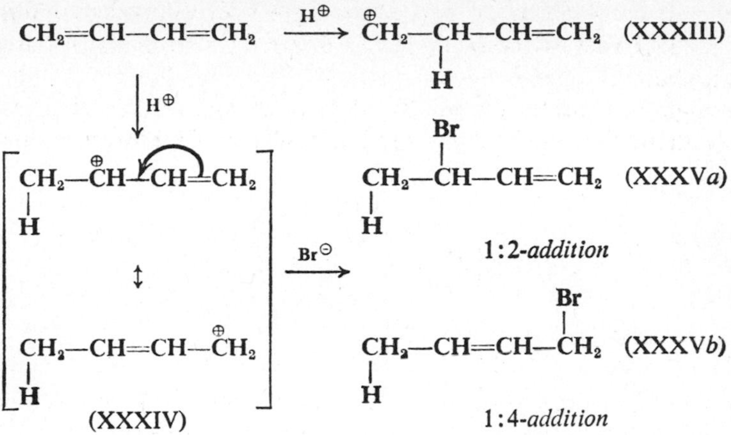

$$CH_2=CH-CH=CH_2 \xrightarrow{H^\oplus} \overset{\oplus}{C}H_2-\underset{\underset{H}{|}}{C}H-CH=CH_2 \quad (XXXIII)$$

$$\downarrow H^\oplus$$

$$\left[\begin{array}{c} CH_2-\overset{\oplus}{C}H\overset{\frown}{-}CH=CH_2 \\ \underset{H}{|} \\ \\ \updownarrow \\ \\ CH_2-CH=CH-\overset{\oplus}{C}H_2 \\ \underset{H}{|} \\ (XXXIV) \end{array}\right] \xrightarrow{Br^\ominus}$$

$$CH_2-\underset{\underset{H}{|}}{C}H-\overset{\overset{Br}{|}}{C}H-CH=CH_2 \quad (XXXVa)$$

1:2-*addition*

$$CH_2-CH=CH-\overset{\overset{Br}{|}}{C}H_2 \quad (XXXVb)$$
$$\underset{H}{|}$$

1:4-*addition*

to occur preferentially at lower temperatures in non-polar solvents and 1:4-addition at higher temperatures in polar solvents; the temperature effect is due to the fact that the activation energy for 1:4-addition is usually higher than that for 1:2-addition (*cf.* p. 203).

For addition to an unsymmetrical diene the same considerations apply as in the case of mono-alkenes, thus:

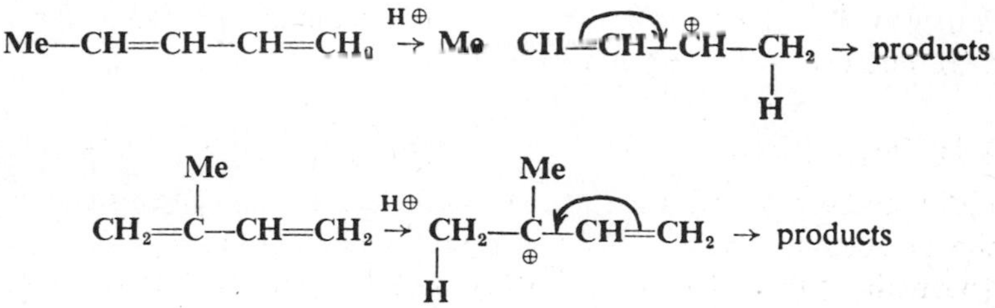

$$Me-CH=CH-CH=CH_2 \xrightarrow{H^\oplus} Me \quad CH=CH-\overset{\oplus}{C}H-CH_2 \rightarrow products$$
$$\underset{H}{|}$$

$$CH_2=\overset{\overset{Me}{|}}{C}-CH=CH_2 \xrightarrow{H^\oplus} CH_2-\overset{\overset{Me}{|}}{\underset{\oplus}{C}}CH=CH_2 \rightarrow products$$
$$\underset{H}{|}$$

(ii) Diels-Alder reaction

The classic example is with butadiene and maleic anhydride

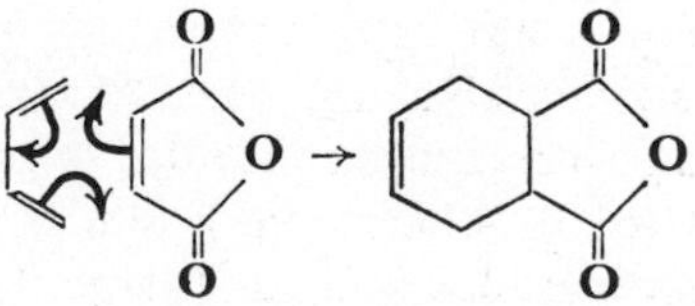

151

i.e. 1:4-addition, proceeding *cis*, via a cyclic transition state (*cf.* the pyrolysis of esters, p. 208), to yield a cyclic product. It has been used as a diagnostic test for determining whether the double bonds in a diene are conjugated or not (though this is normally more readily determined spectroscopically) and also has considerable synthetic importance. The reaction is promoted by the presence of electron-donating substituents in the diene and of electron-withdrawing substituents in the, so-called, *dienophile*; their presence in the latter is, indeed, all but imperative for the reaction proceeds very poorly if at all with a simple double-bonded compound. Other common dienophiles are *p*-benzoquinone, $CH_2{=}CH{\cdot}CHO$ and $EtO_2C{\cdot}C{\equiv}C{\cdot}CO_2Et$. The reaction is also sensitive to steric effects; thus of the three 1,4-diphenylbutadienes only the *trans/trans* form undergoes reaction with maleic anhydride:

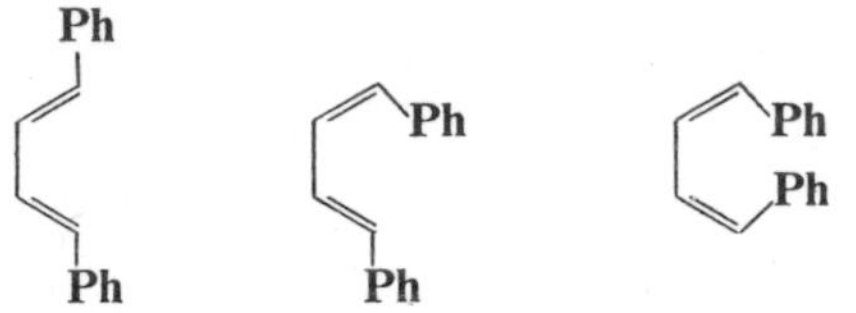

Trans/Trans	*Cis/Trans*	*Cis/Cis*

Similarly the reactivity of the diene is promoted when the double bonds are locked in a *cis* conformation with respect to each other as in cyclopentadiene.

Where there is the possibility of more than one product, depending on which way round the addition takes place, e.g. with maleic anhydride and cyclopentadiene, that product is formed in which there is the maximum concentration of double bonds in the transition state when the centres that are to react are placed over each other; interaction between the π electron systems of the two reactants will then be at a maximum. Thus (XXXVI), the more stable *endo* structure, is obtained rather than the *exo* (XXXVII):

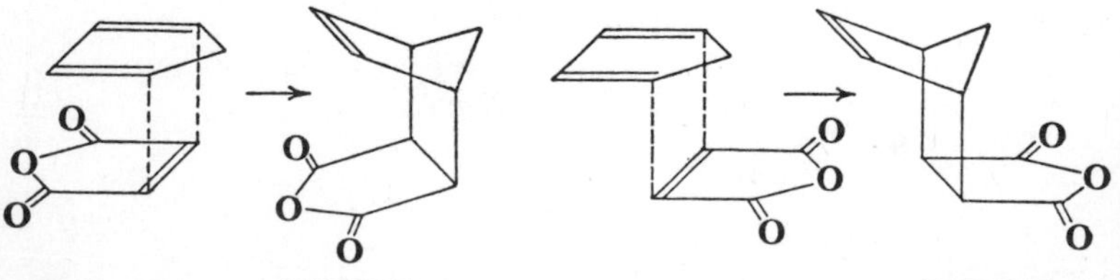

(XXXVI)		(XXXVII)

ADDITION OF ANIONS

As has already been seen (p. 130) the introduction of electron-with-drawing groups into an aromatic nucleus tends to inhibit electro-philic substitution and to make nucleophilic substitution possible. The same is true of addition reactions: the introduction of F, NO_2, CN, $>C=O$, CO_2Et, etc., on the carbon atoms of a double bond causes the π electrons to become less available and attack by an anion then becomes possible, though it would not have taken place with the unmodified double bond:

$$Ph \cdot CH\!=\!CH\!-\!\overset{\overset{\displaystyle O^{\ominus}}{|}}{\underset{\underset{\displaystyle O^{\ominus}}{|}}{S}}\!-\!C_6H_4\cdot Me\text{-}p \xrightarrow[\quad\quad]{\overset{\delta-\;\;\delta+}{R\cdot MgBr}} Ph\cdot CH\!-\!\overset{}{\underset{\underset{\displaystyle R}{|}}{CH}}\!-\!\overset{\overset{\displaystyle O^{\ominus}}{|}}{\underset{\underset{\displaystyle O^{\ominus}}{|}}{S}}\!-\!C_6H_4\cdot Me\text{-}p$$

$$\Big\downarrow H^{\oplus}$$

$$Ph\cdot CH\!-\!\underset{\underset{\displaystyle R}{|}}{CH_2}\!-\!\overset{\overset{\displaystyle O^{\ominus}}{|}}{\underset{\underset{\displaystyle O^{\ominus}}{|}}{S}}\!-\!C_6H_4\cdot Me\text{-}p$$

$$\underset{\underset{\displaystyle F}{|}}{\overset{\overset{\displaystyle F}{|}}{C}}\!=\!\underset{\underset{\displaystyle F}{|}}{\overset{\overset{\displaystyle F}{|}}{C}} \xrightarrow{\ominus OEt} EtO\!-\!\underset{\underset{\displaystyle F}{|}}{\overset{\overset{\displaystyle F}{|}}{C}}\!-\!\!-\!\underset{\underset{\displaystyle F}{|}}{\overset{\overset{\displaystyle F}{|}}{C}}^{\ominus} \xrightarrow{EtOH} EtO\!-\!\underset{\underset{\displaystyle F}{|}}{\overset{\overset{\displaystyle F}{|}}{C}}\!-\!\!-\!\underset{\underset{\displaystyle F}{|}}{\overset{\overset{\displaystyle F}{|}}{C}}\!-\!\!-\!H$$

Some of the reactions have important synthetic applications.

(i) Cyanoethylation

The cyano-group in acrylonitrile, $CH_2\!=\!CH\cdot CN$, makes the β-carbon atom of the double bond respond readily to the attack of anions or other powerful nucleophiles, the addition being completed by the abstraction of a proton from the solvent:

$$CH_2\!=\!CH\!-\!C\!\equiv\!N \begin{array}{l} \xrightarrow{ROH} RO\cdot CH_2\cdot CH_2\cdot CN \\[4pt] \xrightarrow{PhOH} PhO\cdot CH_2\cdot CH_2\cdot CN \\[4pt] \xrightarrow{H_2S} HS\cdot CH_2\cdot CH_2\cdot CN \\[4pt] \xrightarrow{RNH_2} RNH\cdot CH_2\cdot CH_2\cdot CN \end{array}$$

The reaction is normally carried out in the presence of base in order to obtain an anion from the would-be adduct. Carbon–carbon bonds may also be formed:

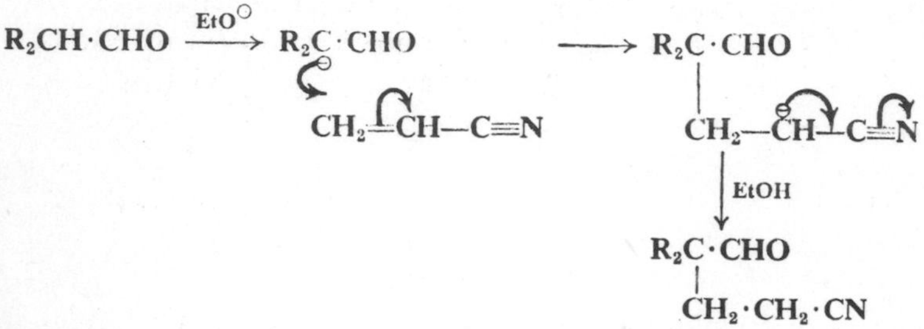

$$R_2CH \cdot CHO \xrightarrow{EtO^\ominus} R_2\overset{\ominus}{C} \cdot CHO \qquad\qquad \longrightarrow R_2C \cdot CHO$$

$$CH_2 {=} CH - C {\equiv} N \qquad\qquad CH_2 - \overset{\ominus}{CH} - C {\equiv} N$$

$$\Big\downarrow EtOH$$

$$R_2C \cdot CHO$$
$$CH_2 \cdot CH_2 \cdot CN$$

The value of cyanoethylation is that three carbon atoms are added, of which the terminal one may be further modified by reduction, hydrolysis, etc., preparatory to further synthetic operations.

ADDITION TO αβ-UNSATURATED CARBONYL COMPOUNDS

The most important electron-withdrawing group is probably $>C{=}O$, found in αβ-unsaturated aldehydes, ketones, esters, etc. These systems will add on hydrogen halide, etc., by a 1:4-mechanism involving initial protonation of oxygen:

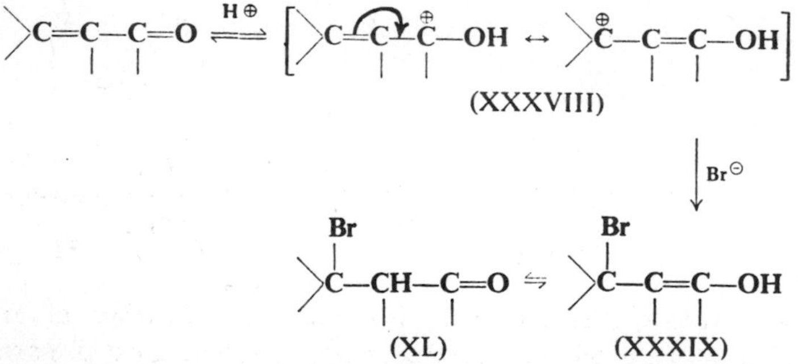

$$>C{=}C{-}C{=}O \overset{H^\oplus}{\rightleftharpoons} \left[>C{=}C{-}\overset{\oplus}{C}{-}OH \leftrightarrow >\overset{\oplus}{C}{-}C{=}C{-}OH \right]$$

(XXXVIII)

$$\Big\downarrow Br^\ominus$$

$$\overset{Br}{\underset{|}{>}}C{-}CH{-}C{=}O \rightleftharpoons \overset{Br}{\underset{|}{>}}C{-}C{=}C{-}OH$$

(XL)   (XXXIX)

Attack by $Br^\ominus$ on the ion (XXXVIII) at C_1 (1:2-addition) would lead to formation of a *gem*-bromohydrin which is highly unstable, losing HBr, hence preferential attack at C_3 (1:4-addition) yields (XXXIX) which is, of course, the enol of the β-bromoketone (XL). Addition to αβ-unsaturated acids proceeds somewhat similarly.

With more pronouncedly nucleophilic reagents, e.g. Grignard reagents, $^\ominus$CN, etc., overall 1:4-addition will take place without need for initial protonation of the carbonyl oxygen atom:

$$\underset{\underset{Y^\ominus}{}}{>\!\!C\!\!-\!\!C\!\!-\!\!C\!\!=\!\!O} \longrightarrow \underset{Y}{>\!\!C\!\!-\!\!C\!\!=\!\!C\!\!-\!\!O^\ominus} \xrightarrow{H_2O} \underset{Y}{>\!\!C\!\!-\!\!C\!\!=\!\!C\!\!-\!\!OH}$$

(Y=R, CN etc.)

$$\underset{Y}{>\!\!C\!\!-\!\!CH\!\!-\!\!C\!\!=\!\!O}$$

This occurs readily with αβ-unsaturated ketones, but with αβ-unsaturated aldehydes direct attack on the carbonyl carbon atom (1:2-addition) also takes place because of the more positive character of this atom in aldehydes as compared with ketones (p. 159).

With even more powerful nucleophiles, e.g. $^\ominus$OH, addition at the β-carbon atom takes place, even with αβ-unsaturated aldehydes. This can lead, under suitable conditions, to reversal of the aldol/dehydration reaction (p. 175):

$$\underset{\underset{^\ominus OH}{}}{\underset{R\cdot C=CH}{\overset{H}{|}}}\!\!-\!\!C\!\!=\!\!O \rightleftharpoons \underset{\underset{OH}{}}{\overset{H}{R\cdot C}}\!\!-\!\!\underset{H}{\overset{}{CH}} \quad C\!\!=\!\!O \xrightarrow{H_2O} \underset{\underset{OH}{}}{\overset{H}{R\ C}}\!\!-\!\!CH_2\!\!-\!\!\underset{H}{\overset{}{C}}\!\!=\!\!O$$

$$\Big\updownarrow {^\ominus OH}$$

$$\underset{\underset{O}{\|}}{\overset{H}{R\cdot C}}\!\!+\ \underset{H}{\overset{\ominus}{CH_2}}\!\!-\!\!C\!\!=\!\!O \rightleftharpoons \underset{\underset{O^\ominus}{}}{\overset{H}{R\cdot C}}\!\!-\!\!CH_2\!\!-\!\!\underset{H}{\overset{}{C}}\!\!=\!\!O$$

Amines, mercaptans, etc., will also add to the β-carbon atom of αβ-unsaturated aldehydes, ketones and esters. The most important addition reactions of αβ-unsaturated carbonyl compounds, however, are with carbanions in which carbon–carbon bonds are formed.

(i) Michael reaction

The most frequently employed carbanions are probably those derived from diethyl malonate, ethyl acetoacetate, ethyl cyanoacetate and aliphatic nitro-compounds, e.g. CH_3NO_2. Thus in the formation of dimedone (XLI) from diethyl malonate and mesityl oxide (XLII) the carbanion (XLIII) derived from diethyl malonate attacks the β-carbon atom of mesityl oxide to yield the ion (XLIV), which is converted, via its enol, to the ketone (XLV). This constitutes the Michael reaction proper, i.e. the carbanion addition to an αβ-unsaturated carbonyl compound. In this case, however, the reaction proceeds further for (XLV) is converted by $^{\ominus}$OEt to the carbanion (XLVI) which cyclises by expelling $^{\ominus}$OEt from the ester group (*cf.* the Dieckmann reaction, p. 178) to yield (XLVII). Hydrolysis and decarboxylation of the β-keto-ester then yields dimedone (XLI):

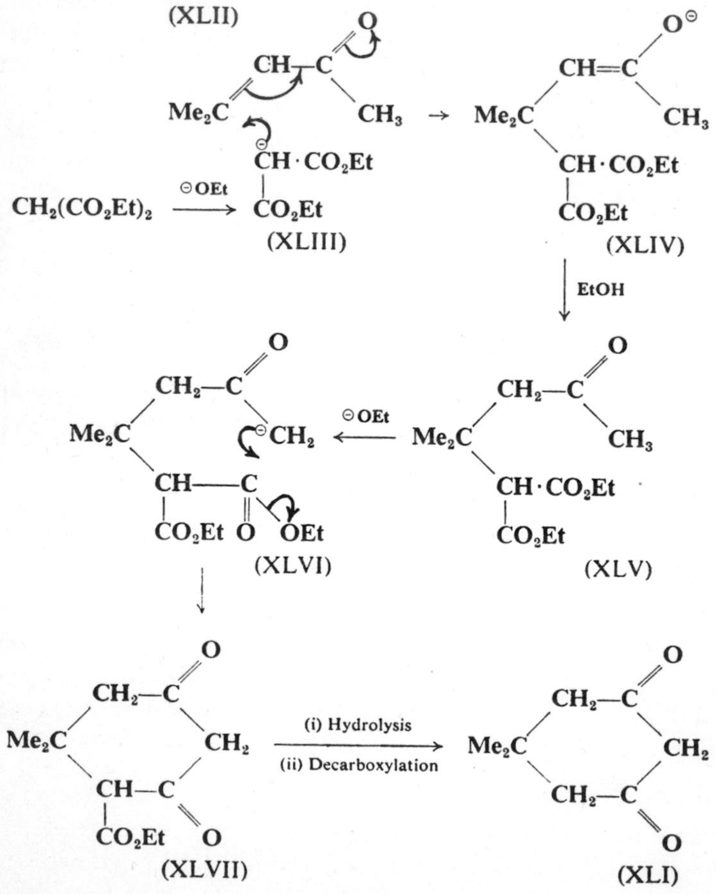

The compound does in fact exist virtually entirely in the enol form:

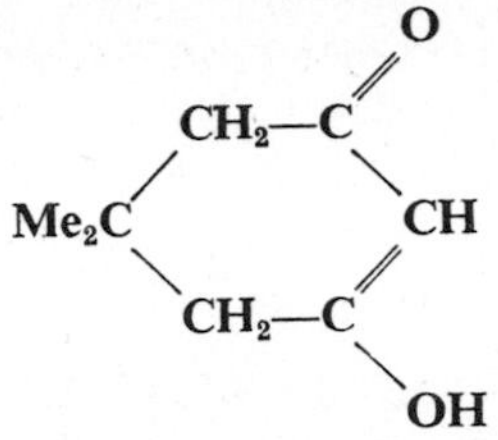

$$
\begin{array}{c}
\text{O} \\
\| \\
\text{CH}_2\text{—C} \\
\text{Me}_2\text{C} \qquad \text{CH} \\
\text{CH}_2\text{—C} \\
\text{OH}
\end{array}
$$

Dimedone is of value as a reagent for the differential characterisation of carbonyl compounds for it readily yields derivatives (XLVIII) with aldehydes but not with ketones, from a mixture of the two:

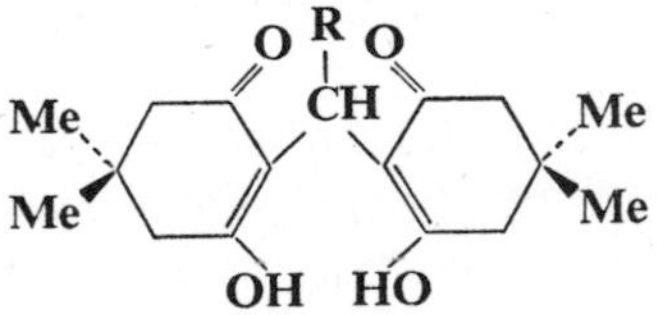

$$
\begin{array}{c}
\text{O} \quad \text{R} \quad \text{O} \\
\text{Me} \qquad \text{CH} \qquad \text{Me} \\
\text{Me} \qquad\qquad\qquad \text{Me} \\
\text{OH} \quad \text{HO}
\end{array}
$$

(XLVIII)

The Michael reaction is promoted by a variety of bases, present in catalytic quantities only, and its synthetic usefulness resides in the large number of carbanions and αβ-unsaturated carbonyl compounds that may be employed. The Michael reaction is reversible (*cf.* the Claisen ester condensation, p. 176) and the rate-determining step is believed to be the formation of the carbon–carbon bond, i.e. (XLIII) → (XLIV), though this has not been definitely proved.

7 ADDITION TO CARBON–OXYGEN DOUBLE BONDS

THE structure of the carbonyl group in aldehydes and ketones is, to judge from its reactions, not entirely adequately represented by $>\!\!C\!\!=\!\!O$, nor by the obvious alternative $>\!\!\overset{\oplus}{C}\!\!-\!\!\overset{\ominus}{O}$. The reality lies somewhere between them

$$>\!\!C\!\!=\!\!\overset{..}{O} \leftrightarrow >\!\!\overset{\oplus}{C}\!\!-\!\!\overset{\ominus}{O} \quad \text{i.e.} \quad >\!\!C\!\!-\!\!O$$

the electrons of the π bond joining carbon to oxygen being drawn towards oxygen on account of the greater electronegativity of the latter. This would imply that the characteristic reaction of the carbonyl group would be a nucleophilic attack on carbon by an anion, $Y^{\ominus}$ (e.g. $^{\ominus}CN$) or an electron-rich species, and such is, indeed, found to be the case (*cf.* addition to $>\!\!C\!\!=\!\!C\!\!<$ which is usually initiated by $X^{\oplus}$ or an electron-deficient complex). Reaction could, of course, equally well be initiated by attack of an electrophile on the oxygen atom of the $>\!\!C\!\!=\!\!O$ group, but this is usually of significance only where the electrophile is $H^{\oplus}$ (or a Lewis acid), amounting to acid-catalysis of the subsequent addition of a nucleophile.

EFFECT OF pH

It might be expected that carbonyl addition reactions would be powerfully acid-catalysed, for after attack on oxygen by a proton the carbon atom will become considerably more positive and hence readier to react with a nucleophile:

$$>\!\!C\!\!=\!\!O \overset{H^{\oplus}}{\rightleftharpoons} >\!\!\overset{\oplus}{C}\!\!-\!\!OH$$

Though this is true, most of the anions that are used as adducts are derived from weak acids so that as the solution becomes more acid their dissociation is suppressed, leading to a drop in $[Y^{\ominus}]$, e.g. $^{\ominus}CN \rightarrow HCN$. Where the nucleophile is not an anion, e.g. $R\cdot\overset{..}{N}H_2$, a

158

similar situation obtains for any quantity of acid will convert it to the unreactive species, $R \cdot \overset{\oplus}{N}H_3$. We should thus expect to find that the rate of addition shows a maximum at a moderately acid **pH**, falling off sharply on each side. This is, indeed, observed in practice, the curve below representing the **pH** dependence of the addition of many different reagents to carbonyl compounds:

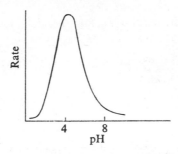

Apart from actual protonation, the positive character of the carbonyl carbon atom will also be enhanced, albeit to a smaller extent, on formation of a hydrogen-bonded complex by an acid with the carbonyl oxygen atom:

$$\overset{\delta+}{\underset{}{C}} = \overset{\delta-}{O} \cdots HA$$

STRUCTURE AND REACTIVITY

As high reactivity will depend on the carbon atom of the carbonyl group being positive, the introduction of groups having an electron-donating effect towards this atom will reduce its reactivity; thus the following sequence is observed:

$$\underset{H-C-H}{\overset{O}{\parallel}} > \underset{R \rightarrow C-H}{\overset{O}{\parallel}} > \underset{R \rightarrow C \leftarrow R}{\overset{O}{\parallel}} \gg$$

$$\underset{R \rightarrow C \leftarrow \ddot{O}R'}{\overset{O}{\parallel}} > \underset{R \rightarrow C \leftarrow \ddot{N}H_2}{\overset{O}{\parallel}} > \underset{R \rightarrow C \leftarrow O^{\ominus}}{\overset{O}{\parallel}}$$

The electron-withdrawing inductive effect of oxygen and nitrogen, in esters and amides, respectively, is more than outweighed by the tendency of their unshared electron pairs to interact with the π orbital of the carbonyl group (mesomeric effect). Reactivity is also reduced by attaching, to the carbonyl carbon atom, an aromatic nucleus, for its delocalised π orbitals also act as an electron source:

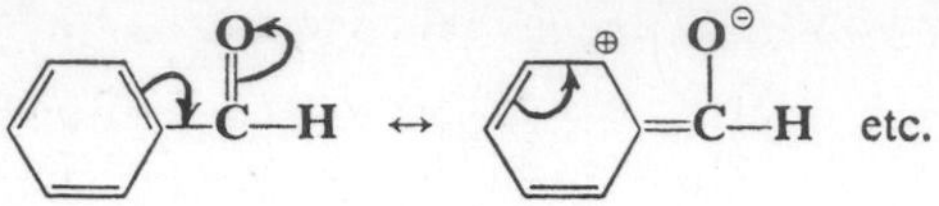

$$\text{(structure)} \leftrightarrow \text{(structure)} \quad \text{etc.}$$

Thus benzaldehyde is less reactive than aliphatic aldehydes. This effect is heightened by the presence, in the benzene nucleus, of electron-donating substituents (e.g. OH) and lessened by electron-withdrawing substituents (e.g. NO_2). This is naturally also observed with aliphatic aldehydes, e.g.:

$$O_2N{\leftarrow}CH_2{\leftarrow}\overset{O}{\overset{\|}{C}}{-}H \;>\; Cl{\leftarrow}CH_2{\leftarrow}\overset{O}{\overset{\|}{C}}{-}H \;>$$

$$CH_3{\rightarrow}\overset{O}{\overset{\|}{C}}{-}H \;>\; CH_3{\rightarrow}{-}CH_2{\rightarrow}{-}\overset{O}{\overset{\|}{C}}{-}H$$

Part of the loss of reactivity in aromatic aldehydes and ketones is also due to the relatively large nucleus inhibiting attack on $>C{=}O$ sterically. Similarly, the bulkier the alkyl groups in aliphatic carbonyl compounds the less the reactivity, due to the crowding that results on adding nucleophiles to the carbonyl carbon atom, e.g.:

$$Me{-}\overset{O}{\overset{\|}{C}}{-}Me \;>\; Me{-}\overset{O}{\overset{\|}{C}}{-}CMe_3 \;>\; Me_3C{-}\overset{O}{\overset{\|}{C}}{-}CMe_3$$

Comparison of the relative reactivity of aldehydes and ketones is complicated by the fact that, in aqueous solution, they are hydrated to varying degrees (see below), so that it is difficult to discover the proportion that is actually available in the reactive carbonyl form in any particular case. A group of characteristic addition reactions will now be studied in more detail.

ADDITION REACTIONS

(i) Hydration

Many carbonyl compounds form hydrates in solution:

$$R{-}\overset{O}{\overset{\|}{C}}{-}H + H_2O \rightleftharpoons R{-}\overset{OH}{\underset{OH}{\overset{|}{C}}}{-}H$$

Thus it has been shown that the percentage hydration at 20° of formaldehyde, acetaldehyde and acetone is 99·99, 58 and ≈ 0 per cent, respectively. The latter is confirmed by the fact that if acetone is dissolved in $H_2{}^{18}O$, when the following equilibrium could, theoretically, be set up,

$$Me_2C{=}O + H_2\overset{18}{O} \rightleftharpoons Me_2C\overset{\displaystyle OH}{\underset{\displaystyle {}^{18}OH}{}} \rightleftharpoons Me_2C{=}\overset{18}{O} + H_2O$$

no ^{18}O is incorporated into the acetone. In the presence of a trace of acid or base, however, while no equilibrium concentration of the hydrate can be detected, the incorporation of ^{18}O occurs too rapidly to measure, indicating that a hydrate must now, transiently, be formed. The acid or base catalysis is presumably proceeding:

$$
\begin{array}{ccc}
\overset{\delta+}{Me_2C}{=}\overset{\delta-}{O}\cdots HA & \xrightarrow{\ H_2O\ } & Me_2C\overset{\displaystyle OH}{\underset{\displaystyle \overset{\oplus}{O}H\ H}{}} \\[2em]
HA\ \updownarrow & & \updownarrow\ -H^{\oplus} \\[2em]
Me_2C{=}O \xrightleftharpoons{\ \ominus OH\ } Me_2C\overset{\displaystyle O^{\ominus}}{\underset{\displaystyle OH}{}} & \xrightleftharpoons{\ H_2O\ } & Me_2C\overset{\displaystyle OH}{\underset{\displaystyle OH}{}}
\end{array}
$$

The acid catalysis exhibited in this case is *general acid catalysis*, that is to say the hydration is catalysed by any acid species present in the aqueous solution and not solely by $H_3O^{\oplus}$ as is so often the case.

The fact that such catalysis is necessary with acetone, but not with the aldehydes, reflects the less positive nature of the carbonyl carbon atom of the ketone, which necessitates initial attack by $^{\ominus}OH$ (or by $H^{\oplus}$ on oxygen), whereas with the aldehydes $H_2O{:}$ will attack the more positive carbon atom directly.

The presence of electron-withdrawing substituents in the alkyl groups makes hydration easier and stabilises the hydrate once formed; thus glyoxal (I), chloral (II) and triketohydrindene (III) all form isolable, crystalline hydrates:

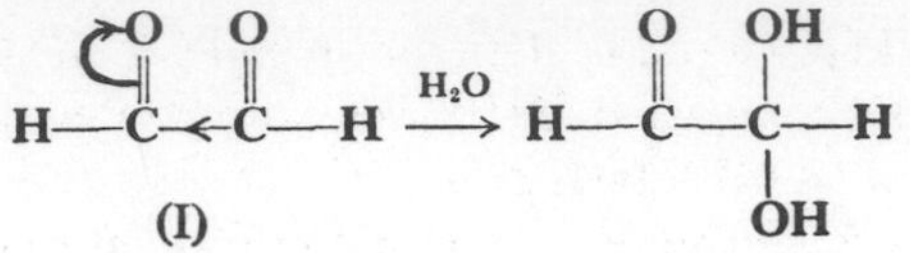

(I)

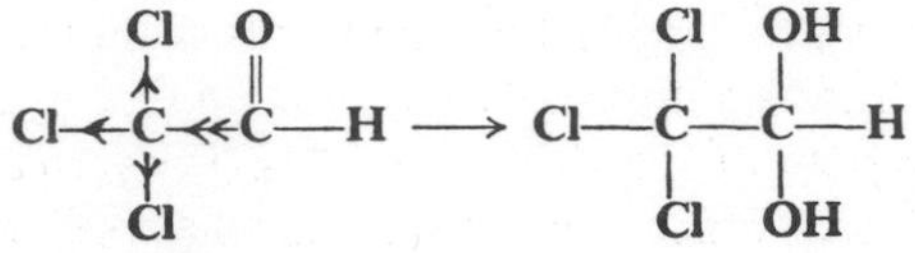

(II)

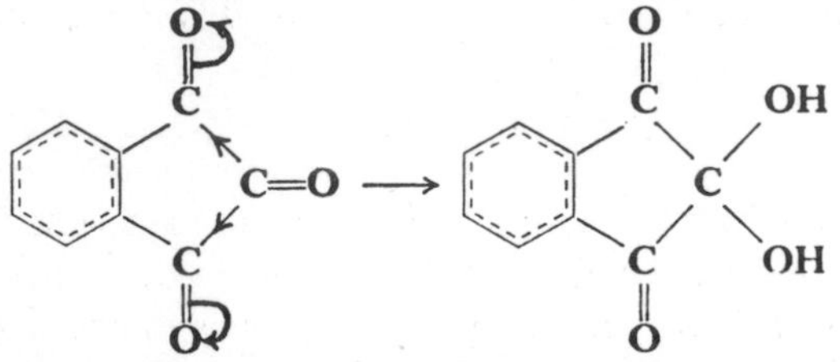

(III)   (IV)

(IV) is ninhydrin, the well-known colour reagent for the detection and estimation of α-amino acids. The hydrates are probably further stabilised by hydrogen bonding between the hydroxyl groups and the electronegative oxygen or chlorine atoms attached to the adjacent α-carbon:

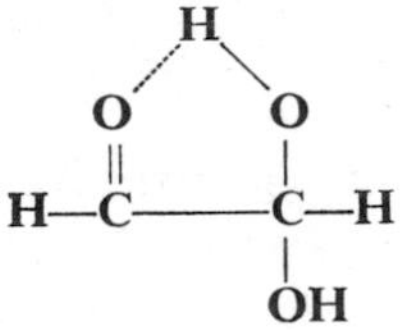

(ii) R·OH

Aldehydes with alcohols, in the presence of dry hydrogen chloride, yield acetals:

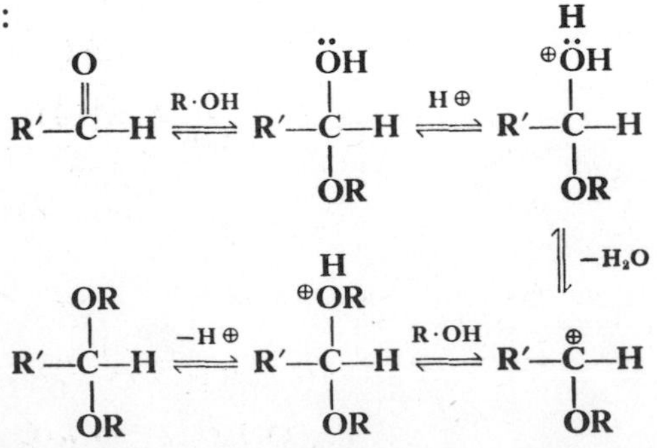

An $\rightleftharpoons$ with the hemi-acetal is often set up on dissolving the aldehyde in the alcohol but conversion to the acetal proper does not take place in the absence of added catalysts.

With ketones the carbonyl carbon atom is not sufficiently positive to undergo initial attack by $R \cdot OH$ and ketals cannot readily be made in this way. Both acetals and ketals may, however, be made by reaction with the appropriate alkyl orthoformate, $HC(OR)_3$, in the presence of NH_4Cl as catalyst. These derivatives may be used for protecting carbonyl groups for they are extremely resistant to alkali, but the carbonyl compound may be recovered readily on treatment with dilute acid.

(iii) R·SH

Mercaptans will react with aldehydes *and* ketones to yield thioacetals, $R'CH(SR)_2$, and thioketals $R'_2C(SR)_2$, respectively. The successful attack on the carbonyl carbon atom of ketones indicates the greater tendency of $R \cdot SH$ than $R \cdot OH$ to form an effective nucleophile, $RS^\ominus$, i.e. the greater acidity of thiols than the corresponding alcohols. These derivatives offer, with the acetals, differential protection of the carbonyl group for they are stable to acid but readily decomposed by $HgCl_2/CdCO_3$. They may also be decomposed by Raney nickel

$$R'_2C{=}O \longrightarrow R'_2C(SR)_2 \xrightarrow{\text{Ni/H}_2} R'_2CH_2$$

the overall reaction offering a preparative method of value for the reduction of $-CHO \rightarrow -CH_3$ and $\rangle CO \rightarrow \rangle CH_2$.

(iv) $^\ominus CN$, $HSO_3{}^\ominus$, etc.

These are both normal addition of anions:

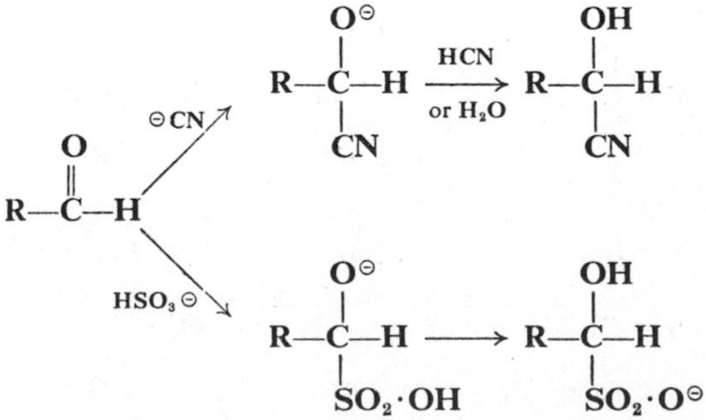

The addition of **HCN** is base-catalysed indicating that the rate-determining step of the reaction is attack by $^\ominus$**CN**. The process is completed by reaction with **HCN** if the reaction is being carried out in liquid **HCN** but by reaction with H_2O if in aqueous solution. This reaction has provided a great deal of the kinetic data on the addition of anions to carbonyl compounds, while the addition of bisulphite has afforded much evidence on the relative steric effect, on such addition, of groups attached to the carbonyl carbon atom. There is evidence that the effective attacking agent in the formation of bisulphite derivatives is actually the more powerfully nucleophilic $SO_3^{\ominus\ominus}$ even under conditions in which its concentration relative to $HSO_3^{\ominus}$ is very small. As is expected, the relative ease of addition, and stability of the derivative once formed, is considerably less with ketones than with aldehydes.

Halide ion will add to a $\rangle C{=}O$ group in the presence of acid, but the equilibrium is so readily reversible that the resultant 1,1-halohydrin cannot be isolated. If the reaction is carried out in alcohol, however, the α-halogeno-ether so produced may be isolated provided the solution is first neutralised:

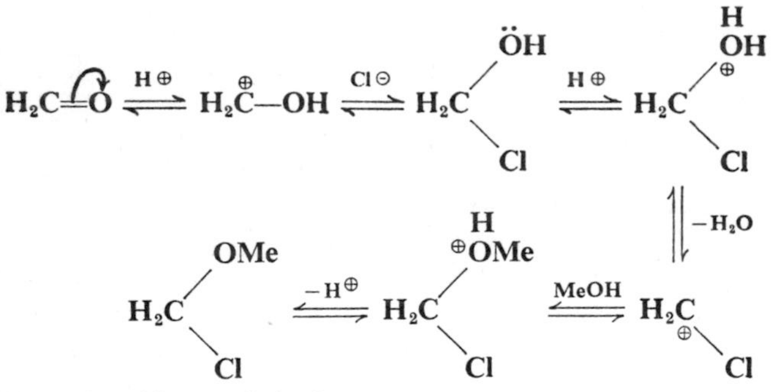

α-Chloromethyl ether

(v) Amine derivatives

Reaction with NH_3, $R \cdot NH_2$ or, more specifically, $HO \cdot NH_2$, $NH_2 \cdot CO \cdot NH \cdot NH_2$ and $Ph \cdot NH \cdot NH_2$ is the classical method by which liquid aldehydes and ketones are characterised.

There is spectroscopic and other evidence that in the formation of oximes, semicarbazones and probably phenylhydrazones, attack of the nucleophile, $R \cdot \ddot{N}H_2$, on the carbonyl compound, to form the adduct (V), is rapid and is followed by rate-determining, acid-catalysed

$$R-\overset{\overset{\displaystyle H}{|}}{\underset{\underset{\displaystyle H}{|}}{N:}} \quad \overset{\overset{\displaystyle O}{||}}{\underset{\displaystyle}{C}}- \longrightarrow R-\overset{\overset{\displaystyle H}{|}}{\underset{\underset{\displaystyle H}{|}}{\overset{\oplus}{N}}}-\overset{\overset{\displaystyle \overset{\ominus}{O}}{|}}{\underset{\displaystyle}{C}}- \xrightarrow{\text{fast}} R-\overset{\overset{\displaystyle HO}{|}}{\underset{\underset{\displaystyle H}{|}}{N}}-\overset{|}{\underset{|}{C}}-$$

(V)

$$R-N{=}C\big\langle \ +H_2O$$

(VI)

dehydration of the latter to yield the final derivative (VI). If the acidity of the solution is increased, however, the rate of dehydration is naturally accelerated and the initial formation of (V) is slowed owing to increasing conversion of the reactive nucleophile $R \cdot NH_2$ into its unreactive conjugate acid, $R \cdot \overset{\oplus}{N}H_3$; initial attack of the nucleophile on the carbonyl compound may then become the rate-determining step of the overall reaction. The fact that oxime formation may also be catalysed by bases at higher **pH** is due to the dehydration step being subject to base—as well as acid—catalysis:

$$\underset{}{\bigg\rangle}C{=}O \xrightarrow{:NH_2OH} \underset{\underset{\displaystyle H}{\underset{\displaystyle N \cdot OH}{|}}}{\overset{\overset{\displaystyle OH}{|}}{\bigg\rangle C}} \xrightarrow{\ominus OH} \underset{\underset{\displaystyle \underset{\ominus}{N} \cdot OH}{}}{\overset{\overset{\displaystyle OH}{}}{\bigg\rangle C}} \longrightarrow \bigg\rangle C{=}N \cdot OH$$

With ammonia some few aldehydes (e.g. chloral) yield the aldehyde ammonia, $R' \cdot CH(OH) \cdot NH_2$, but these derivatives more often react further to yield polymeric products. With primary amines, the derivatives obtained from both aldehydes and ketones eliminate water spontaneously, as above, to yield the Schiff base, e.g. $R' \cdot CH{=}NR$, (VI).

(vi) Hydride ion reactions

(a) **LiAlH₄ reductions**: Here the complex hydride ion, $AlH_4^{\ominus}$, is acting as a carrier of hydride ion, the latter acting as a nucleophile towards the carbonyl carbon atom:

$$R_2C{\overset{\frown}{=}}O + AlH_4^{\ominus} \rightarrow R_2\overset{\underset{\displaystyle H}{|}}{C}-O^{\ominus} \xrightarrow{H_2O} R_2\overset{\underset{\displaystyle H}{|}}{C}-OH$$

With esters, the initial reaction is a nucleophilic displacement, followed by reduction as above:

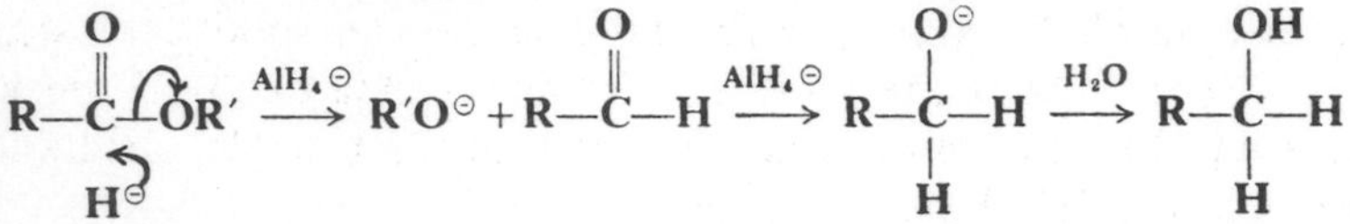

$$R-\underset{\underset{H^{\ominus}}{}}{\overset{\overset{O}{\parallel}}{C}}\!-\!OR' \xrightarrow{\text{AlH}_4{}^{\ominus}} R'O^{\ominus} + R-\overset{\overset{O}{\parallel}}{C}-H \xrightarrow{\text{AlH}_4{}^{\ominus}} R-\underset{\underset{H}{|}}{\overset{\overset{O^{\ominus}}{|}}{C}}-H \xrightarrow{\text{H}_2\text{O}} R-\underset{\underset{H}{|}}{\overset{\overset{OH}{|}}{C}}-H$$

A similar reduction takes place with amides ($R \cdot CO \cdot NH^{\ominus}$ being obtained by a preliminary removal of proton by $AlH_4{}^{\ominus}$, i.e. an 'active hydrogen' reaction) via an addition/elimination stage,

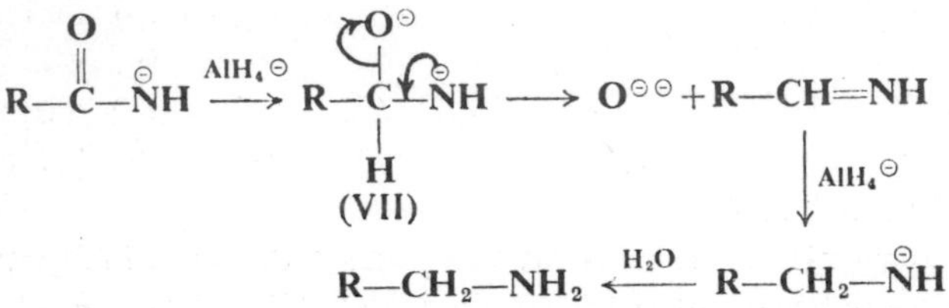

$$R-\overset{\overset{O}{\parallel}}{C}-\overset{\ominus}{N}H \xrightarrow{\text{AlH}_4{}^{\ominus}} R-\underset{\underset{(VII)}{\underset{H}{|}}}{\overset{\overset{O^{\ominus}}{|}}{C}}-NH \longrightarrow O^{\ominus\ominus} + R-CH{=}NH$$

$$R-CH_2-NH_2 \xleftarrow{\text{H}_2\text{O}} R-CH_2-\overset{\ominus}{N}H \quad \Big\downarrow \text{AlH}_4{}^{\ominus}$$

the Schiff base being obtained as it is easier to eliminate $O^{\ominus\ominus}$ than $HN^{\ominus\ominus}$ from (VII). **LiAlH$_4$** may obviously not be employed in hydroxylic solvents ('active hydrogen' reaction) or in those that are readily reduced and ether or tetrahydrofuran $(CH_2)_4O$ is, therefore, commonly used. **NaBH$_4$** may be used in water or alcohol but is, not surprisingly, a less reactive reagent and will not reduce amides.

(b) **Meerwein-Ponndorf reduction:** This is essentially the reduction of ketones to secondary alcohols with aluminium isopropoxide in isopropanol solution:

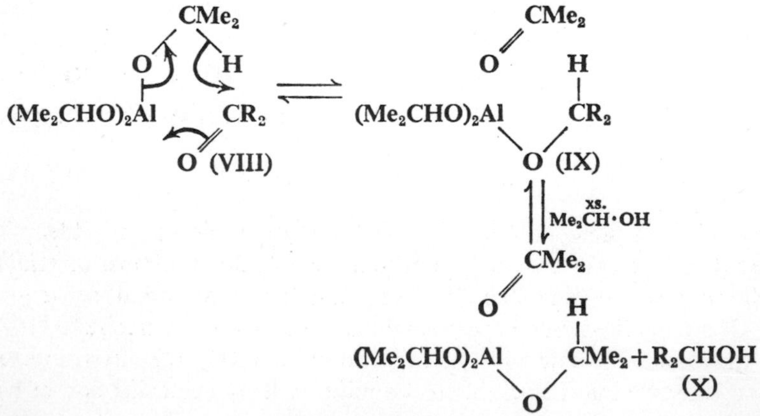

Hydride ion, $H^{\ominus}$, is transferred from aluminium isopropoxide to the ketone (VIII) via a cyclic transition state and an equilibrium thereby set up between this pair on the one hand and the mixed alkoxide (IX) plus acetone on the other. That there is indeed such a specific transfer of hydrogen may be demonstrated by using $(Me_2CDO)_3Al$ when deuterium becomes incorporated in the α-position of the resultant carbinol, $R \cdot CD(OH) \cdot R'$.

Acetone is the lowest boiling species in the system, so by distilling the mixture the equilibrium is displaced to the right, the secondary alçohol (X) being freed from the alkoxide (IX) by the excess isopropanol present. Because the establishment of this equilibrium is the crucial stage, the reaction is, naturally, very highly specific in its action and $>C=C<$, $-C\equiv C-$, NO_2, etc., undergo no reduction. The reaction may be reversed, $R \cdot CH(OH) \cdot R' \longrightarrow R \cdot CO \cdot R'$, by use of aluminium t-butoxide and a large excess of acetone to displace the equilibrium to the left.

(c) **Cannizzaro reaction:** The disproportionation of aldehydes lacking any α-hydrogen atoms (i.e. $Ph \cdot CHO$, CH_2O and $R_3C \cdot CHO$) to acid anion and primary alcohol in the presence of concentrated alkali, is also a hydride transfer reaction. In its simplest form the reaction rate $\propto [Ph \cdot CHO]^2[^{\ominus}OH]$ and the reaction is believed to follow the course:

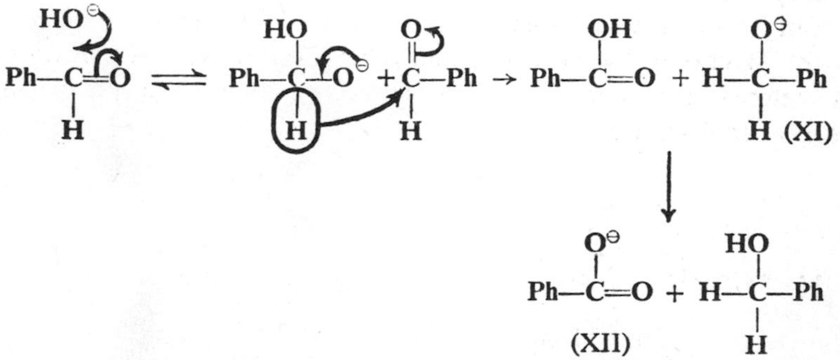

Rapid, reversible addition of $^{\ominus}OH$ to one molecule of aldehyde results in transfer of hydride ion to a second; this is almost certainly the rate-determining step of the reaction. The acid and alkoxide ion (XI) so obtained then become involved in a proton exchange to yield the more stable pair, alcohol and acid anion (XII), the latter, unlike the alkoxide ion, being able to stabilise itself by delocalisation of its

167

charge. That the migrating hydride ion is transferred directly from one molecule of aldehyde to another and does not actually become free in the solution is shown by carrying out the reaction in D_2O, when no deuterium becomes attached to carbon in the alcohol as it would have done if the migrating hydride ion had become free and so able to equilibrate with the solvent. In some cases, e.g. with formaldehyde in very high concentrations of alkali, a fourth-order reaction takes place: rate $\propto [CH_2O]^2[^{\ominus}OH]^2$. This is believed to involve formation of a doubly charged anion and transfer of hydride ion by this to a second molecule of aldehyde to yield carboxylate and alkoxide ions:

$$\underset{\underset{O^{2\ominus}}{|}}{H-C-H} \overset{^{\ominus}OH}{\rightleftharpoons} \underset{\underset{O^{\ominus}}{|}}{\overset{\overset{OH}{|}}{H-C-H}} \overset{^{\ominus}OH}{\rightleftharpoons} \underset{\underset{O^{\ominus}}{|}}{\overset{\overset{O^{\ominus}}{\|}}{H-C-H}} + \underset{\underset{H}{|}}{\overset{\overset{H}{|}}{C=O}}$$

$$\underset{\underset{O^{\ominus}}{|}}{\overset{\overset{O}{\|}}{H-C}} + \underset{\underset{H}{|}}{\overset{\overset{H}{|}}{H-C-O^{\ominus}}}$$

Intramolecular Cannizzaro reactions are also known, e.g. glyoxal → hydroxyacetate (glycollate) anion:

$$\underset{\underset{H}{|}}{\overset{\overset{H}{|}}{O=C-C=O}} \rightarrow \underset{\underset{H}{|}}{\overset{\overset{H}{|}}{HO-C-C=O}} \overset{O^{\ominus}}{|}$$

As expected

$$\text{rate} \propto [OHC \cdot CHO]\,[^{\ominus}OH]$$

and no deuterium attached to carbon is incorporated in the glycollate produced on carrying out the reaction in D_2O.

(vii) Reactions with metals

(a) Magnesium or sodium and ketones: Magnesium, usually in the form of an amalgam to increase its reactivity, will donate one electron each to two molecules of a ketone to yield a bimolecular product (XIII). This contains two unpaired electrons which can then unite to form a carbon–carbon bond yielding the magnesium salt (XIV) of a pinacol; subsequent acidification yields the free pinacol (XV):

$$R_2C\!=\!O \quad\quad R_2\overset{\displaystyle\cdot}{\underset{\displaystyle\cdot}{C}}\!-\!O$$

$$:Mg \rightarrow \qquad\qquad\Big\rangle Mg \rightarrow$$

$$R_2C\!=\!O \quad\quad R_2C\!-\!O$$
$$\text{(XIII)}$$

$$R_2C\!-\!O$$
$$\Big| \qquad \Big\rangle Mg \xrightarrow{\;H\oplus\;}$$
$$R_2C\!-\!O$$
$$\text{(XIV)}$$

$$R_2C\!-\!OH$$
$$\Big|$$
$$R_2C\!-\!OH$$
$$\text{(XV)}$$

This reaction is unusual in involving initial attack on oxygen rather than carbon. Pinacol itself is $Me_2C(OH)\cdot C(OH)Me_2$, but the name has come to be used generally for such tertiary-1,2-diols. The reaction is most readily seen when sodium is dissolved, in the absence of air, in ethereal solutions of aromatic ketones, the blue, paramagnetic radical-ion of the sodium ketyl, $Ar_2\overset{\displaystyle\cdot}{C}\!-\!\overset{\ominus}{O}\leftrightarrow Ar_2\overset{\ominus}{C}\!-\!\overset{\displaystyle\cdot}{O}$, then being in equilibrium with the dianion of the corresponding pinacol:

$$Ar_2C\!-\!O^\ominus$$
$$\Big|$$
$$Ar_2C\!-\!O^\ominus$$

(b) **Sodium and esters:** Sodium will donate an electron to an ester to yield the radical-ion (XVI), two molecules of which unite (XVII) (*cf.* pinacol formation above) and expel $EtO^\ominus$ to yield the α-diketone (XVIII). Further electron donation by sodium yields the diradical-ion (XIX), which again forms a carbon–carbon bond (XX). Acidification yields the α-hydroxyketone or *acyloin* (XXI):

$$\begin{array}{c}O\\ \|\\ 2R\!-\!C\!-\!OEt\end{array} \xrightarrow{2Na\cdot} \begin{array}{c}O^\ominus\\ |\\ R\!-\!\overset{\cdot}{\underset{\cdot}{C}}\!-\!OEt\\ R\!-\!\overset{\cdot}{C}\!-\!OEt\\ |\\ O^\ominus\end{array} \longrightarrow \begin{array}{c}O^\ominus\\ |\\ R\!-\!C\!-\!OEt\\ R\!-\!C\!-\!OEt\\ |\\ O^\ominus\end{array} \longrightarrow \begin{array}{c}O\\ \|\\ R\!-\!C\\ R\!-\!C\\ \|\\ O\end{array}$$

$$\text{(XVI)} \qquad\qquad \text{(XVII)} \qquad\qquad \text{(XVIII)}$$

$$\Big\downarrow 2Na\cdot$$

$$\begin{array}{c}O\\ \|\\ R\!-\!C\\ |\\ R\!-\!CH\\ |\\ OH\end{array} \rightleftharpoons \begin{array}{c}OH\\ |\\ R\!-\!C\\ \|\\ R\!-\!C\\ |\\ OH\end{array} \xleftarrow{\;H\oplus\;} \begin{array}{c}O^\ominus\\ |\\ R\!-\!C\\ \|\\ R\!-\!C\\ |\\ O^\ominus\end{array} \longleftarrow \begin{array}{c}O^\ominus\\ |\\ R\!-\!C\cdot\\ R\!-\!C\cdot\\ |\\ O^\ominus\end{array}$$

$$\text{(XXI)} \qquad\qquad \text{(XX)} \qquad\qquad \text{(XIX)}$$

This acyloin condensation is much used for the ring-closure of long chain dicarboxylic esters, $EtO_2C \cdot (CH_2)_n \cdot CO_2Et$ in the synthesis, in high yield, of large cyclic hydroxyketones.

A larger quantity of sodium in the presence of a little alcohol results in the reaction following a different course. The larger quantity of sodium donates two electrons to the ester to yield the divalent anion (XXII), which liberates $EtO^\ominus$ from the alcohol; the resultant ion (XXIII) then expels $EtO^\ominus$ to form the aldehyde (XXIV). Repetition of the above sequence yields the alkoxide (XXV) and, on acidification, the primary alcohol (XXVI):

$$
\begin{array}{ccccccc}
\overset{\displaystyle O}{\underset{\displaystyle \|}{}} & & \overset{\displaystyle O^\ominus}{\underset{\displaystyle |}{}} & & \overset{\displaystyle O^\ominus}{\underset{\displaystyle |}{}} & & \overset{\displaystyle O}{\underset{\displaystyle \|}{}}
\end{array}
$$

$$R\!-\!\overset{O}{\overset{\|}{C}}\!-\!OEt \xrightarrow{\;2Na\cdot\;} R\!-\!\underset{\underset{\ominus}{}}{\overset{O^\ominus}{\overset{|}{C}}}\!-\!OEt \xrightarrow{\;EtOH\;} R\!-\!\underset{\underset{H}{|}}{\overset{O^\ominus}{\overset{|}{C}}}\!\!-\!\!OEt \longrightarrow R\!-\!\underset{\underset{H}{|}}{\overset{O}{\overset{\|}{C}}}$$

(XXII)   (XXIII)   (XXIV)

2Na·

$$R\!-\!\underset{\underset{H}{|}}{\overset{OH}{\overset{|}{C}}}\!-\!H \xleftarrow{\;H^\oplus\;} R\!-\!\underset{\underset{H}{|}}{\overset{O^\ominus}{\overset{|}{C}}}\!-\!H \xleftarrow{\;EtOH\;} R\!-\!\underset{\underset{H}{|}}{\overset{O^\ominus}{\overset{|}{C}}}{}^{\ominus}$$

(XXVI)   (XXV)

This is the classical Bouveault-Blanc reduction of esters (now largely displaced by $LiAlH_4$, above). It, like pinacol formation, used to be looked upon as a reaction of nascent hydrogen, i.e. from sodium and the alcohol, whose presence is essential; but it would seem that any sodium so used up is merely wasted and best results are obtained by using the calculated quantity of both sodium and alcohol in an inert solvent.

When, in addition, the Claisen ester condensation is considered below (p. 176), something of the complexity of the products that may result from the reaction of sodium on esters will be realised!

(viii) Addition of carbanions and negative carbon

The importance of these reactions resides in the fact that carbon–carbon bonds are formed; many of them are thus of great synthetic importance.

(a) **Grignard reagents:** The actual structure of Grignard reagents themselves is still a matter of some dispute. Phenyl magnesium bromide has, however, been isolated in crystalline form as the com-· pound $C_6H_5MgBr \cdot 2Et_2O$, in which C_6H_5, Br and the two molecules of ether are arranged tetrahedrally about the magnesium atom. The known reactions of Grignard reagents indicate the possible participation of all of the species:

$$2R \cdot Mg \cdot Hal \rightleftharpoons \begin{cases} 2R^\ominus + 2\overset{\oplus}{Mg}Hal \\ 2R \cdot + 2 \cdot MgHal \\ R_2Mg + MgHal_2 \end{cases}$$

Thus free radical reactions with them are known, but in most of their useful synthetic applications they tend to behave as though polarised in the sense $\overset{\delta-}{R} \cdot \overset{\delta+}{Mg} \cdot Hal$, i.e. as sources of negative carbon if not necessarily of carbanions as such.

In reactions with carbonyl groups it appears that *two* molecules of Grignard reagent are involved in the actual addition. One molecule acts as a Lewis acid with the oxygen atom of the carbonyl group, thus enhancing the positive nature of the carbonyl carbon atom, and so promotes attack on it by the R group of a second molecule of Grignard reagent via a cyclic transition state:

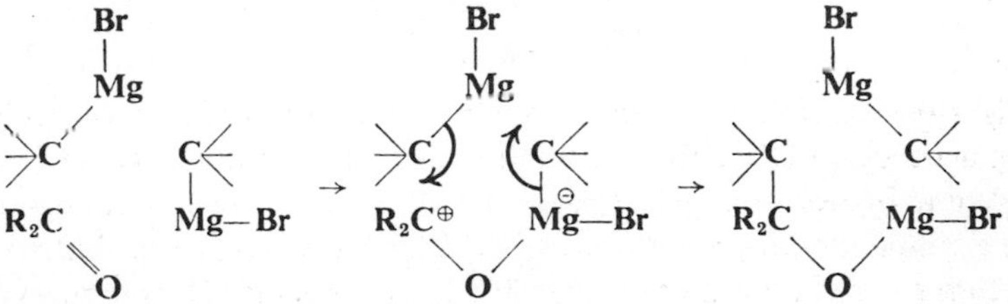

If such a course is followed it might be expected that Grignard reagents of suitable structure, i.e. those having hydrogen atoms on a β-carbon, might undergo conversion to olefines as a side-reaction, transfer of hydride ion to the positive carbon atom of the carbonyl group taking place:

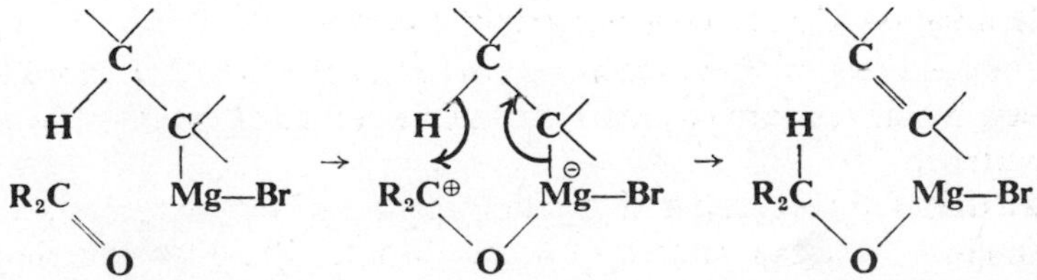

171

This is, indeed, observed in practice; the ketone is in part reduced to the secondary alcohol in the process, via a cyclic transition state closely resembling that already encountered in the Meerwein-Ponndorf reaction (p. 166).

If Grignard additions do proceed via initial attack of one molecule of the reagent on the carbonyl oxygen, it might be expected that the reaction would be promoted if a more effective Lewis acid were introduced into the solution, for this would co-ordinate preferentially to yield an even more positive carbonyl carbon atom. Thus introduction of $MgBr_2$ has been observed to double the yield of tertiary alcohol in the reactions of some ketones with Grignard reagents.

Grignard reagents are however being increasingly superseded by other organo-metallic compounds for preparative addition of this kind, particularly by the more reactive lithium derivatives.

(b) **Acetylide ion:** A very useful reaction is the addition of acetylide ion to carbonyl compounds, the reaction often being carried out in liquid ammonia in the presence of sodamide to convert acetylene into its carbanion (p. 211). Hydrogenation of the resultant acetylenic carbinol (XXVII) in the presence of Lindlar catalyst (partially poisoned palladium) yields the olefine (XXVIII); the latter undergoes an acid-catalysed allylic rearrangement (p. 29) to the primary alcohol (XXIX), which, as the corresponding halide, can be made to undergo further synthetic reactions. The series constitutes a useful preparative sequence:

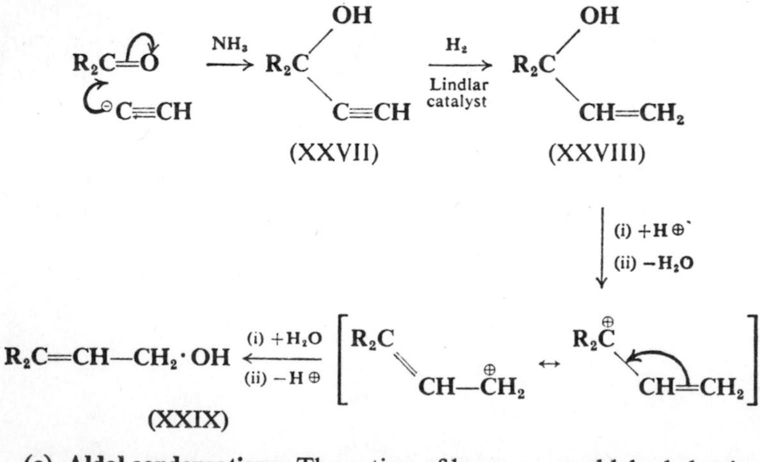

(c) **Aldol condensations:** The action of bases on an aldehyde having α-hydrogen atoms results in the formation of a stabilised carbanion

(XXX) which can attack the carbonyl carbon atom of a second molecule of aldehyde to yield, ultimately, the aldol (XXXI):

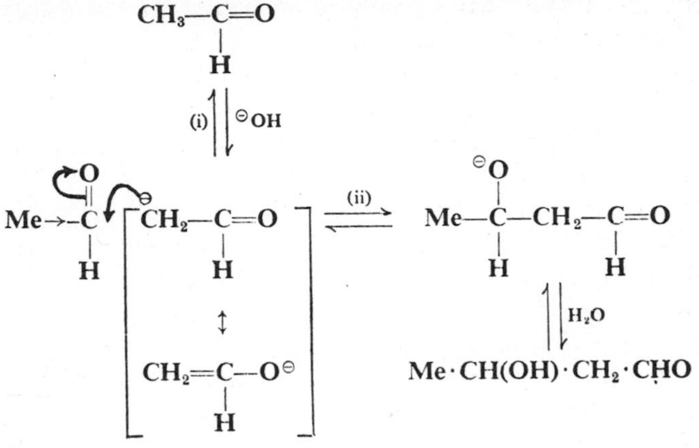
CH₃—C=O
H
(i)
⊖OH
O
Me→-C
H
CH₂—C=O
H
CH₂=C—O⊖
H
(ii)
⊖O
Me—C—CH₂—C=O
H
H
H₂O
Me·CH(OH)·CH₂·CHO

(XXX) (XXXI)

The forward reaction (ii) and the reversal of (i) are essentially in competition with each other but, as carrying out the reaction in $\mathbf{D_2O}$ fails to result in the incorporation of any deuterium in the methyl group, (ii) must be so much more rapid than the reversal of (i) as to make the latter virtually irreversible. The corresponding reaction of acetone to diacetone alcohol (XXXII) proceeds much more slowly and, when carried out in $\mathbf{D_2O}$, deuterium is incorporated into the methyl group; this is the result of a less rapid attack of the carbanion on a carbonyl carbon atom which is markedly less positive than that in an aldehyde:

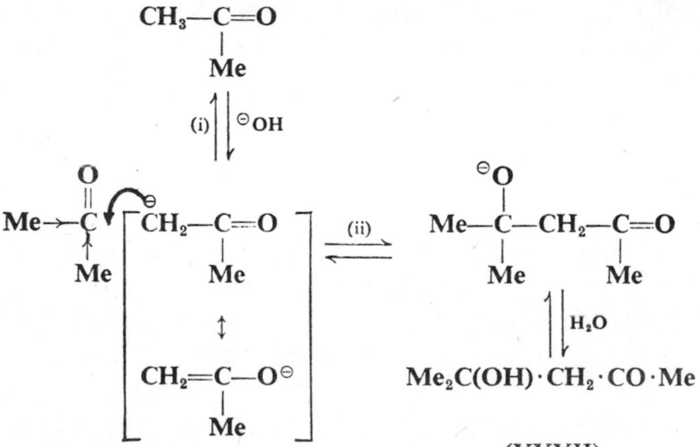
CH₃—C=O
Me
(i)
⊖OH
O
Me→C
Me
CH₂—C=O
Me
CH₂=C—O⊖
Me
(ii)
⊖O
Me—C—CH₂—C=O
Me
Me
H₂O
Me₂C(OH)·CH₂·CO·Me

(XXXII)

Aldehydes having no α-hydrogen atoms cannot form carbanions and they therefore, undergo the Cannizzaro reaction (p. 167) with concentrated alkali; but as this reaction is slow, such aldehydes are often able to function as carbanion acceptors. Thus formaldehyde, in excess, reacts with acetaldehyde:

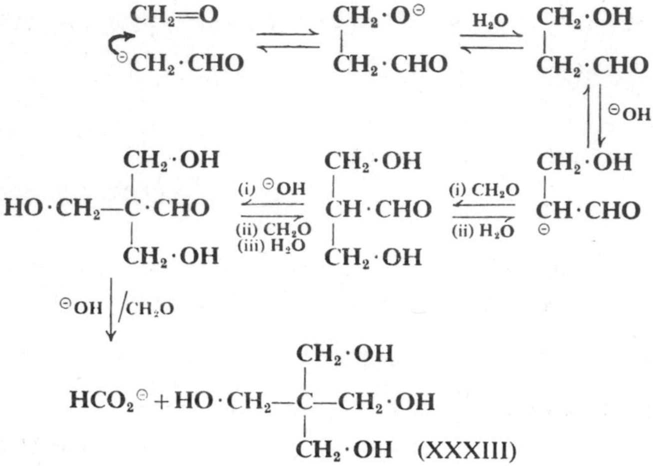

$$
\begin{array}{ccccc}
\mathrm{CH_2{=}O} & \longrightarrow & \mathrm{CH_2{\cdot}O^{\ominus}} & \xrightarrow{\;\mathrm{H_2O}\;} & \mathrm{CH_2{\cdot}OH} \\
\overset{\displaystyle\curvearrowleft}{{}^{\ominus}\mathrm{CH_2{\cdot}CHO}} & \rightleftharpoons & |\;\;\;\;\mathrm{CH_2{\cdot}CHO} & \longleftarrow & |\;\;\;\;\mathrm{CH_2{\cdot}CHO}
\end{array}
$$

$$\Big\Updownarrow {}^{\ominus}\mathrm{OH}$$

$$
\begin{array}{ccccc}
\mathrm{CH_2{\cdot}OH} & & \mathrm{CH_2{\cdot}OH} & & \mathrm{CH_2{\cdot}OH} \\
\;\;\;\;\;| & \xleftarrow[\text{(ii) CH}_2\text{O}]{\text{(i) }^{\ominus}\mathrm{OH}} & | & \xleftarrow[\text{(ii) H}_2\mathrm{O}]{\text{(i) CH}_2\mathrm{O}} & | \\
\mathrm{HO{\cdot}CH_2{-}C{\cdot}CHO} & & \mathrm{CH{\cdot}CHO} & & \mathrm{CH{\cdot}CHO} \\
\;\;\;\;\;| & \scriptstyle\text{(iii) H}_2\mathrm{O} & | & & \;\;\;{}^{\ominus} \\
\mathrm{CH_2{\cdot}OH} & & \mathrm{CH_2{\cdot}OH} & &
\end{array}
$$

$$\;{}^{\ominus}\mathrm{OH}\Big\downarrow\Big/\mathrm{CH_2O}$$

$$
\begin{array}{c}
\mathrm{CH_2{\cdot}OH} \\
| \\
\mathrm{HCO_2^{\ominus} + HO{\cdot}CH_2{-}C{-}CH_2{\cdot}OH} \\
| \\
\mathrm{CH_2{\cdot}OH} \quad \text{(XXXIII)}
\end{array}
$$

In the last stage $(\mathrm{HO{\cdot}CH_2})_3\mathrm{C{\cdot}CHO}$, which can no longer form a carbanion, undergoes a crossed Cannizzaro reaction with formaldehyde to yield pentaerythritol (XXXIII) and formate anion. The reaction proceeds this way rather than to yield $(\mathrm{HO{\cdot}CH_2})_3\mathrm{C{\cdot}CO_2}^{\ominus}$ and $\mathrm{CH_3OH}$ as the carbonyl carbon atom of formaldehyde is the more positive of the two aldehydes so that it is attacked preferentially by ${}^{\ominus}\mathrm{OH}$, with resultant transfer of $\mathrm{H}^{\ominus}$ to $(\mathrm{HO{\cdot}CH_2})_3\mathrm{C{\cdot}CHO}$ rather than the other way round.

A further useful synthetic reaction is the base-catalysed addition of aliphatic nitro-compounds to carbonyl groups (see p. 175). Here the aldehyde itself can also form a carbanion and aldol formation could be a competing reaction, but the carbanion from the nitro-compound tends to be the more stable (due to the more effective delocalisation of its charge) and is thus formed more readily, resulting in the preponderance of the above reaction.

The elimination of water from a hydroxy compound usually requires acid-catalysis (p. 192) but the possibility of carbanion formation in the first formed aldol, coupled with the presence of a group

$$
\begin{array}{c}
\overset{\displaystyle O}{\underset{\displaystyle \oplus}{CH_3-N}}-O^{\ominus} \\[4pt]
\Big\updownarrow \;\ominus OH
\end{array}
$$

$$
R \cdot CH_2-\overset{O}{\underset{H}{C}}\left[CH_2-\underset{\oplus}{\overset{O}{N}}-O^{\ominus}\right] \rightleftharpoons R \cdot CH_2-\overset{\ominus O}{\underset{H}{C}}-CH_2-\underset{\oplus}{\overset{O}{N}}-O^{\ominus}
$$

$$
\begin{array}{c}
O^{\ominus} \\
\big\updownarrow \\
\underset{\oplus}{CH_2{=}N}-O^{\ominus}
\end{array}
$$

$$\Big\updownarrow \; H_2O$$

$$R \cdot CH_2 \cdot CH(OH) \cdot CH_2 \cdot NO_2$$

in the adjacent β-position that can be readily expelled as an anion, results in an easy 'attack from the back' by an electron pair:

$$
\underset{Me \cdot CH-CH_2 \cdot CHO}{\overset{OH}{|}} \overset{\ominus OH}{\rightleftharpoons} \underset{Me \cdot CH-CH \cdot CHO}{\overset{OH}{|}} \overset{\ominus OH}{\longrightarrow}
$$

$$Me \cdot CH{=}CH \cdot CHO$$

Thus the dehydration of aldols is subject to base-catalysis and carbanion additions are often followed by elimination of water resulting in an overall condensation reaction. The successive additions of carbanion, followed by elimination of water induced by strong base, result in the formation of low molecular weight polymers from simple aliphatic aldehydes; if the process is to be halted at the simple aldol, a weak base such as K_2CO_3 is used. A preparative use of carbanion addition followed by elimination is seen in the Claisen-Schmidt condensation of aromatic aldehydes with aliphatic aldehydes or ketones in the presence of 10 per cent mineral alkali:

$$+ \overset{\ominus}{C}H_2 \cdot CO \cdot Me \;\rightarrow\; Ph \cdot CH{=}CH \cdot CO \cdot Me$$

$$Ph-\overset{O}{\underset{}{C}}-H$$

$$+ \overset{\ominus}{C}H_2 \cdot CHO \;\rightarrow\; Ph \cdot CH{=}CH \cdot CHO$$

With aliphatic aldehydes, self-condensation can, of course, constitute an important side reaction. The presence of electron-donating groups in the aromatic nucleus will reduce the positive nature of the carbonyl carbon atom, and p-MeO·C$_6$H$_4$·CHO is found to react at only about one-seventh the rate of benzaldehyde.

(d) **Perkin reaction:** Closely related to the above is the Perkin reaction for the synthesis of $\alpha\beta$-unsaturated acids from aromatic aldehydes and aliphatic acid anhydrides in the presence of an alkali metal salt of the corresponding acid, e.g. for cinnamic acid, Ph·CH=CH·CO$_2$H:

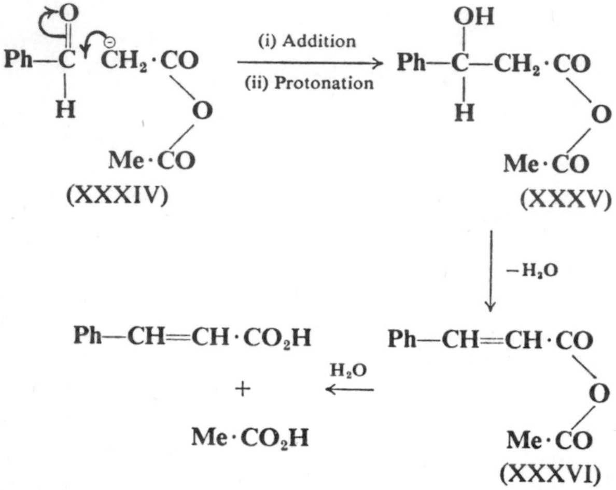

In acetic anhydride solution, acetate ion is a sufficiently strong base to remove a proton from the activated α-position of the anhydride to yield the carbanion (XXXIV), which adds to the carbonyl group of the aldehyde, the product, after protonation, being the aldol-like species (XXXV). Under the conditions of the reaction (*ca.* 140°), (XXXV) undergoes dehydration in the presence of acetic anhydride and the resultant mixed anhydride (XXXVI), on being poured into water at the end of the reaction, is hydrolysed to cinnamic and acetic acids. The reaction is a general one, depending only on the presence of a CH$_2$ group in the α-position of the anhydride. That the reaction follows the above course is confirmed by the fact that aromatic aldehydes will, in the presence of suitable basic catalysts, react with anhydrides but not with the corresponding acid anions, and aldol-like intermediates such as (XXXV) have in some cases been isolated.

(e) **Claisen ester condensation:** This too is effectively an aldol type reaction, e.g. with ethyl acetate:

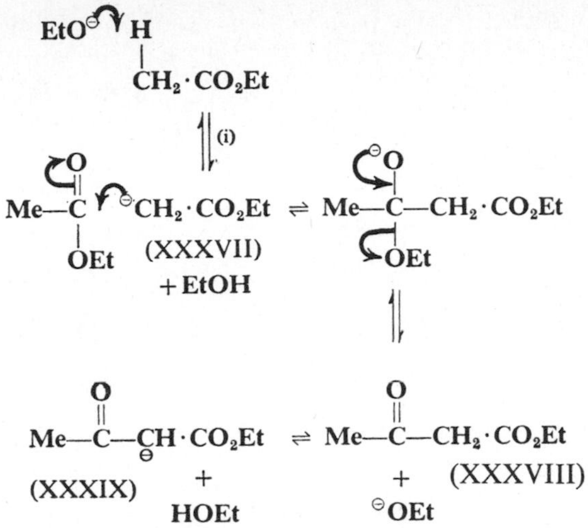

EtO⊖ H
|
CH₂·CO₂Et

‖ (i)

Me—C—CH₂·CO₂Et ⇌ Me—C—CH₂·CO₂Et
(XXXVII)   OEt
+ EtOH

‖

O
‖
Me—C—CH·CO₂Et ⇌ Me—C—CH₂·CO₂Et
(XXXIX)   ⊖   (XXXVIII)
      +   +
    HOEt   ⊖OEt

Normally a gram equivalent of sodium is employed as a source of the sodium ethoxide catalyst required, but only a little ethanol need be added initially as more is liberated as soon as the reaction starts, with the formation of the carbanion (XXXVII). This adds to the carbonyl group of a second molecule of ester, followed by the expulsion of EtO⊖ to yield the β-keto ester (XXXVIII), which is finally converted into the carbanion (XXXIX), i.e. the 'sodio-derivative' (hence the need for the employment of a whole gram equivalent of sodium). The formation of (XXXIX) is an essential feature of the reaction for it helps to drive the equilibrium (i) over to the right; this is made necessary by the fact that the carbanion (XXXVII) is not as highly stabilised as,

for example, $\underset{\ominus CH_2 - C - H}{O}$, and is consequently more reluctant to

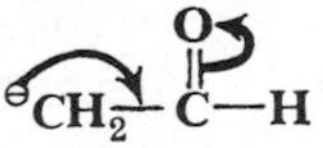

form. This is reflected in the fact that $R_2CH \cdot CO_2Et$ does not undergo the reaction in the presence of EtO⊖ despite the fact that it has an α-hydrogen atom and so could form a carbanion, because the product $R_2CH \cdot CO \cdot CR_2 \cdot CO_2Et$ cannot be converted to a carbanion such as (XXXIX) and so fails to drive the equilibrium over to the right.

Such esters can however be made to condense satisfactorily in the presence of very strong bases such as $Ph_3C^\ominus Na^\oplus$, for here the initial carbanion formation is essentially irreversible:

$$R_2CH \cdot CO_2Et + Ph_3C^\ominus \rightarrow R_2\overset{\ominus}{C} \cdot CO_2Et + Ph_3CH$$

Crossed condensation of two different esters is not always practicable because of the formation of mixed products, but it can be of synthetic value, particularly where one of the esters used is incapable of forming a carbanion, e.g. $(CO_2Et)_2$, HCO_2Et and $Ph \cdot CO_2Et$. The complexity of the alternative reactions that can take place from the action of sodium on esters has already been referred to (p. 170).

Where the two ester groups are part of the same molecule and cyclisation can therefore result, the condensation is known as a Dieckmann reaction:

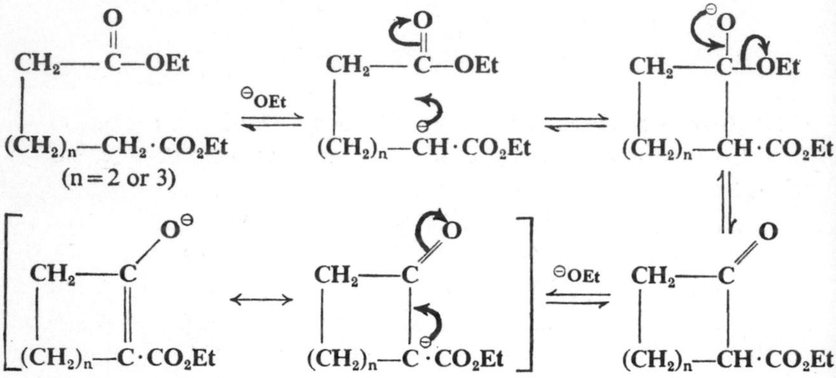

Here as in the simple Claisen ester condensation it is necessary, if ethoxide is used as the catalyst, to be able to form the anion of the final β-keto ester in order to drive the overall reaction in the desired direction.

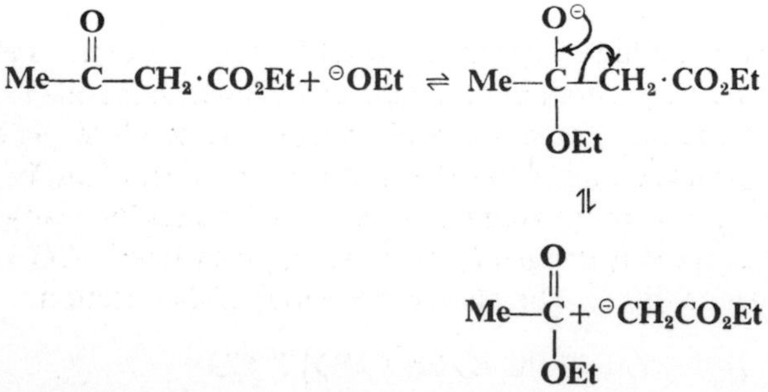

Like all aldol-type reactions, the Claisen ester condensation is reversible i.e. the so-called 'acid decomposition' of β-keto esters. An exactly analogous fission of β-diketones also takes place:

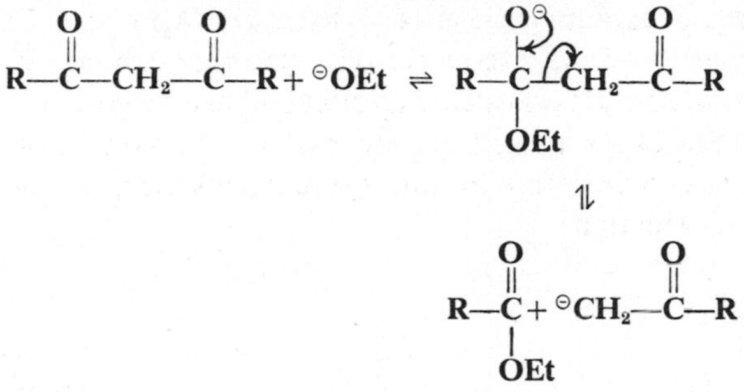

$$R-\overset{O}{\overset{\|}{C}}-CH_2-\overset{O}{\overset{\|}{C}}-R + {}^{\ominus}OEt \rightleftharpoons R-\overset{O^{\ominus}}{\underset{OEt}{\overset{|}{C}}}-CH_2-\overset{O}{\overset{\|}{C}}-R$$

$$R-\overset{O}{\overset{\|}{C}} + {}^{\ominus}\underset{OEt}{\overset{|}{C}}H_2-\overset{O}{\overset{\|}{C}}-R$$

(f) Benzoin condensation: Another carbanion addition is that observed with aromatic aldehydes in alcoholic solution in the presence of $^{\ominus}$CN:

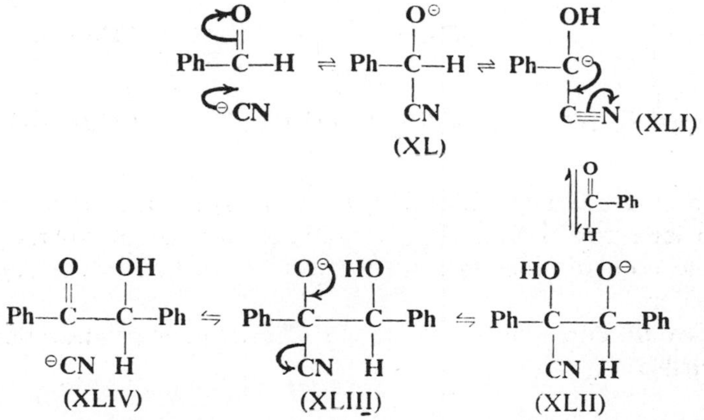

$$Ph-\overset{O}{\overset{\|}{C}}-H \rightleftharpoons Ph-\underset{CN}{\overset{O^{\ominus}}{\overset{|}{C}}}-H \rightleftharpoons Ph-\overset{OH}{\underset{C\equiv N}{\overset{|}{C}}}{}^{\ominus}$$

$$(XL) \qquad (XLI)$$

$$\overset{O}{\overset{\|}{C}}-Ph$$
$$H$$

$$Ph-\overset{O}{\overset{\|}{C}}-\underset{H}{\overset{OH}{\overset{|}{C}}}-Ph \leftrightharpoons Ph-\underset{CN}{\overset{O^{\ominus}}{\overset{|}{C}}}-\underset{H}{\overset{HO}{\overset{|}{C}}}-Ph \leftrightharpoons Ph-\underset{CN}{\overset{HO}{\overset{|}{C}}}-\underset{H}{\overset{O^{\ominus}}{\overset{|}{C}}}-Ph$$

$$^{\ominus}CN \quad H$$

$$(XLIV) \qquad (XLIII) \qquad (XLII)$$

Cyanide ion is a highly specific catalyst for this reaction, its effectiveness depending presumably on the ease with which it adds to benzaldehyde in the first place and with which it is finally expelled from (XLIII) to yield benzoin (XLIV). But perhaps most of all, it depends on its electron-withdrawing power which promotes the ready release, as proton, of the hydrogen atom attached to carbon in (XL) to yield the carbanion (XLI). The observed kinetics of the reaction

$$\text{Rate} \propto [\text{Ph} \cdot \text{CHO}]^2 [{}^{\ominus}\text{CN}]$$

179

support the above formulation and the rate-determining step is believed to be the reaction of the carbanion (XLI) with a second molecule of aldehyde to yield (XLII).

(g) **Benzilic acid change**: An interesting intramolecular reaction, which can be looked upon as essentially a carbanion addition, is the base-catalysed conversion of benzil to benzilic acid anion, $Ph \cdot CO \cdot CO \cdot Ph \rightarrow Ph_2C(OH) \cdot CO_2^{\ominus}$:

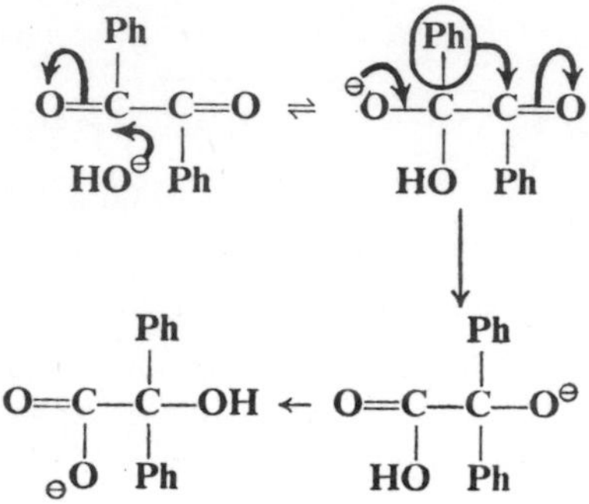

It is found that

$$Rate \propto [Ph \cdot CO \cdot CO \cdot Ph]\,[^{\ominus}OH]$$

and a rapid, reversible addition of $^{\ominus}OH$ to benzil is followed by the migration of **Ph** with its electron pair to the slightly positive carbon atom of the adjacent carbonyl group. The reaction is exactly analogous to the intramolecular Cannizzaro reaction of glyoxal (p. 168) except that there it was hydrogen that migrated with its electron pair while here it is phenyl.

(h) **Mannich reaction**: This carbanion addition, albeit an indirect one so far as the carbonyl group is concerned, is an extremely useful synthetic reaction in which an active hydrogen containing compound (i.e. one that will readily form a carbanion) reacts with formaldehyde and a secondary amine (or, less frequently, ammonia or a primary amine):

$$\text{>C—H} + CH_2O + HNR_2 \rightarrow \text{>C—CH}_2\text{—NR}_2 + H_2O$$

$$Rate \propto [\text{>C—H}]\,[CH_2O]\,[R_2NH]$$

The reactions to form the so-called Mannich bases (XLVII) are believed to proceed as follows, e.g. with $Ph \cdot CO \cdot Me$:

$$H_2C \overset{O}{\underset{H}{\underset{|}{C}}} :NR_2 \longrightarrow H_2C \overset{\overset{\ominus}{O}}{\underset{H}{\underset{|}{\overset{|}{N}R_2}}} \overset{H^\oplus}{\longrightarrow} H_2C \overset{\overset{HO}{|}}{\underset{H}{\underset{|}{\overset{\oplus}{N}R_2}}}$$

$$\downarrow -H_2O$$

$$Ph \cdot CO \cdot CH_2 \cdot CH_2 \cdot NR_2 \overset{Ph \cdot CO \cdot \overset{\ominus}{C}H_2}{\longleftarrow} \left[H_2\overset{\oplus}{C} - \overset{..}{N}R_2 \leftrightarrow H_2C = \overset{\oplus}{N}R_2 \right]$$

(XLVII)   (XLVI)

Initial attack by the unshared electron pair of nitrogen on the carbonyl carbon atom is followed by protonation and elimination of water to yield the ion (XLVI). Attack by the carbanion derived from acetophenone on the positive carbon atom of (XLVI) then yields the Mannich base (XLVII). If ammonia or primary amines are used, the first formed Mannich base, still carrying hydrogen on the nitrogen atom, can itself participate further in the reaction leading to more complex products, hence the preference for secondary amines.

The Mannich base formed will readily eliminate R_2NH, hence the synthetic usefulness of the reaction:

$$Ph \cdot CO \cdot CH_2 \cdot CH_2 \cdot NR_2 \quad \begin{matrix} \overset{heat}{\nearrow} & Ph \cdot CO \cdot CH = CH_2 \\ \overset{Ni/H_2}{\longrightarrow} & Ph \cdot CO \cdot CH_2 \cdot Me \\ \underset{Ac_2O}{\searrow} & Ph \cdot CO \cdot CH_2 \cdot CH_2 \cdot OAc \end{matrix}$$

STEREOCHEMISTRY OF ADDITION TO CARBONYL COMPOUNDS

Whether the mechanism of addition to a carbon–oxygen double bond is *cis* or *trans* clearly has no meaning for, unlike a carbon–carbon double bond, (p. 139) different products will not be obtained by the two mechanisms because of free rotation about the C—O single bond that results:

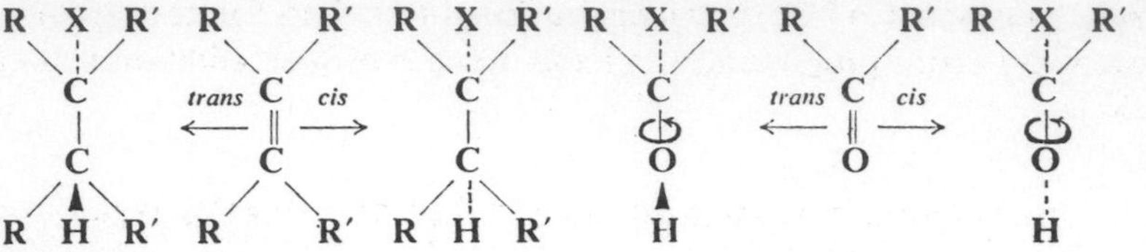

A new asymmetric centre has been introduced but, as always, a racemate will be produced. If, however, an asymmetric centre is already present, e.g. **R·CHMe·CO·Me**, and if the addition is carried out on one of the pure optical isomers, the addition is taking place in an asymmetric environment and different quantities of the two possible products are often formed. This is due to the preferential formation of that isomer whose production involves a transition state in which steric interaction is at a minimum. Thus where **R** is a large group and the reaction is, for example, addition of a Grignard reagent, the initial attack of the reagent, as a Lewis acid on oxygen, will yield a complex (XLVIII) in which the now complexed oxygen atom will be as far away from the bulky **R** group as possible. As the nucleophile now attacks the carbon atom of the carbonyl complex it will tend to move in preferentially from the side on which its approach is hindered only by hydrogen rather than by the bulkier methyl group:

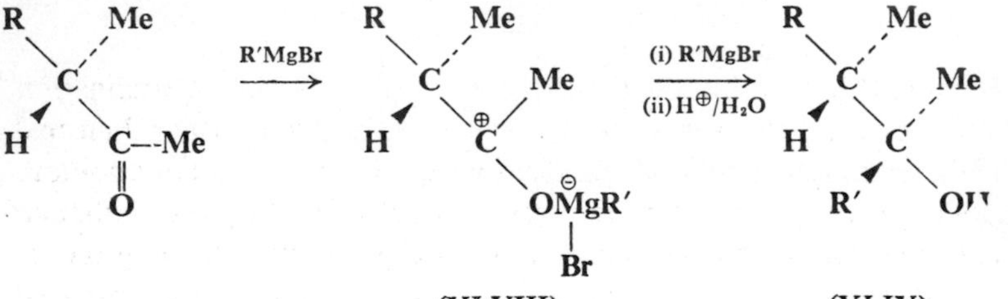

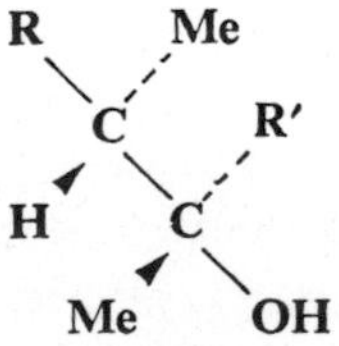

The overall result being the formation of (XLIX) rather than (L) as the major product. The above argument is essentially the working rule enunciated by Cram which has been found to forecast accurately the major product from a large number of such addition reactions.

NUCLEOPHILIC ATTACK ON CARBOXYLIC ACID DERIVATIVES

The observed sequence of reactivity, in general terms, of derivatives of acids:

$$R-C\overset{O}{\underset{Cl}{\Big\langle}} > R-C\overset{O}{\underset{OEt}{\Big\langle}} > R-C\overset{O}{\underset{NH_2}{\Big\langle}} > R-C\overset{O}{\underset{N}{\Big\langle}}\overset{R}{\underset{R}{}}$$

is in accord with the view that their characteristic reactions, e.g. alkaline hydrolysis, can be looked upon as nucleophilic addition followed by elimination:

$$R-C\underset{OH}{\overset{O}{-}}Y \rightarrow R-C\underset{OH}{\overset{O}{-}}Y \rightarrow R-C\underset{OH}{\overset{O}{-}} + {}^{\ominus}Y$$

It should be said that the difference between an addition/elimination and a direct displacement reaction may be apparent rather than real if the elimination follows sufficiently rapidly on the initial addition.

The observed reactivity sequence is due to the fact that although chlorine, oxygen and nitrogen exert an electron-withdrawing inductive effect on the carbonyl carbon atom, they all have unshared electron pairs which can interact to form a π orbital with the carbonyl carbon atom (mesomeric effect) thus decreasing the positive character of this atom and, hence, the ease with which nucleophiles will attack it. This effect increases as we go $Cl \rightarrow OEt \rightarrow NH_2 \rightarrow NR_2$, the difference between NH_2 and NR_2 being due to the inductive effect of the two alkyl groups increasing electron-availability on the nitrogen atom. There may also be a slight fall in the reactivity of any one derivative as the R group of the acid is changed from methyl to an alkyl-substituted methyl group as its slightly greater inductive effect also reduces the positive nature of the carbonyl carbon atom.

The reactivity sequence is well illustrated by the fact that acid chlorides react readily with alcohols and amines to yield esters and amides, respectively, while esters react with amines to give amides, but the simple reversal of any of these reactions on an amide though possible is usually very difficult.

(i) Base induced reactions

The example that has been the subject of most investigation is almost certainly the alkaline hydrolysis of esters. This has been shown to be a second-order reaction and, by the use of ^{18}O labelling, it is seen to involve *acyl-oxygen* cleavage (*cf*. p. 35) in most cases

$$\underset{\substack{\| \\ \text{R}\cdot\text{C}-\text{OR}'}}{\text{O}} \overset{^{18}}{\underset{}{}} \xrightarrow{\ominus\text{OH}} \underset{\substack{\| \\ \text{R}\cdot\text{C}-\text{O}^\ominus}}{\text{O}} + \text{H}-\overset{^{18}}{\text{OR}}'$$

the labelled oxygen appearing in the alcohol but not in the acid anion from the hydrolysis. The reaction is believed to proceed:

$$\underset{\substack{| \\ \text{OH}}}{\overset{\substack{\text{O} \\ \|}}{\text{R}-\text{C}-\text{OEt}}} \rightleftharpoons \underset{\substack{| \\ \text{OH}}}{\overset{\substack{\text{O} \\ \|}}{\text{R}-\text{C}-\text{OEt}}} \rightleftharpoons \underset{\substack{| \\ \text{OH}}}{\overset{\substack{\text{O} \\ \|}}{\text{R}-\text{C}}} + {}^\ominus\text{OEt} \rightarrow \underset{\substack{| \\ \text{O}^\ominus}}{\overset{\substack{\text{O} \\ \|}}{\text{R}-\text{C}}} + \text{HOEt}$$

The rate-determining step is almost certainly the initial attack of $^\ominus$OH on the ester and the overall reaction is irreversible due to the insusceptibility of $\text{R}\cdot\text{CO}_2{}^\ominus$ to attack by **EtOH** or **EtO**$^\ominus$. The alkaline hydrolysis of amides, **R·CO·NHR′**, follows a very similar course in which it is $\overset{\ominus}{\text{RNH}}$ that undergoes expulsion. The action of $^\ominus$**OR** in place of $^\ominus$**OH** on an ester results in *transesterification* to yield **R·CO·OR′** and the action of amines on esters to form amides also follows an essentially similar course:

$$\underset{\substack{| \\ \text{NH}_2\text{R}}}{\overset{\substack{\text{O} \\ \|}}{\text{R}-\text{C}-\text{OEt}}} \rightleftharpoons \underset{\substack{| \\ {}^\oplus\text{NH}_2\text{R}}}{\overset{\substack{\ominus\text{O} \\ |}}{\text{R}-\text{C}-\text{OEt}}} \overset{-\text{H}^\oplus}{\rightleftharpoons} \underset{\substack{| \\ \text{NHR}}}{\overset{\substack{\text{O} \\ \|}}{\text{R}-\text{C}-\text{OEt}}} \rightleftharpoons \underset{\substack{| \\ \text{NHR}}}{\overset{\substack{\text{O} \\ \|}}{\text{R}-\text{C}}} + {}^\ominus\text{OEt}$$

It has been shown that the conjugate base of the amine, **RNH** does not play any significant part in the amide formation. Both transesterification and amide formation from the ester are reversible, unlike alkaline ester hydrolysis, as the carboxylate anion is not involved.

The reactions of acid chlorides show a number of resemblances to the nucleophilic displacement reactions of alkyl halides, proceeding by uni- and bi-molecular mechanisms, the actual path followed being markedly affected by the polarity and ion-solvating ability of the medium (*cf.* p. 60) as well as by the structure of the substrate. The reactions of acid anhydrides are in many ways intermediate between those of acyl halides, in which the group that is ultimately expelled shows a considerable readiness to be lost as an anion, and esters in which the leaving group normally requires assistance for its ultimate displacement.

(ii) Acid catalysed reactions

Esters also undergo acidic hydrolysis, initial protonation being followed by nucleophilic attack by H_2O; acyl-oxygen cleavage is again observed:

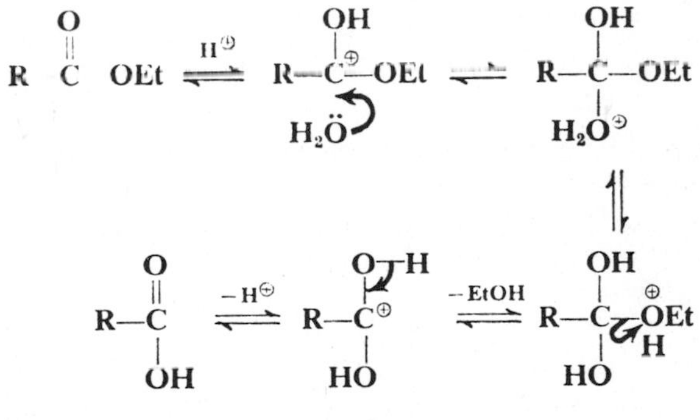

Unlike alkaline hydrolysis, the overall reaction is experimentally reversible and esters are commonly made by protonation of the carboxylic acid followed by nucleophilic attack of **ROH**, an excess of the latter normally being employed so as to displace the $\rightleftharpoons$ in the desired direction. Esters, **R·CO·OR**, also undergo ester exchange with **R'OH** under these conditions. Esters of tertiary alcohols, however, have been shown by ^{18}O labelling experiments to undergo *alkyl-oxygen* cleavage on hydrolysis

$$R_3CO-\overset{\overset{\displaystyle O}{\|}}{C}-R' \underset{}{\overset{H^{\oplus}}{\rightleftharpoons}} R_3C-O-\overset{\overset{\displaystyle HO}{|}}{\underset{\oplus}{C}}-R' \rightleftharpoons R_3C^{\oplus} + O=\overset{\overset{\displaystyle HO}{|}}{C}-R'$$

$$\Big\updownarrow H_2O$$

$$R_3COH \underset{\longrightarrow}{\overset{-H^{\oplus}}{\rightleftharpoons}} R_3C-\overset{\oplus}{\underset{\overset{\displaystyle |}{H}}{O}}H$$

reflecting the tendency of the tertiary alkyl group to form a relatively stable carbonium ion. Similar alkyl-oxygen cleavage also tends to occur with esters of secondary alcohols that yield the most stable carbonium ions, e.g. **Ph₂CHOH**. Attempts at ester-exchange with esters of such alcohols lead not surprisingly to acid + ether rather than to the expected new ester:

$$R_3CO-\overset{\overset{\displaystyle O}{\|}}{C}-R \underset{}{\overset{H^{\oplus}}{\rightleftharpoons}} R_3C^{\oplus} + O=\overset{\overset{\displaystyle HO}{|}}{C}-R$$

$$\Big\updownarrow R'OH$$

$$R_3COR' \underset{\longrightarrow}{\overset{-H^{\oplus}}{\rightleftharpoons}} R_3\overset{\oplus}{C}\underset{\overset{\displaystyle |}{H}}{O}R'$$

Acid catalysed esterification or hydrolysis is found to be highly susceptible to steric hindrance, thus 2,4,6-trimethyl-benzoic acid is insusceptible to esterification under the normal conditions (*cf.* p. 24). This is due to the fact that such relatively bulky *ortho* substituents force the initially protonated carboxyl group (LI) out of the plane of the benzene nucleus:

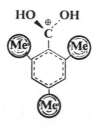

(LI)

Attack by the nucleophile, **ROH**, apparently needs to occur from a direction more or less at right angles to the plane in which the proton-ated carboxyl group lies and such line of approach is now blocked, from either side, by a bulky methyl group: no esterification thus takes place. It is found however, that if the acid is dissolved in concentrated H_2SO_4 and the resultant solution poured into cold methanol, ready esterification takes place. Similarly the methyl ester, which is highly resistant to acid hydrolysis under normal conditions, may be reconverted to the acid merely by dissolving it in concentrated H_2SO_4 and then pouring this solution into cold water.

The clue to what is taking place is provided by the fact that dissolving 2,4,6-trimethylbenzoic acid in H_2SO_4 results in a four-fold depression of the latter's freezing point due to the ionisation:

$$R \cdot CO_2H + 2H_2SO_4 \ \rightleftharpoons \ R \cdot \overset{\oplus}{C} {=} O + H_3O^{\oplus} + 2HSO_4{}^{\ominus}$$
$$(LII)$$

The resultant acylium ion (LII) would be expected to undergo extremely ready nucleophilic attack, e.g., by **MeOH**, and as $-\overset{\oplus}{C}{=}O$ has a linear structure

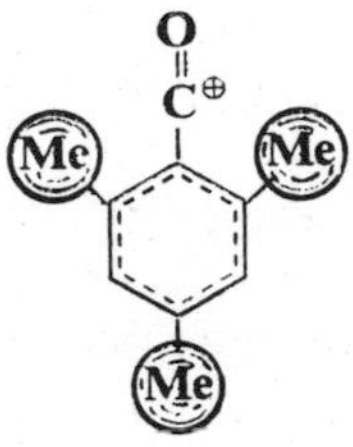

(LII)

attack by **MeOH** can take place at right angles to the plane of the benzene ring and is thus not impeded by the two flanking methyl groups. The same acylium ion is obtained on dissolving the methyl ester in H_2SO_4 and this undergoes equally ready attack by H_2O to yield the acid. Benzoic acid itself and its esters do not form acylium ions under these conditions, however. This is probably due to the fact that whereas protonated benzoic acid can stabilise itself by delocalisation (LIII),

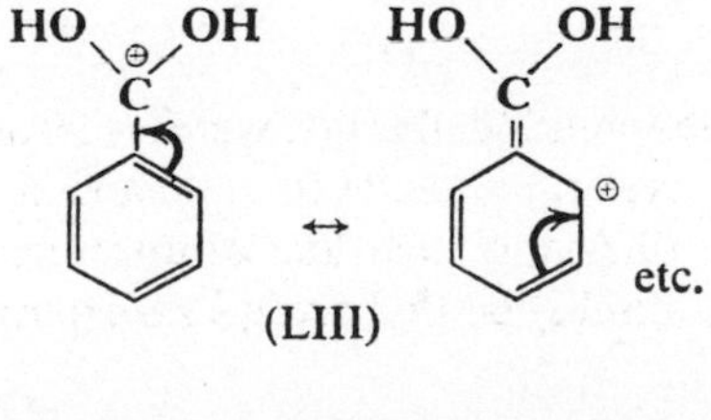

(LIII)

187

protonated 2,4,6-trimethylbenzoic acid çannot as the *o*-methyl groups prevent the atoms of the carboxyl group from lying in the same plane as the benzene ring and π orbital interaction is thus much reduced or prevented. With the acylium ion (LII) however, there is no such restriction and the substituent methyl groups can indeed further delocalise the positive charge by hyperconjugation:

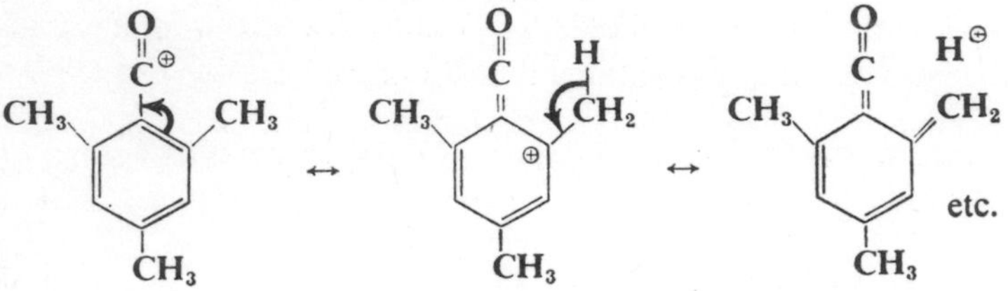

(LII)

(iii) Addition reactions of nitriles

Nitriles also undergo nucleophilic addition reactions due to:

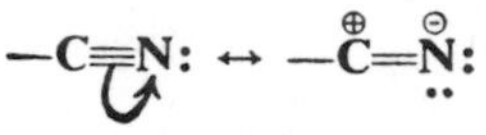

$$-C\equiv N: \leftrightarrow -\overset{\oplus}{C}=\overset{\ominus}{\underset{\cdot\cdot}{N}}:$$

Thus they will undergo acid-catalysed addition of ethanol to yield salts of imino-ethers (LIV)

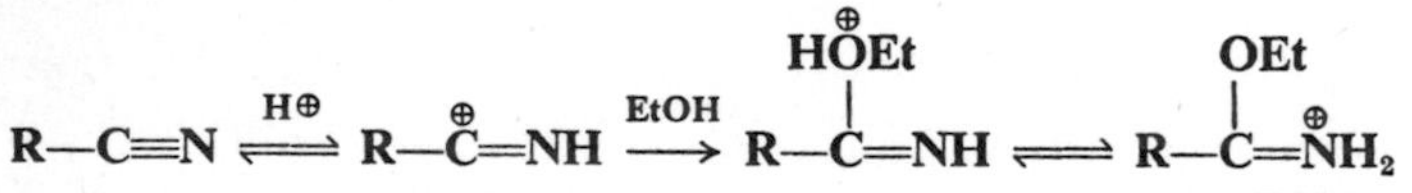

and also acid or base catalysed addition of water:

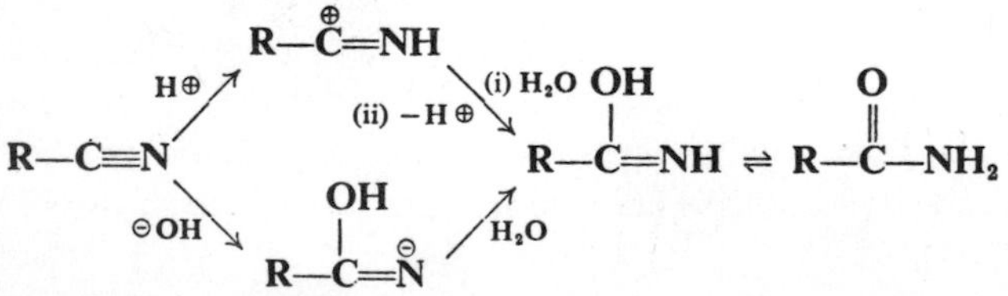

It is often difficult to isolate the amide, however, for this undergoes readier hydrolysis than the original nitrile yielding the acid or its anion.

Nitriles will, of course, also undergo addition of Grignard reagents to yield ketones and of hydrogen to yield primary amines.

188

8 ELIMINATION REACTIONS

ELIMINATION reactions are those in which two groups are removed from a molecule without being replaced by other groups. In the great majority of such reactions the groups are lost from adjacent carbon atoms, one of the groups eliminated commonly being a proton and the other a nucleophile, $Y:$ or $Y^{\ominus}$, resulting in the formation of a multiple bond:

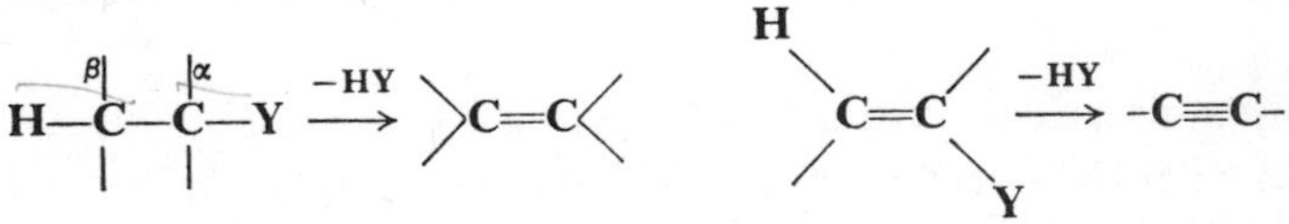

$$H-\overset{\beta|}{\underset{|}{C}}-\overset{|\alpha}{\underset{|}{C}}-Y \xrightarrow{-HY} >C=C< \qquad \overset{H}{\underset{}{}}>C=C<\xrightarrow{-HY} -C\equiv C-$$

Among the most familiar examples are the base-induced elimination of hydrogen halide from alkyl halides

$$R\cdot CH_2\cdot CH_2\cdot Hal \xrightarrow{\ominus OH} R\cdot CH=CH_2+H_2O+Hal^{\ominus}$$

the acid-catalysed dehydration of alcohols

$$R\cdot CH_2\cdot CH_2\cdot OH \xrightarrow{H^{\oplus}} R\cdot CH=CH_2+H_3O^{\oplus}$$

and the Hofmann degradation of quaternary alkylammonium hydroxides:

$$R\cdot CH_2\cdot CH_2\cdot \overset{\oplus}{N}R_3 \xrightarrow{\ominus OH} R\cdot CH=CH_2+H_2O+NR_3$$

β-ELIMINATION

The carbon atom from which Y is removed is generally referred to as the α-carbon and that losing a proton as the β-carbon, the overall process being designated as a β-elimination, though as this type of elimination reaction is by far the most common the β- is often omitted. Some estimate of the driving force behind such elimination reactions may be gained from calculations of the energy released in forming the multiple bond. Thus $>C-C< \rightarrow >C=C<$ releases approximately

189

41 kcal/mole and $\rangle C{=}C\langle \rightarrow -C{\equiv}C-$, 23 kcal/mole, though it should be emphasised that these figures may be modified considerably, depending on the structure of the original compound or the actual atoms or groups that are eliminated during the change.

Some α-elimination reactions are known, however, in which both groups are lost from the same carbon atom (p. 206) and also many reactions in which the two carbon atoms losing groups are further apart resulting in a cyclisation, as in the Dieckmann reaction (p. 178), for example:

$$
\begin{array}{c}
\text{CH}_2{-}\text{CH}_2 \\
| \quad\quad | \\
\text{CH}_2 \quad \text{CH}_2\cdot\text{CO}_2\text{Et} \\
\diagdown \quad\;\; \\
\text{C}\cdot\text{OEt} \\
\|\; \\
\text{O}
\end{array}
\xrightarrow{\ominus\text{OEt}}
\begin{array}{c}
\text{CH}_2{-}\text{CH}_2 \\
| \quad\quad | \\
\text{CH}_2 \quad \text{CH}\cdot\text{CO}_2\text{Et} + \text{EtOH} \\
\diagdown\;\;\diagup \\
\text{C} \\
\|\; \\
\text{O}
\end{array}
$$

Elimination reactions are also known in which groups are lost from atoms other than carbon: in the conversion of the acetates of aldoximes to nitriles, for example,

$$\text{Ar}\cdot\text{CH}{=}\text{N}\cdot\text{O}\cdot\text{CO}\cdot\text{Me} \xrightarrow{-\text{Me}\cdot\text{CO}_2\text{H}} \text{Ar}\cdot\text{C}{\equiv}\text{N}$$

or in the reversal of the addition reactions of carbonyl groups (p. 163)

$$
\begin{array}{c}
\text{H} \\
| \\
\text{R}{-}\text{C}{-}\text{OH} \\
| \\
\text{CN}
\end{array}
\xrightarrow{-\text{HCN}}
\begin{array}{c}
\text{H} \\
| \\
\text{R}{-}\text{C}{=}\text{O}
\end{array}
$$

though these reactions have been studied in less detail.

Elimination reactions have been shown to take place by either a uni- or a bimolecular mechanism, designated as E1 and E2 respectively, by analogy with the S_N1 and S_N2 mechanisms of nucleophilic substitution which they often accompany in, for example, the attack of base on an alkyl halide:

$$
\text{R}\cdot\text{CH}_2\cdot\text{CH}_2\text{Br}
\begin{array}{c}
\xrightarrow{\ominus\text{OH}} \quad \text{R}\cdot\text{CH}{=}\text{CH}_2 + \text{H}_2\text{O} + \text{Br}^{\ominus} \\
\qquad\qquad\qquad \textit{Elimination} \\
\\
\xrightarrow{\ominus\text{OH}} \quad \text{R}\cdot\text{CH}_2\cdot\text{CH}_2\cdot\text{OH} + \text{Br}^{\ominus} \\
\qquad\qquad\qquad \textit{Substitution}
\end{array}
$$

THE E1 MECHANISM

This mechanism, like the S_N1, envisages the rate of the reaction as being dependent on the substrate concentration only, the rate-determining stage involving this species alone. Thus with the halide, Me_3CBr

$$\text{Rate} \propto [Me_3CBr]$$

the reaction rate being measured is that of the formation of the carbonium ion (I):

$$Me_3CBr \rightarrow Me_3C^{\oplus} + Br^{\ominus}$$
$$\text{(I)}$$

Rapid, non rate-determining attack by other species in the system, for example $^{\ominus}OH$ or H_2O, can then take place. If these act as nucleophiles (i.e. electron pair donors towards carbon) the result is an overall substitution

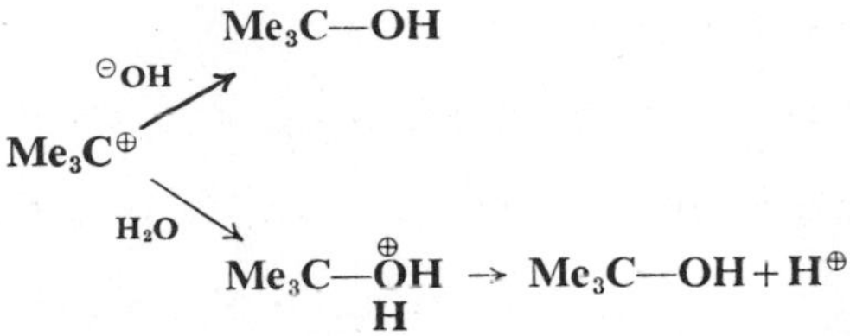

$$
\begin{array}{c}
\phantom{Me_3C^{\oplus}}\quad Me_3C\!-\!OH \\
\phantom{Me_3C^{\oplus}}\;^{\ominus}OH \nearrow \\
Me_3C^{\oplus} \\
\phantom{Me_3C^{\oplus}}H_2O \searrow \\
\phantom{Me_3C^{\oplus}}Me_3C\!-\!\overset{\oplus}{O}H \rightarrow Me_3C\!-\!OH + H^{\oplus} \\
\phantom{Me_3C^{\oplus}}\quad\; H
\end{array}
$$

while if they act as bases (electron pair donors towards hydrogen), the result is removal of a proton from a β-carbon atom to yield an olefine:

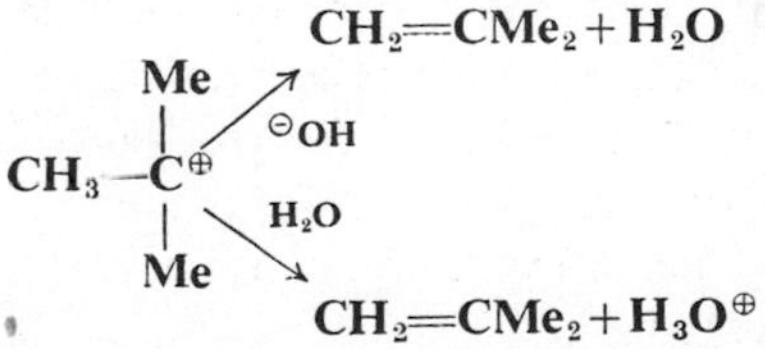

$$
\begin{array}{c}
\phantom{CH_3-C^{\oplus}}CH_2\!\!=\!\!CMe_2 + H_2O \\
Me \nearrow \\
| \;\;^{\ominus}OH \\
CH_3-C^{\oplus} \\
| \;\;H_2O \\
Me \searrow \\
\phantom{CH_3-C^{\oplus}}CH_2\!\!=\!\!CMe_2 + H_3O^{\oplus}
\end{array}
$$

Obviously conditions that promote S_N1 reactions (p. 60) will lead to E1 reactions also, for carbonium ion formation is the significant stage in both. Thus the ratio of unimolecular elimination to substitution has, in a number of cases, been shown to be fairly constant for a given alkyl group, no matter what the halogen atom or other group lost as an anion from it. This shows that E1 and S_N1 are *not* proceeding as quite separate competing reactions and lends support to a carbonium ion as the common intermediate; for otherwise the nature of the leaving group would be expected to play a significant role leading to a change in the proportion of elimination to substitution products as it was varied. Variation of the structure of the alkyl group, however, has a considerable effect on the relative amounts of elimination and substitution that take place. It is found that branching at the β-carbon atom tends to favour E1 elimination; thus $Me \cdot CH_2 \cdot CMe_2Cl$ yields only 34 per cent of olefine whereas $Me_2CH \cdot CMe_2Cl$ yields 62 per cent. The reason for this may, in part at least, be steric: the more branched the halide, the more crowding is released when it is converted to the carbonium ion intermediate, but crowding is again introduced when the latter reacts with an entering group ($\rightarrow$ substitution); by contrast, loss of a proton ($\rightarrow$ elimination) results, if anything, in further relief of strain and so is preferred. Study of a range of halides shows that this is not the whole of the story however. Hyperconjugation may also play a part, as will be seen below (p. 197) in considering the preferential formation of one isomeric olefine rather than another from a carbonium ion in which there is more than one β-carbon atom which can lose a proton. The E1 mechanism is also encountered in the acid-induced dehydration of alcohols:

$$Me_3C \cdot OH \xrightarrow{H^\oplus} Me_3C \cdot \overset{\oplus}{\underset{H}{O}H} \xrightarrow{-H_2O} Me_3C^\oplus \xrightarrow{-H^\oplus} Me_2C{=}CH_2$$

THE E2 MECHANISM

In the alternative E2 mechanism, the rate of elimination of, for example, hydrogen halide from an alkyl halide induced by $^\ominus OH$ is given by:

$$\text{Rate} \propto [R \cdot Hal][^\ominus OH]$$

This rate law has been interpreted as involving the abstraction of a proton from the β-carbon atom by base, accompanied by a *simultaneous* loss of halide ion from the α-carbon atom:

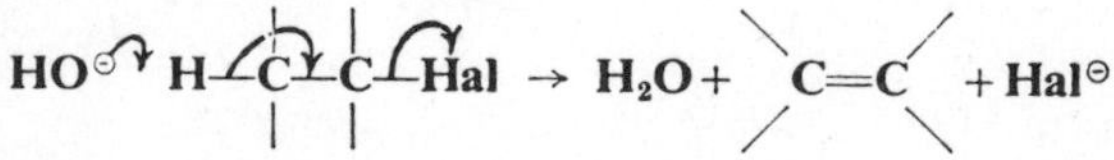

$$HO^\ominus \quad H{-}\overset{|}{\underset{|}{C}}{-}\overset{|}{\underset{|}{C}}{-}Hal \rightarrow H_2O + \;\;\diagdown\!\!\diagup\!\!C{=}C\diagdown\!\!\diagup\;\; + Hal^\ominus$$

It might be objected that there is no necessity for proton abstraction and halide elimination to be simultaneous, that initial removal

192

of proton by base followed by the faster, non rate-determining elimination of halide ion from the resultant carbanion, *as a separate step*, would still conform to the above rate law:

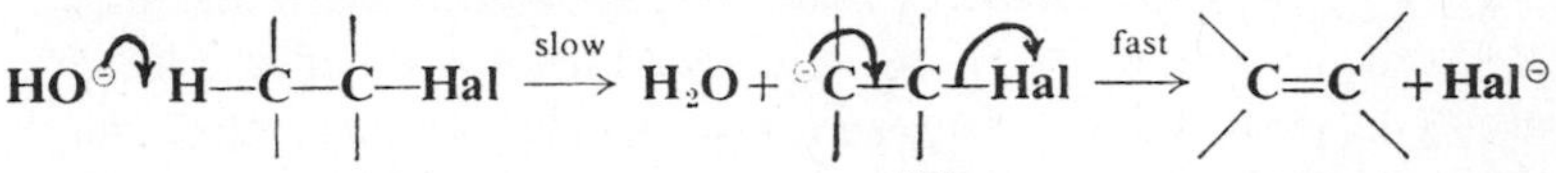

$$HO^{\ominus} \quad H—\overset{|}{\underset{|}{C}}—\overset{|}{\underset{|}{C}}—Hal \xrightarrow{slow} H_2O + \overset{|}{\underset{|}{C}}—\overset{|}{\underset{|}{C}}—Hal \xrightarrow{fast} \quad \overset{\diagdown}{\diagup}C=C\overset{\diagup}{\diagdown} + Hal^{\ominus}$$

(II)

The formation of a carbanion such as (II) with so little possibility of stabilisation (*cf.* p. 211) seems inherently unlikely and evidence against the actual participation of carbanions is provided by a study of the reaction of β-phenylethyl bromide (III) with $^{\ominus}$**OEt** in **EtOD**. Carbanion formation would, *a priori*, be expected to be particularly easy with this halide because of the stabilisation that can occur by delocalisation of the negative charge via the π orbitals of the benzene nucleus (III*a*):

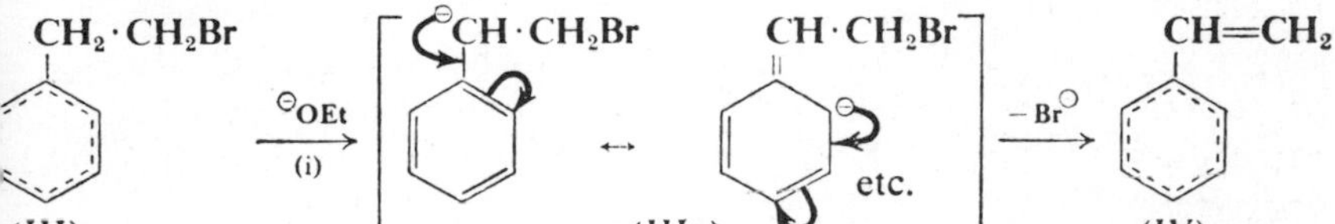

Carrying out the reaction in **EtOD** should lead to the formation of **Ph·CHD·CH$_2$Br** by reversal of (i) and this in its turn should yield some **Ph·CD=CH$_2$** as well as **Ph·CH=CH$_2$** in the final product. If, however, the reaction in **EtOD** is stopped short of completion, i.e. while some bromide is still left, it is found that neither this nor the styrene (IV) formed contain any deuterium. Thus a carbanion is not formed as an intermediate even in this especially favourable case, and it seems likely that in such E2 eliminations, abstraction of proton, formation of the double bond and elimination of the halide ion or other nucleophile normally occur simultaneously as a concerted process.

Though this is generally true there is, in the highly special case of the elimination reactions of trichloro- and some dihalo-ethylenes, some evidence that carbanions are involved:

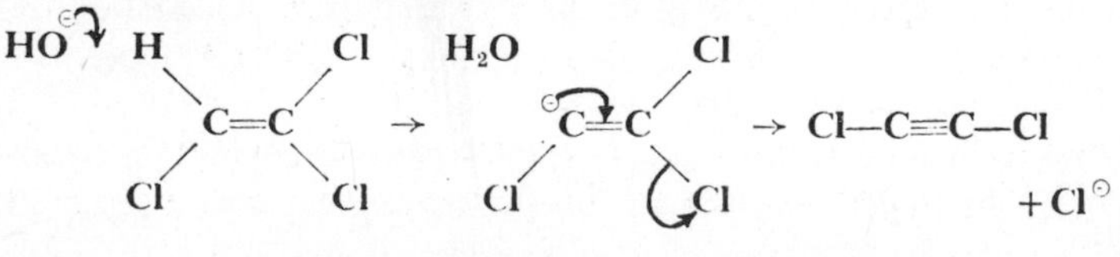

193

we have thus now seen elimination reactions in which the **H—C** bond is broken *before* (trichlorethylene above), *simultaneously* with (**E2**), and *after* (**E1**), the **C—Y** bond.

An **E2** elimination will naturally be promoted, relative to an S_N2 substitution, by any features that serve to stabilise the resultant olefine or, more particularly, the transition state leading to it; a good example is substitution by phenyl on the β-carbon atom:

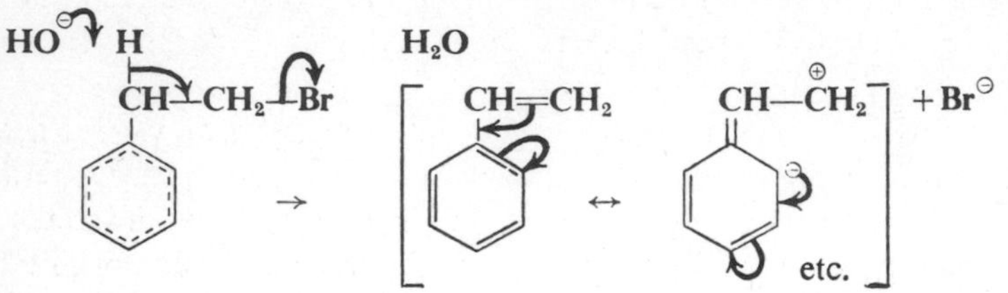

(i) Stereospecificity in E2 eliminations

It has been found that **E2** elimination reactions exhibit a high degree of stereospecificity, proceeding considerably more readily if the groups to be eliminated are *trans* to each other.

Thus it is found that of the stereoisomerides of benzene hexachloride, $C_6H_6Cl_6$, one isomer loses **HCl** 10,000 times more slowly than any of the others and this is found to be the one (V) that has *no* adjacent chlorine and hydrogen atoms *trans* with respect to each other:

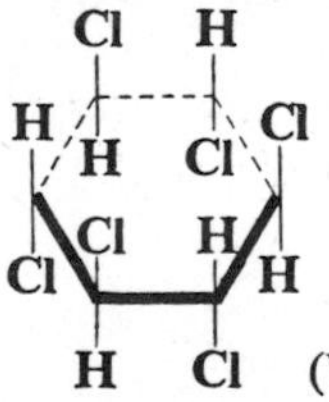

This stereospecificity brings to mind the characteristic 'attack from the back' of the S_N2 reaction (p. 65) and probably results from the electrons released by removal of the proton from the β-carbon atom attacking the α-carbon atom, 'from the back', with displacement of the leaving group (VI → VII, see p. 195).

It has been suggested that it is necessary that the attacking atom of the base, the hydrogen atom to be eliminated, C_β, C_α and the other

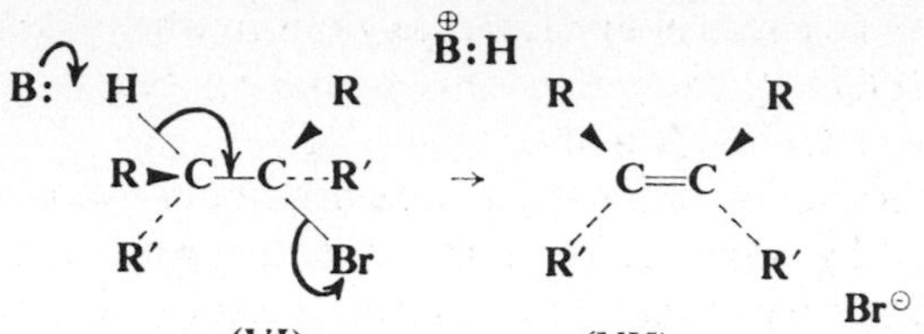

(VI)   (VII)

leaving group should all be coplanar in the transition state in an E2 elimination, but other factors may well play a part in securing stereospecific *trans* elimination.

In the case of benzene hexachloride (V) considered above, restricted rotation about a single bond prevents the leaving groups from getting into this preferred orientation and elimination is thus inhibited: a similar phenomenon is also encountered in the conversion of suitably substituted olefines to acetylenes for the same reason. Thus base-induced elimination of HCl to yield acetylene dicarboxylic acid (VIII) proceeds much more rapidly from chlorofumaric acid (IX) than from chloromaleic acid (X),

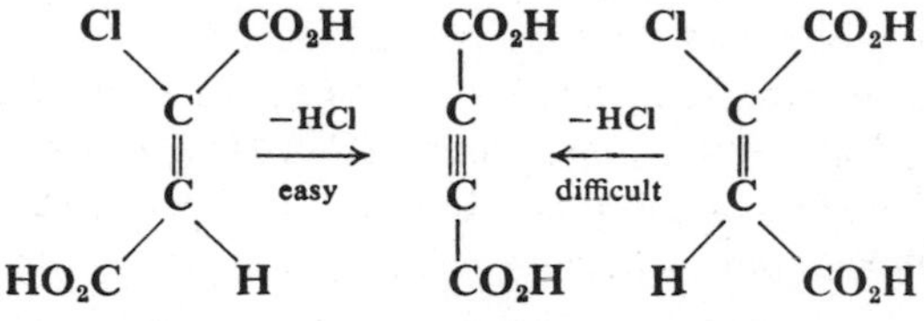

(IX)   (VIII)   (X)

as does the elimination of acetic acid from *anti-* as compared with *syn*-benzaldoxime acetate (XI and XII, respectively) to yield benzonitrile (XIII):

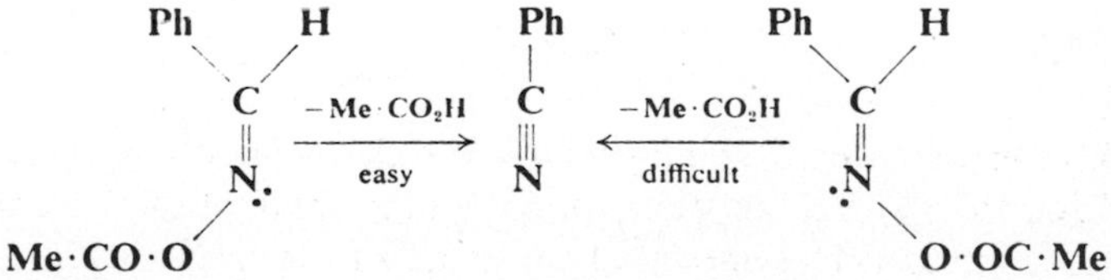

(XI)   (XIII)   (XII)

A fact that may be made use of in assigning configurations to a pair of stereoisomeric aldoximes.

195

In cases such as (V) where a sterospecific *trans* elimination cannot take place *cis* elimination can be made to occur, though normally only with considerable difficulty. The reaction then probably proceeds via carbanion formation (*cf*. p. 193), a route that normally involves a considerably higher free energy of activation than that via a normal E2 'trans' transition state with consequent increase in the severity of the conditions necessary to effect it.

In compounds in which no restriction of rotation about a bond is imposed, the leaving groups will arrange themselves so as to be as far apart as possible when they are eliminated. Thus *meso* dibromostilbene (XIV) yields a *cis* unsaturated compound (XV), whereas the corresponding DL-compound (XVI) yields the *trans* form (XVII):

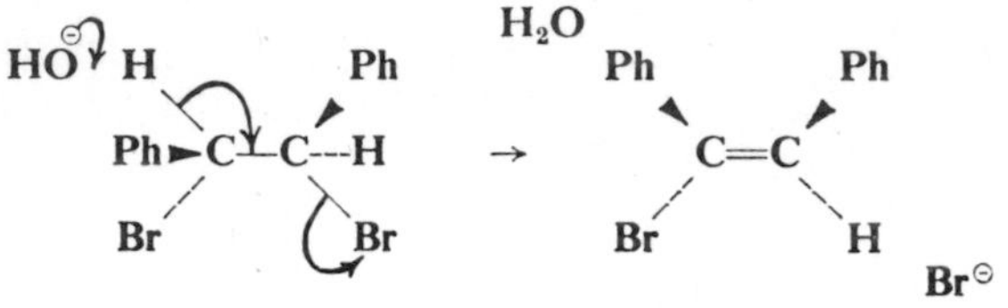

(XIV)   (XV)

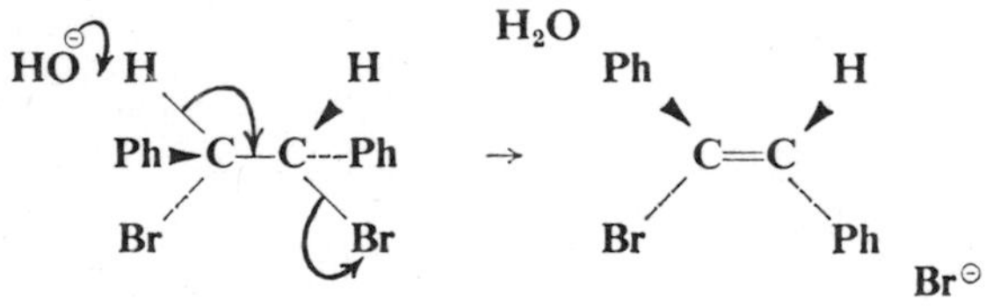

(XVI)   (XVII)

A 'ball-and-stick' model will be found useful for confirming the true stereochemical course of these eliminations.

(ii) Orientation in E2 eliminations: Saytzeff v. Hofmann

The situation frequently arises in base-induced elimination reactions of alkyl halides, $R \cdot Hal$, and alkyl *onium* salts, such as $R \cdot \overset{\oplus}{N}R'_3$ and $R \cdot \overset{\oplus}{S}R'_2$, that more than one olefine can, in theory, be produced:

$$R \cdot CH_2 \cdot CH_2 \cdot CH{=}CH_2$$
$$(XIX)$$

$$R \cdot CH_2 \cdot CH_2 {-} CH {-} CH_3 \overset{\nearrow}{\underset{\searrow}{}}$$
$$\underset{Y}{|}$$

$$R \cdot CH_2 \cdot CH{=}CH \cdot CH_3$$

$$(XVIII) \qquad\qquad (XX)$$

$$(Y = Hal, \overset{\oplus}{NR'_3} \text{ or } \overset{\oplus}{SR'_2})$$

Three factors, essentially, influence the relative proportions of olefine that are actually obtained: (*a*) the relative ease with which a proton can be lost from the available, alternative β-positions, (*b*) the relative stability of the olefines, once formed (more accurately, the relative stability of the transition states leading to them), and (*c*) steric effects (arising from substitution at the β-positions, the size of the leaving group Y, and the size of the base used to induce the elimination). The relative significance of, and conflict between, these factors has led in the past to the empirical recognition of two opposing modes of elimination: *Saytzeff elimination*, leading preferentially to the olefine carrying the *larger* number of alkyl groups, i.e. (XX) rather than (XIX), and *Hofmann elimination*, leading preferentially to the olefine carrying the *smaller* number of alkyl groups, i.e. (XIX) rather than (XX).

The Saytzeff mode, which is principally encountered in the elimination reactions of halides, is easy to justify in terms of (*b*) for the olefine carrying the larger number of alkyl groups can be shown by combustion experiments to be more stable than its less alkylated isomers, a fact that may be explained by hyperconjugation. Thus (XX) has *five* C—H linkages adjacent to the double bond compared with only *two* for (XIX) and a greater number of forms such as (XXI) can therefore contribute to its stabilisation by delocalisation (*cf.* p. 21):

$$R \cdot CH_2 \cdot \overset{\ominus}{CH} {-} CH{=}CH_2 \ \overset{\oplus}{H}$$
$$(XXI)$$

It should be remembered, however, that it is the hyperconjugative effect of alkyl groups in the E2 transition state rather than in the end product, that is of prime importance: alkyl hyperconjugation with the forming double bond lowers the energy of that transition state in which it occurs and hence favours its preferential formation.

At first sight, therefore, it might be concluded that the Saytzeff mode of elimination was the normal one and the Hofmann mode merely an occasional, abnormal departure therefrom. In fact, it is the latter that predominates with onium salts. Thus on heating (XXII), it is largely ethylene, rather than propylene, that is obtained despite the greater stability (due to hyperconjugation) of the latter:

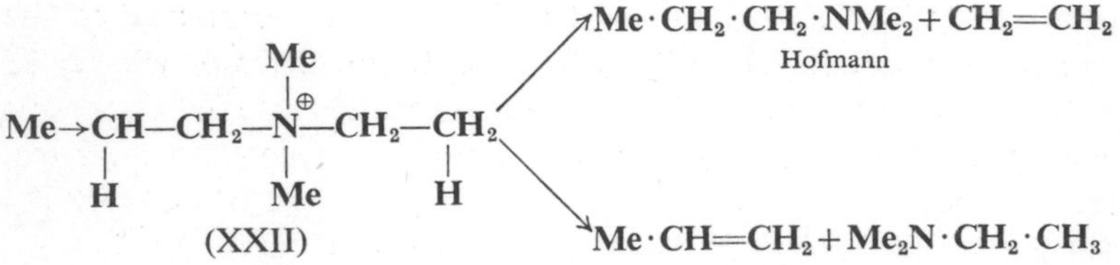

$$
\text{Me} \rightarrow \overset{\displaystyle \text{Me}}{\underset{\displaystyle \text{H}}{\text{CH}}} - \text{CH}_2 - \overset{\displaystyle \oplus}{\underset{\displaystyle \text{Me}}{\text{N}}} - \text{CH}_2 - \overset{}{\underset{\displaystyle \text{H}}{\text{CH}_2}}
$$

$$\nearrow \text{Me} \cdot \text{CH}_2 \cdot \text{CH}_2 \cdot \text{NMe}_2 + \text{CH}_2{=}\text{CH}_2 \quad \text{Hofmann}$$

$$\searrow \text{Me} \cdot \text{CH}{=}\text{CH}_2 + \text{Me}_2\text{N} \cdot \text{CH}_2 \cdot \text{CH}_3$$

(XXII)

This can be explained by assuming that, in this case, (*a*) is of prime importance: the inductive effect of the methyl group in the n-propyl substituent causes a lowering of the acidity of the hydrogens attached to the β-carbon atom in this group and thus leads to preferential removal of a proton from the β-carbon atom of the ethyl substituent which is not so affected.

Thus it could be claimed that in Satyzeff elimination the hyperconjugative effects of alkyl groups are in control while in Hofmann elimination it is their inductive effects that predominate. But this leaves unanswered the question as to what causes the shift from the former mode to the latter. As has already been observed, Hofmann elimination is more common in the elimination reactions of onium salts and undoubtedly groups such as $\overset{\oplus}{\text{R}_3\text{N}}-$ and $\overset{\oplus}{\text{R}_2\text{S}}-$ will be much more potent in promoting acidity in β-hydrogens by their inductive effects than will halogen atoms so that the relative acidity of the β-hydrogen atoms could well come to be the controlling influence in the reaction. But this is not the whole of the story: another obvious difference is that the groups eliminated from onium compounds are usually considerably *larger* than those lost in the elimination reactions of halides; so much so that the preferential formation of that E2 transition state in which there is least crowding becomes imperative, even though this may not be the one favoured by hyperconjugative stabilisation.

The importance of the steric factor has been confirmed in a number of ways. Thus increase in the size of the leaving group in a compound of given structure leads to a corresponding increase in the proportion of Hofmann product produced, and the same result is observed when branching is introduced into the structure of a compound (with halides as well as onium salts) that might be expected to lead to increasing crowding in the E2 transition state. Perhaps most cogent of all, an increase in the proportion of Hofmann product is seen when the size of the initiating base is increased. Thus in the dehydro-bromination of $Me \cdot CH_2CMe_2Br$ the change from $Me \cdot CH_2 \cdot O^{\ominus}$ $\rightarrow Me_3C \cdot O^{\ominus} \rightarrow EtMe_2C \cdot O^{\ominus} \rightarrow Et_3C \cdot O^{\ominus}$ leads to formation of the Hofmann product, $Me \cdot CH_2 \cdot C(Me){=}CH_2$, in yields of 29, 72, 78 and 89 per cent respectively. The importance that steric factors can play in deciding which type of elimination will result can, perhaps, best be seen by comparing the transition states (XXIII) and (XXIV) for the two modes of E2 elimination from $R \cdot CH_2 \cdot CMe_2X$:

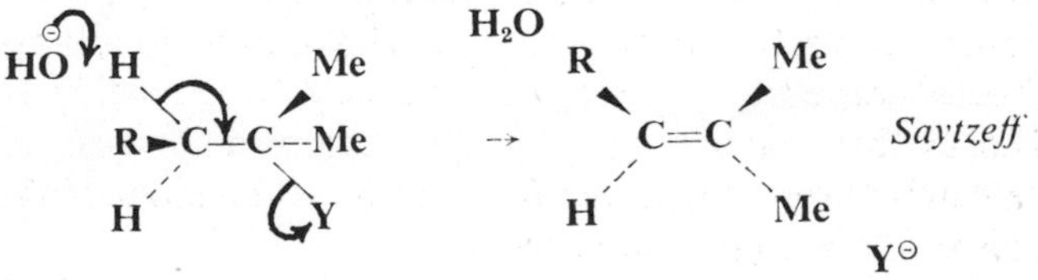

(XXIII)

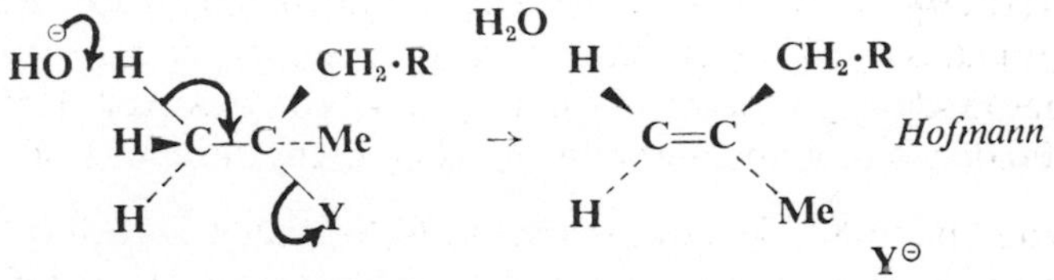

(XXIV)

It can be seen that if **Y** is large, and especially if **R** is large as well, transition state (XXIV) will be favoured over (XXIII) as, in the former, **R** is much better able to get out of **Y**'s way; as indeed will be the case if $^{\ominus}OH$ is replaced by a bulkier base, **Y** being the same distance away in both cases but **R** being much less of a hindrance in (XXIV) than in (XXIII).

The classical Hofmann elimination reaction has been of the utmost value in structure elucidation, particularly in the alkaloid field. Any basic nitrogen atom present is converted to the quaternary salt by exhaustive methylation and the corresponding quaternary hydroxide then heated. Removal of the nitrogen from the compound by one such treatment indicates that it was present in a side-chain while elimination after two or three treatments, indicates its presence in a saturated ring or at a ring junction, respectively. The resultant olefine is then investigated so as to shed further light on the structure of the original natural product.

The presence of a phenyl group on the α- or β-carbon atom very markedly promotes E2 eliminations because of its stabilisation of the resultant olefine by delocalisation. The effect is more marked in the β- than in the α-position, however, because of the additional effect of phenyl in increasing the acidity of the β-hydrogens from this position and so facilitating their removal. The effect is sufficiently pronounced so as to control the orientation of elimination, resulting in the Saytzeff mode even with onium salts:

$$Ph \cdot CH_2 \cdot CH_2 \overset{\overset{\displaystyle Me}{|}}{\underset{\underset{\displaystyle Me}{|}}{N}}{}^{\oplus} \hspace{-0.5em}- CH_2 \cdot CH_3 \xrightarrow{\ominus OH} Ph \cdot CH{=}CH_2 + Me_2N \cdot CH_2 \cdot CH_3$$

A vinyl group will have much the same effect.

A steric limitation on elimination reactions is codified in Bredt's rule that reactions which would introduce a double bond on to a bridgehead carbon atom in bicyclic systems do not take place. Thus (XXV) does not yield the bicycloheptene (XXVI) which has, indeed, never been prepared:

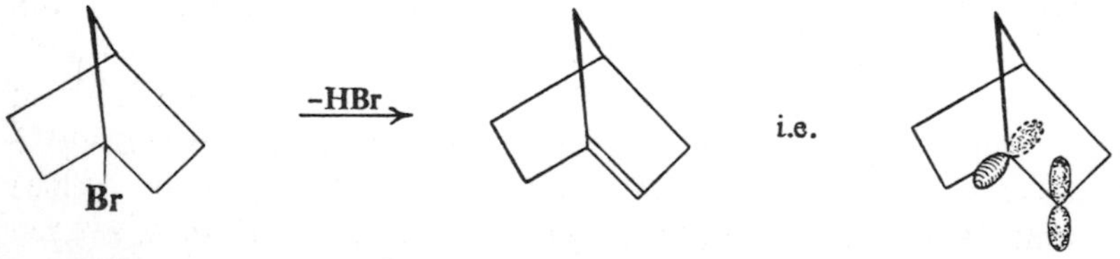

(XXV) (XXVI)

This is presumably due to the bond angles required by the rigid ring system preventing any degree of attainment of the planar configuration required for significant π bonding to the adjacent carbon atom. It should be emphasised in this connection that the Bredt rule does not thus apply to compounds such as (XXVII)

(XXVII)

nor to compounds in which the bridge comprises five or more atoms, for a sufficiently planar conformation can then be attained without too great an overall straining of the system.

Finally, it should be emphasised that in E1 eliminations where more than one possible olefine can be obtained, the product which is stabilised by hyperconjugation will almost always predominate. The leaving group, having already departed, can exert no influence, and the process is completed by loss of proton from that β-position which will yield the stabler olefine, i.e. (XXVIII) rather than (XXIX):

$$R \cdot CH_2 \cdot CMe_2Br \rightarrow R \cdot CH_2 \cdot \overset{\oplus}{C} \overset{\nearrow \; Me}{\underset{\searrow Me}{}} \quad \begin{matrix} \nearrow & R \cdot CH{=}CMe_2 \\ & (XXVIII) \\ \\ \searrow & R \cdot CH_2 \cdot C(Me){=}CH_2 \\ & (XXIX) \end{matrix}$$

ELIMINATION v. SUBSTITUTION

Broadly speaking changes in reaction conditions that would be expected to promote an S_N2 reaction at the expense of an S_N1 (p. 60) will promote the often competing E2 reaction at the expense of an E1 and, of course, vice-versa. The features that will favour overall elimination at the expense of substitution are a little more subtle, though some passing attention has already been paid to them; thus in the E1 reaction reference has already been made to steric features. The more crowded a halide, for example, the greater is the release of strain when the carbonium ion intermediate is formed. This strain is reintroduced on attack by a nucleophile but is not increased, and may even be further reduced, on removal of a proton to yield the olefine. The sheer steric effect here becomes merged with other features, however, for increasing alkyl substitution may also lead to the possible formation of olefines that are increasingly stabilised by hyperconjugation, thus favouring their formation at the expense of substitution. This, of course, is the reason for the greater tendency of tertiary and secondary, as compared with primary, halides to undergo unimolecular elimination rather than substitution reactions whatever the reagent employed:

$$
\begin{array}{ccc}
\mathbf{R \cdot CH_2 \cdot CH_2 \cdot Hal} & \mathbf{R \cdot CH_2 \cdot CHMe \cdot Hal} & \mathbf{R \cdot CH_2 \cdot CMe_2 \cdot Hal} \\
\downarrow & \downarrow & \downarrow \\
\mathbf{R \cdot CH{=}CH_2} & \mathbf{R \cdot CH{=}CH \cdot Me} & \mathbf{R \cdot CH{=}CMe_2}
\end{array}
$$

$$\mathbf{R \cdot CH_2 \cdot CH_2 \cdot Hal} \,<\, \mathbf{R \cdot CH_2 \cdot CHMe \cdot Hal} \,<\, \mathbf{R \cdot CH_2 \cdot CMe_2 \cdot Hal}$$

In bimolecular reactions also it is found that increasing alkyl substitution favours elimination at the expense of substitution, for while it retards S_N2 because of overcrowding in the transition state that would lead to substitution, it promotes E2 because of the hyperconjugative stabilisation of the incipient olefine in the alternative transition state that would lead to elimination.

One of the most potent factors influencing the elimination/substitution ratio with a given substrate, however, is change of mechanism from uni- to bimolecular. The $E1/S_N1$ product ratio will be fixed, as will the $E2/S_N2$ ratio, and, provided the reaction is proceeding by a purely uni- *or* bimolecular mechanism, the ratio will thus be independent of the concentration of, e.g. $^{\ominus}OH$. As the concentration of $^{\ominus}OH$ is increased, however, there will come a changeover from an initially unimolecular to a bimolecular mechanism, a changeover that takes place quite suddenly with strong bases such as $^{\ominus}OH$ and which leads to a different, usually higher, proportion of the elimination product. This reflects the well-known use of high concentrations of strong bases for the actual preparation of olefines.

It might be expected that the reagent employed would be of great significance in influencing the relative amounts of $E2/S_N2$ in a particular system, for basicity (i.e. electron pair donation to hydrogen) and nucleophilicity (i.e. electron pair donation to carbon) do not run wholly in parallel in a series of reagents, $Y^{\ominus}$ or $Y:$. Thus the use of tertiary amines, e.g. triethylamine, rather than $^{\ominus}OH$ or $^{\ominus}OEt$ for converting halides to olefines depends on the amines being moderately strong bases but weak nucleophiles while the latter reagents are powerful nucleophiles as well as being strong bases. The particular preparative value of pyridine for this purpose, despite its being a considerably weaker base than simple tertiary amines, R_3N: (*cf.* p. 55), arises in part at least from the stability of the pyridinium cation once formed; reversal of the abstraction of $H^{\oplus}$ by pyridine is thus unlikely. Reagents such as $^{\ominus}SR$ which show the widest divergences between their basicity and nucleophilicity, are in general too weak bases to be of much value in inducing elimination reactions.

Careful investigation has shown that where substitution and elimination reactions compete in a given system, elimination normally has the higher activation energy and is thus the more favoured of the two by rise in temperature: a fact that has long been recognised in preparative chemistry.

EFFECT OF ACTIVATING GROUPS

Thus far we have only considered the effect of alkyl, and occasionally aryl, substituents in influencing elimination reactions, but a far more potent influence is exerted by strongly electron-withdrawing groups such as $-NO_2$, $>SO_2$, $-CN$, $>C=O$, $-CO_2Et$, etc., in facilitating eliminations. Their influence is primarily on increasing the acidity of the β-hydrogen atoms:

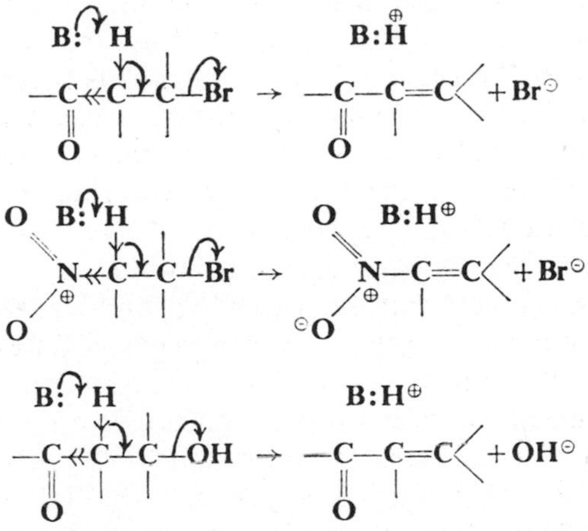

(XXX)

The reactions can proceed by a one- or a two-stage mechanism depending on whether the removal of proton and the other leaving group is concerted or whether an intermediate anion is actually formed. An added effect of substituents like the above is, of course, to stabilise such an anion by delocalisation

203

$$-\overset{\overset{\displaystyle O}{\|}}{C}-\overset{\ominus}{C}-\overset{|}{C}-Y \quad \leftrightarrow \quad -\overset{\overset{\displaystyle \ominus O}{|}}{C}=\overset{|}{C}-\overset{|}{C}-Y$$

$$\underset{\overset{|}{\underset{\ominus O}{\oplus}}}{N}\overset{\ominus}{-}\overset{|}{C}-\overset{|}{C}-Y \quad \leftrightarrow \quad \underset{\overset{|}{\underset{\ominus O}{\oplus}}}{N}=\overset{|}{C}-\overset{|}{C}-Y$$

but it is not certain that such intermediates are formed as a matter of course in all these reactions, however. An interesting example above is the way in which the $\searrow$C=O group makes possible a *base*-induced elimination of water from the aldol (XXX), whereas the elimination of water from a compound not so activated is nearly always acid-induced (*cf*. p. 174).

It has been suggested that a good deal of the driving force for the elimination reactions of suitably substituted carbonyl compounds is due to the product being conjugated and so able to stabilise itself by delocalisation (XXXI):

$$\underset{\underset{B:\,H}{|}}{Me\cdot CH}{-}CH{-}CH{=}O \quad \rightarrow \quad \left[\begin{array}{c} Me\cdot \overset{\oplus}{CH}{-}CH{=}CH{-}\overset{\ominus}{O} \\ \updownarrow \\ Me\cdot CH{=}CH{-}CH{-}O \end{array} \right] \quad \text{(XXXI)}$$

$$\|$$

$$Me\cdot CH{-}CH{-}CH{-}O$$

That this is not the most important feature, however, is revealed by the difference in behaviour exhibited by 1- and 2-halogenoketones (XXXII and XXXIII, respectively). Both could eliminate hydrogen halide to yield the same olefine (see p. 205) as the product of reaction, so if its stability were the prime driving force little difference would be expected in their rates of elimination. In fact (XXXIII) eliminates very much more rapidly than (XXXII) suggesting that the main effect of the carbonyl substituent is in increasing the acidity of the hydrogens on the adjacent carbon atom: this is the one that loses proton in (XXXIII) but *not* in (XXXII). It is indeed found to be generally true that the elimination-promoting effect of a particular

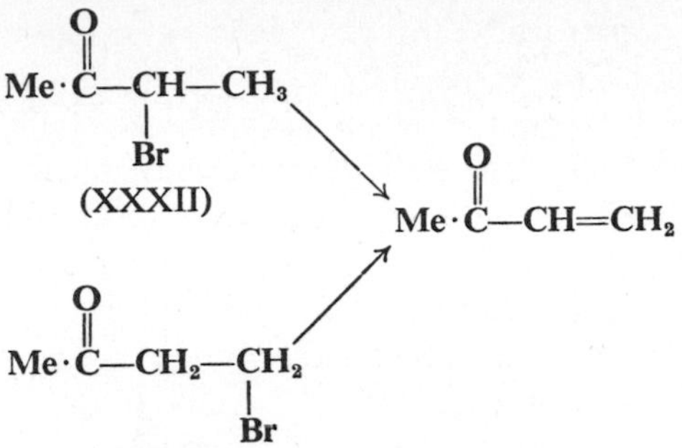

$$Me \cdot \overset{O}{\overset{\|}{C}} - \underset{Br}{\overset{|}{CH}} - CH_3$$

(XXXII)

$$Me \cdot \overset{O}{\overset{\|}{C}} - CH = CH_2$$

$$Me \cdot \overset{O}{\overset{\|}{C}} - CH_2 - \underset{Br}{\overset{|}{CH_2}}$$

(XXXIII)

electron-withdrawing substituent is much greater in the β- than in the α-position. The influence of such activating groups is often sufficiently great to lead to the elimination of more unusual leaving groups such as **OR** and **NH$_2$**.

A rather interesting intramolecular reaction of this type is the loss of **CO$_2$** and bromide ion from the anion of a β-bromo-acid, for example cinnamic acid dibromide (XXXIV):

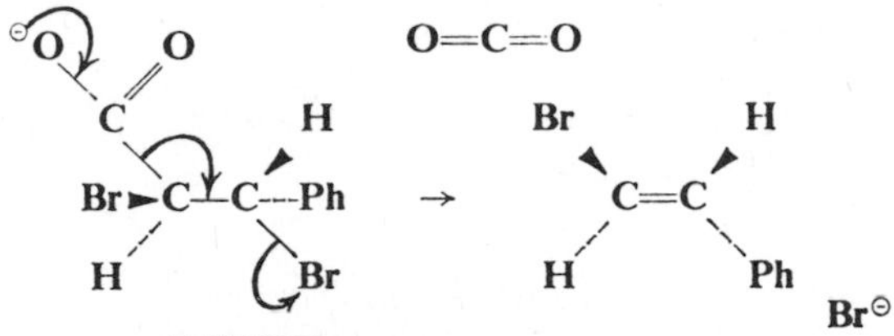

(XXXIV)

DEBROMINATION

Attention has been confined so far almost wholly to reactions in which one of the leaving groups has been hydrogen, and although these are the most common and important eliminations, the dehalo-genation of 1,2-dihalides, particularly bromides, also has some mechanistic and preparative interest. The most common classical reagents for the purpose are metals such as zinc:

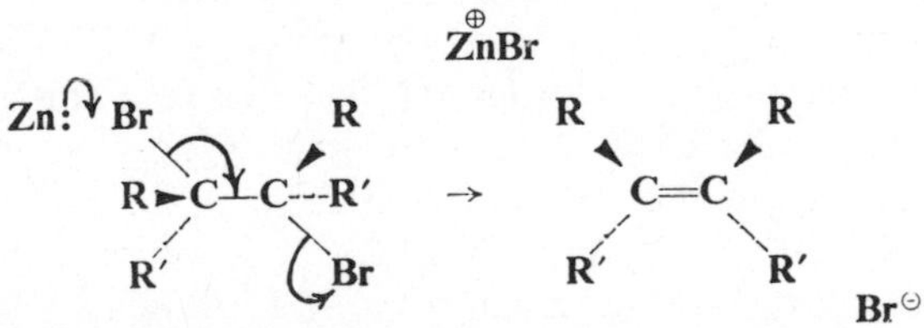

205

Apart from any preparative or diagnostic value the reaction may have, it is of course the above state of affairs that makes impossible the preparation of Grignard and similar organo-metallic compounds from 1,2-dihalides. Similar eliminations can be made to proceed with 1,2-halo-esters and 1,2-halo-ethers. The reactions normally proceed stereospecifically *trans*.

A similar stereospecificity has been observed in the preparatively more useful debromination of 1,2-dibromides by iodide ion. The kinetic law followed is of the form:

$$\text{Rate} \propto [I^{\ominus}] [1,2\text{-dibromide}]$$

but there is reason to believe that the mechanism, in some cases at least, is a little more complicated than that with zinc, involving an S_N2 displacement to form the bromo-iodide as the rate-determining step

$$I^{\ominus} + BrCH_2 \cdot CH_2Br \rightarrow Br^{\ominus} + ICH_2 \cdot CH_2Br$$

followed by attack by iodide ion on the iodine atom that has been introduced:

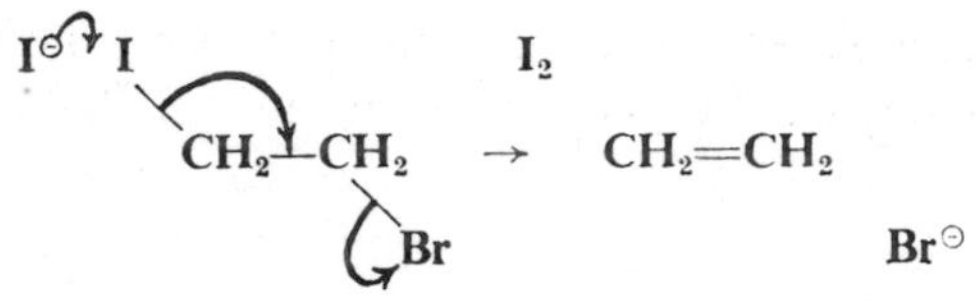

Practical use is made of this reaction in the purification of olefines. The usually crystalline dibromides are purified by recrystallisation and the pure olefine then regenerated, as above, under extremely mild conditions.

α-ELIMINATION

A small number of cases are known of the elimination of hydrogen halide where both atoms are lost from the same carbon: these are known as α-elimination reactions. The best known example occurs in the hydrolysis of chloroform with strong base:

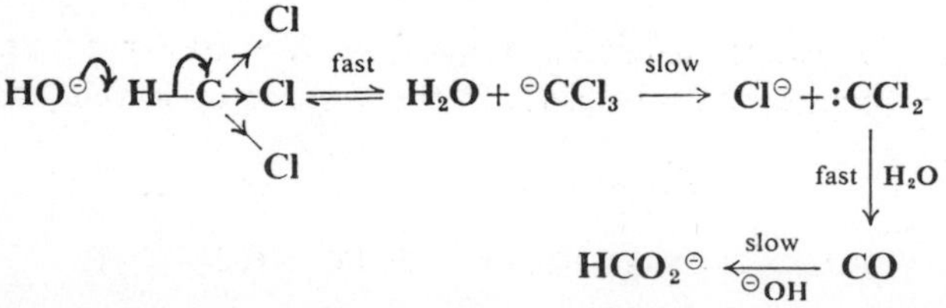

Hydrogen halide is lost in a two-stage process to yield carbon dichloride, a carbene (*cf.* p. 93), as an intermediate in the hydrolysis. The latter then reacts with water to yield **CO** as the primary product and this then undergoes further slow attack by $^\ominus$**OH** to yield formate anion. The initial attack on **H** rather than **C** (with expulsion of **Cl**$^\ominus$) by $^\ominus$**OH** is due to the electron-withdrawing effect of the chlorine atoms increasing the acidity of the hydrogen atom, a property which is reflected in its ready base-catalysed exchange with deuterium in **D$_2$O**. Confirmation of the existence of **CCl$_2$**, i.e. of an α-elimination, is provided by the introduction of substrates into the system that would be expected to react readily with such a species; thus olefines have been converted into cyclo-propane derivatives:

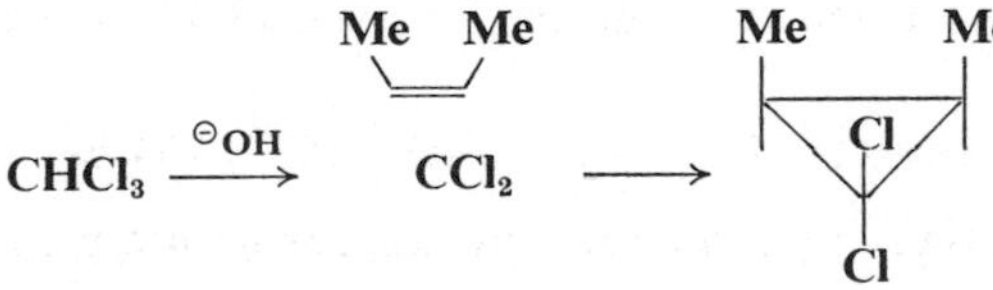

$$\text{CHCl}_3 \xrightarrow{\ ^\ominus\text{OH}\ } \text{CCl}_2 \longrightarrow$$

Another example of an α-elimination is seen in the action of potassium amide on 2,2-diphenylvinyl bromide (**XXXV**):

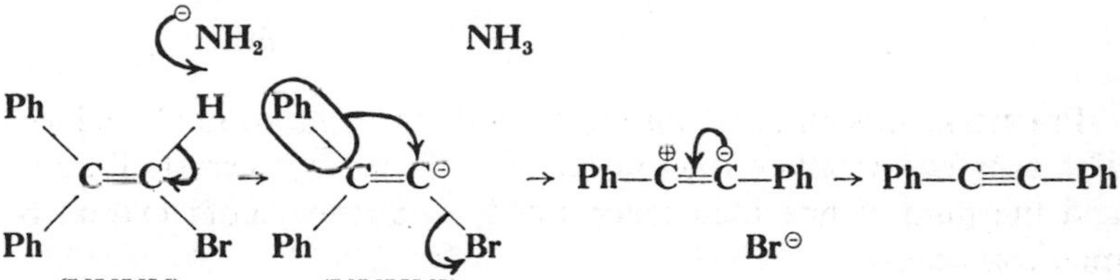

$$\text{Ph}-\overset{\oplus}{\text{C}}\overset{\ominus}{=}\text{C}-\text{Ph} \to \text{Ph}-\text{C}\equiv\text{C}-\text{Ph}$$

(XXXV)   (XXXVI)   Br$^\ominus$

Whether the whole process proceeds as a concerted operation or whether the carbanion (**XXXVI**) is actually formed, as such, is not known however.

CIS-ELIMINATION

A number of esters, particularly acetates, are known to undergo elimination reactions on heating, in the absence of solvent, to yield olefines:

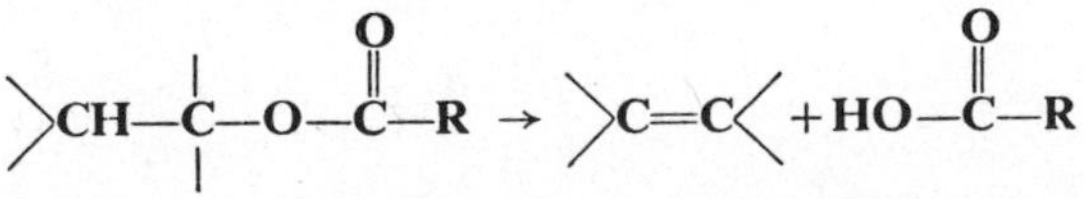

$$\underset{\displaystyle}{\text{>CH}-\overset{\text{O}}{\overset{\|}{\text{C}}}-\text{O}-\overset{\text{O}}{\overset{\|}{\text{C}}}-\text{R}} \to \text{>C=C<} + \text{HO}-\overset{\text{O}}{\overset{\|}{\text{C}}}-\text{R}$$

The kinetic law followed is of the form

$$\text{Rate} \propto [\text{ester}]$$

and the reaction is believed to proceed through a cyclic transition state (XXXVII):

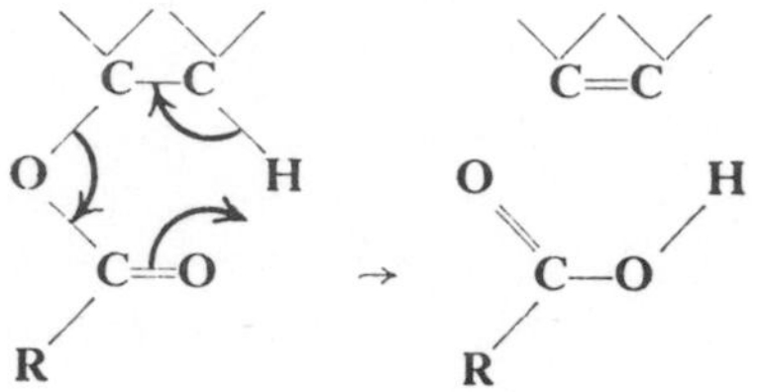

(XXXVII)

The strongest evidence in favour of such a route is that these eliminations are found to proceed stereospecifically *cis* in contrast to the almost universal *trans* eliminations that we have encountered to date. It is thus probable, in most cases, that the breakage of the C—H and C—O bonds occur simultaneously, but the fact that small, though detectable, amounts of *trans* elimination have been observed to take place suggests that in some cases the latter breaks before the former, leading to the transient formation of an ion pair, which can then undergo mutual reorientation. It seems unlikely in such cases that radicals, rather than ion pairs, are ever formed as the reactions appear to be unaffected by either radical initiators or inhibitors (*cf.* p. 231).

A very closely analogous elimination is the Chugaev reaction which involves the indirect conversion of an alcohol to the corresponding olefine via pyrolysis of the methyl xanthate (XXXVIII) obtained by the action of $CS_2/^{\ominus}OH/MeI$ on the original alcohol:

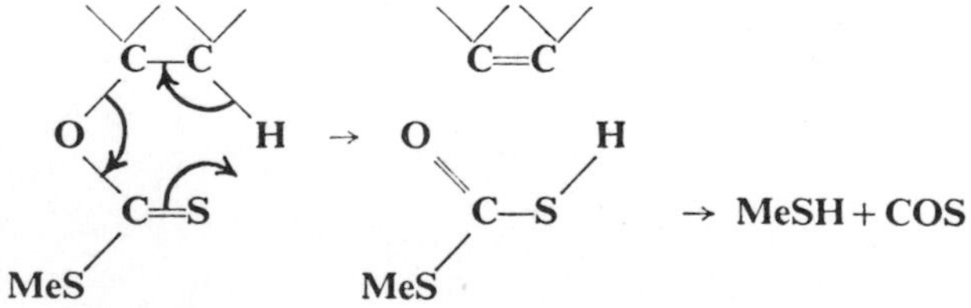

$$\rightarrow \text{MeSH} + \text{COS}$$

(XXXVIII)

This reaction has the greater preparative value as the pyrolysis may be successfully carried out at lower temperatures (*ca.* 150° as compared with *ca.* 400° for acetates); the advantage of both, compared with other methods of olefine formation in complicated structures, is their relative freedom from simultaneous molecular rearrangement.

A more recent elimination reaction of preparative value analogous to the above is that of tertiary amine oxides (XXXIX); this elimination proceeds smoothly at even lower temperatures with the elimination of a dialkylhydroxylamine (XL):

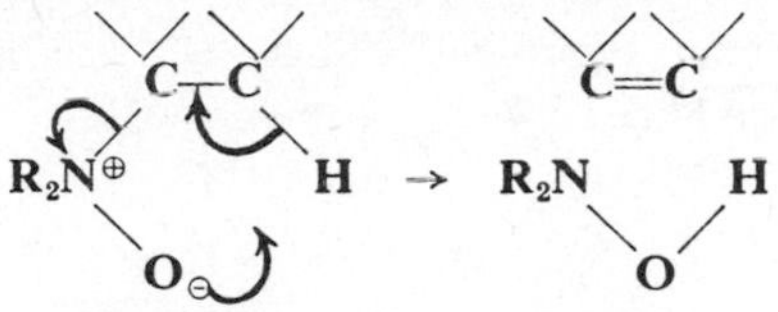

(XXXIX)   (XL)

9 CARBANIONS AND THEIR REACTIONS

SOME organic compounds are known which function as acids, in the classical sense, in that a proton is liberated from a C—H bond, the resultant conjugate base (I) being known as a *carbanion*:

$$\diagdown\!\!\overset{\curvearrowright}{\underset{\diagup}{C}}\!\!-\!H \;\rightleftharpoons\; \diagdown\!\!\underset{\diagup}{C}^{\ominus}+H^{\oplus}$$

(I)

This tendency is, not surprisingly, but little marked with aliphatic hydrocarbons for the C—H bond is a fairly strong one and there is normally no structural feature that either promotes acidity in the hydrogen atom or that leads to significant stabilisation of the carbanion with respect to the original undissociated molecule (*cf.* p. 40); thus methane has been estimated to have a pK_a of ≈ 58, compared with $4\cdot76$ for acetic acid. Triphenylmethane (II), however, whose related carbanion (III) can be stabilised by delocalisation

$$\text{Ph}_3\text{C}\!-\!\text{H} \rightleftharpoons \text{H}^{\oplus} + \left[\text{Ph}_2\overset{\ominus}{\text{C}} \!\!\diagdown\!\!\bigcirc \;\leftrightarrow\; \text{Ph}_2\text{C}\!\!=\!\!\bigcirc \;\; \text{etc.} \right]$$

(II)   (III)

is a much stronger acid ($pK_a \approx 25$) by relative, if not by absolute, standards. The presence of one or more strongly electron-withdrawing groups has an even more marked effect; thus tricyanomethane (IV)

$$(\text{NC})_3\text{C}\!-\!\text{H} \;\rightleftharpoons\; \text{H}^{\oplus} + \left[(\text{NC})_2\overset{\ominus}{\text{C}}\!\!-\!\text{C}\!\!\equiv\!\!\text{N} \;\leftrightarrow\; (\text{NC})_2\text{C}\!\!=\!\!\text{C}\!\!=\!\!\overset{\ominus}{\text{N}} \;\; \text{etc.} \right]$$

(IV)

approaches the mineral acids in strength. The cumulative effect of introducing successive cyano groups is of interest here for acetonitrile (V), containing only one such group, still has a pK_a as high as 25:

$$\text{CH}_3\!-\!\text{C}\!\!\equiv\!\!\text{N} \;\rightleftharpoons\; \text{H}^{\oplus} + \left[\overset{\ominus}{\text{CH}}_2\!\!-\!\text{C}\!\!\equiv\!\!\text{N} \;\leftrightarrow\; \text{CH}_2\!\!=\!\!\text{C}\!\!=\!\!\overset{\ominus}{\text{N}} \right]$$

(V)

FORMATION OF CARBANIONS

Although the tendency of many C—H bonds to such spontaneous dissociation is but low, structural factors, particularly the presence of electron-withdrawing groups, can lead to sufficient acidity in such hydrogen atoms as to permit their ready removal by bases:

$$R \cdot CH_2 \cdot X + B: \rightarrow R \cdot \overset{\ominus}{C}H \cdot X + \overset{\oplus}{B}:H$$

Thus the following compounds

$$EtO_2C \cdot CH_2 \cdot CO_2Et \qquad\qquad CH_3 \cdot NO_2$$
$$\text{(VI)} \quad pK_a \approx 15 \qquad\qquad\qquad pK_a = 10 \cdot 2$$

$$Me \cdot CO \cdot CH_2 \cdot CO_2Et \qquad\qquad Me \cdot CO \cdot CH_2 \cdot CO \cdot Me$$
$$\text{(VII)} \quad pK_a = 10 \cdot 1 \qquad\qquad \text{(VIII)} \quad pK_a = 8 \cdot 8$$

readily yield carbanions in this way which are, with similar ones, of the utmost importance as intermediates in a wide variety of reactions. Other compounds which lose a proton less readily may sometimes be converted into carbanions by treatment with very strong bases in anhydrous media, as is the case with acetylene ($pK_a = 26$):

$$HC \equiv CH \xrightarrow[\substack{\text{liq.} \\ NH_3}]{\ominus NH_2} HC \equiv C^{\ominus} + NH_3$$

Where the actual isolation or ready detection of a carbanion as such is not feasible, the transient formation of such a species may be inferred from dissolving the compound, in the presence of base, in D_2O or EtOD and observing if deuterium becomes incorporated. Thus chloroform is found to undergo such an incorporation:

$$HCCl_3 \underset{H_2O}{\overset{-H^{\oplus}}{\rightleftharpoons}} {}^{\ominus}CCl_3 \underset{-D^{\oplus}}{\overset{D_2O}{\rightleftharpoons}} DCCl_3$$

STABILITY OF CARBANIONS

As might be expected, the effect of electron-withdrawing (i.e. *activating*) groups is most pronounced when they can exert a mesomeric as well as an inductive effect; for then they not only promote acidity in the relevant hydrogen atom but stabilise the resultant carbanion as well. Thus a carbonyl or a nitro-group will be more effective than, for example, $\overset{\oplus}{N}R_3$, CF_3, etc.:

$$R-\underset{H}{CH} \rightarrow \underset{\underset{O^\ominus}{\overset{\oplus}{}}}{N} \overset{O}{\underset{}{}} \quad \overset{B:}{\rightarrow} \quad \left[R-\overset{\ominus}{CH} - \underset{\underset{O^\ominus}{\overset{\oplus}{}}}{N} \overset{O}{\underset{}{}} \quad \leftrightarrow \quad R-CH=\underset{\underset{O^\ominus}{\overset{\oplus}{}}}{N} \overset{O^\ominus}{\underset{}{}} \right]$$

$$R-\underset{H}{CH} \rightarrow \overset{O}{\underset{}{C}} - R \quad \overset{B:}{\rightarrow} \quad \left[R-\overset{\ominus}{CH} - \overset{O}{\underset{}{C}} - R \quad \leftrightarrow \quad R-CH=\overset{O^\ominus}{\underset{}{C}} - R \right]$$

$$R-\underset{H}{C} \rightarrow \overset{F}{\underset{\underset{F}{}}{C}} \rightarrow F \quad \overset{B:}{\rightarrow} \quad R-\overset{\ominus}{CH}-CF_3$$

The smaller pK_a, and hence greater stability of the carbanion, of acetylacetone (VIII) compared with ethyl acetoacetate (VII), and of the latter compared with diethyl malonate (VI) arises from the carbonyl group in a ketone being more effective at electron-withdrawal and delocalisation than the carbonyl group in an ester. This springs from the occurrence in the latter of

which lowers the effectiveness of the $>C=O$ group at withdrawing electrons from the rest of the molecule. The decreasing activating effect of $-CO\cdot Y$ on going $-CO\cdot H \rightarrow -CO\cdot R \rightarrow -CO\cdot OR \rightarrow -CO\cdot NH_2 \rightarrow -CO\cdot O^\ominus$ being due to Y becoming more electron-donating as the series is traversed.

An interesting carbanion, the cyclopentadienyl anion (IX)

(IX)

owes its considerable stability to the fact that, in the system, a total of six π electrons is available and these can distribute themselves so as to form delocalised π orbitals covering all five carbon atoms, leading to the quasi-aromatic structure (IX*a*):

(IX*a*)

The stability of the ion is reflected in the acidity of cyclopentadiene itself, demonstrating the readiness with which the latter is prepared to lose a proton in order to attain a more stable state as a carbanion. The quasi-aromaticity cannot be demonstrated by electrophilic substitution, for attack by $X^{\oplus}$ would merely lead to direct combination with the ion, but true aromatic character (Friedel-Crafts reactions, etc.) is shown by the remarkable series of extremely stable compounds such as *ferrocene* (X), (obtained by attack of (IX) on metallic halides such as $FeCl_2$)

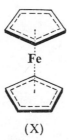

(X)

in which the metal atom is held by π bonds in a kind of molecular 'sandwich' between two cyclopentadienyl structures.

STEREOCHEMISTRY OF CARBANIONS

The question of whether a simple carbanion of the form $R_3C^{\ominus}$ is planar or pyramidal (like a tertiary amine with which it is isoelectronic) cannot be answered with any degree of confidence. A pyramidal structure would seem more likely but direct experimental confirmation thereof is somewhat inadequate. As soon as one or more of the groups attached to the carbanion carbon atom are capable of stabilising the ion by delocalisation, then limitations are imposed on its configuration because of the near coplanarity necessary if significant delocalisation via the overlapping of parallel p orbitals is to take place. This will apply to the three bonds to the carbanion carbon in the triphenyl-methyl anion (XI)

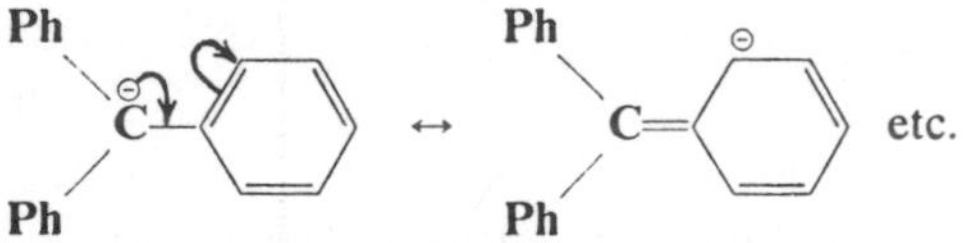

(XI)

and also in cases where the carbanion carbon is adjacent to $>C=O$ NO_2, etc. A good example of this is seen in the compound (XII):

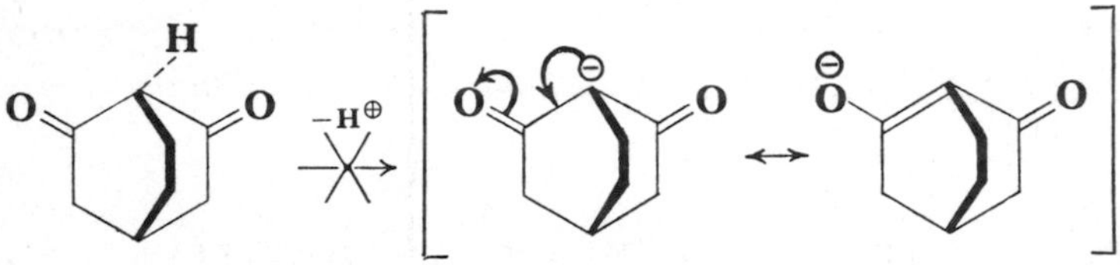

(XII)   (XIII)

Here the hydrogen, despite being flanked by *two* carbonyl groups, shows little sign of acidity (*cf.* $Me \cdot CO \cdot CH_2 \cdot CO \cdot Me$) because the carbanion (XIII) that would be obtained by its removal is unable to stabilise itself by delocalisation owing to the rigid ring structure preventing the p orbitals on the two carbon atoms involved from becoming parallel; significant overlapping thus could not take place and the carbanion does not form.

In simpler examples, it is well known that asymmetric centres carrying a hydrogen atom adjacent to carbonyl groups (e.g. XIV) are very readily racemised in the presence of base. This can, never-theless, *not* be taken as entirely unambiguous confirmation of the planar nature of any carbanion intermediate involved (e.g. XV), despite its likelihood on other grounds, for the enol form (XVI) which *must* be planar will also be in equilibrium with it:

$$\underset{R'}{\overset{H}{\underset{\diagdown}{R \blacktriangleright \overset{*}{C}}} - \overset{O}{\overset{\|}{C}} - \quad \underset{(XIV)}{\rightleftharpoons}} \quad \overset{B:}{\qquad} \quad \underset{R'}{\overset{R}{\underset{\diagdown}{C}} \overset{O}{\overset{\|}{C}} -}{\underset{(XV)}{}}$$

B:H ⊕ ↕   ↕ B:H ⊕

$$\underset{R'}{\overset{R}{\underset{\diagdown}{C}} = \overset{O^\ominus}{\underset{}{C}} - \quad \underset{(XV)}{\rightleftharpoons}} \quad \overset{B:}{\qquad} \quad \underset{R'}{\overset{R}{\underset{\diagdown}{C}} = \overset{OH}{\underset{|}{C}} -}{\underset{(XVI)}{}}$$

CARBANIONS AND TAUTOMERISM

The enolisation mentioned above, is, of course, an example of the larger phenomenon of *tautomerism*: the existence of two or more readily interconvertible structures that differ only in electron distribution and in the position of a mobile atom. The mobile atom concerned is hydrogen in the overwhelming majority of examples, in which case the phenomenon is known as *prototropy*; familiar examples are ethyl acetoacetate and aliphatic nitro-compounds:

$$\underset{Keto}{Me \cdot \overset{O}{\overset{\|}{C}} - CH_2 \cdot CO_2Et} \quad \rightleftharpoons \quad \underset{Enol}{Me \cdot \overset{OH}{\overset{|}{C}} = CH \cdot CO_2Et}$$

$$\underset{Pseudo\text{-}acid\ form}{R \cdot CH_2 - \overset{O}{\underset{\oplus}{N}} \diagdown_{O^\ominus}} \quad \rightleftharpoons \quad \underset{Aci\text{-}form}{R \cdot CH = \overset{OH}{\underset{\oplus}{N}} \diagup^{O^\ominus}}$$

(i) Concerted *v.* stepwise mechanism

These interconversions could, in theory, take place by either a stepwise or a concerted mechanism depending on whether the abstraction of hydrogen from one atom takes place prior to, or simultaneously with, the addition of hydrogen to the other; both types are encountered in practice. If the conversion is base-induced, the former mechanism would, in suitable cases, involve the participation of a carbanion, while the second would not. Many common examples, including β-keto-esters, β-diketones, aliphatic nitro-compounds, i.e. the common keto/enol systems and their relatives, are believed to involve the stepwise mechanism

$$
\underset{\text{(XVII)}}{\overset{\displaystyle \text{B:} \overset{\frown}{} \text{H}}{\underset{\displaystyle \underset{O}{\overset{|}{R-C-C-R'}}}{}}} \rightleftharpoons
\left[
\begin{array}{c}
R-C=C-R' \\
\overset{|}{\underset{\ominus}{O}} \\
\updownarrow \\
R-\overset{\ominus}{C}-C-R' \\
\overset{|}{\underset{O}{}}
\end{array}
\right]_{\text{(XVIII)}}
\xrightleftharpoons{H^{\oplus}}
\underset{\text{(XIX)}}{\overset{|}{R-C=C-R'} \atop OH}
$$

and, as might be expected, the more stable the carbanion intermediate (XVIII), i.e. the more acidic the substrate from which it may be derived, the more is the stepwise mechanism favoured with respect to the concerted one. The above example enables emphasis to be laid on the distinction between tautomerism and mesomerism which so often apparently leads to confusion. Thus (XVII) and (XIX) are tautomers, the so-called keto and enol forms respectively, and are quite distinct chemical entities. Although often readily interconvertible *both* can, in suitable cases (e.g. ethyl acetoacetate), actually be isolated and characterised. By contrast, the intermediate involved in their inter-conversion, the carbanion (XVIII), is a *single species*, a mesomeric hybrid of the two hypothetical structures written, neither of which has any real existence. It is, of course, a commonplace to find a pair of tautomers underlain, as it were, by a carbanion stabilised by delocalisation in this way.

By contrast, the tautomerisation of a number of compounds of the form $R_2CH-N=CR'_2$, the azomethines, has been shown to proceed via the concerted mechanism. Thus tautomerisation of (XX) → (XXI) has been carried out in EtOD with EtO$^{\ominus}$ as catalyst, and been found to result in deuterium exchange as well as tautomerisation. A concerted mechanism must lead to deuteration and tautomerisation proceeding at exactly the same rate for the latter cannot take place without the former

$$
\begin{array}{c}
\text{EtO}\overset{\ominus}{} \text{H} \\
p\text{-Ph}\cdot\text{C}_6\text{H}_4\blacktriangleright\text{C} \overset{|}{\underset{*}{}}\text{N}{=}\text{C} \\
\text{Ph} \quad \text{(XX)} \quad \text{H} \\
\text{D} \\
\overset{\curvearrowright}{\text{OEt}}
\end{array}
\rightleftharpoons
\begin{array}{c}
\text{EtO} \\
\text{H} \\
p\text{-Ph}\cdot\text{C}_6\text{H}_4 \quad \text{Ph} \\
\text{C}{=}\text{N}{-}\underset{*}{\text{C}}\blacktriangleleft\text{H} \\
\text{Ph} \quad \text{(XXI)} \quad \text{D} \\
\overset{\ominus}{\text{OEt}}
\end{array}
$$

whereas with a stepwise mechanism

$$
\begin{array}{c}
\text{EtO}\overset{\ominus}{} \text{H} \quad \text{Ph} \\
p\text{-Ph}\cdot\text{C}_6\text{H}_4\blacktriangleright\underset{*}{\text{C}}{-}\text{N}{=}\text{C} \\
\text{Ph} \quad\quad\quad \text{H} \\
\text{(XX)}
\end{array}
$$

$$
\text{EtOD} \Big\Updownarrow \overset{\ominus}{\text{OEt}}
\quad \text{(i)}
$$

$$
\left[
\begin{array}{c}
p\text{-Ph}\cdot\text{C}_6\text{H}_4 \quad\quad \text{Ph} \\
\overset{\ominus}{\text{C}}{-}\text{N}{=}\text{C} \\
\text{Ph} \quad\quad \text{H}
\end{array}
\leftrightarrow
\begin{array}{c}
p\text{-Ph}\cdot\text{C}_6\text{H}_4 \quad\quad \text{Ph} \\
\text{C}{=}\text{N}{-}\text{C} \\
\text{Ph} \quad\quad \overset{\ominus}{}\text{H}
\end{array}
\right]
$$

$$
\overset{\ominus}{\text{OEt}} \Big\Updownarrow \text{EtOD}
\quad \text{(ii)}
$$

$$
\begin{array}{c}
p\text{-Ph}\cdot\text{C}_6\text{H}_4 \quad\quad \text{Ph} \\
\text{C}{=}\text{N}{-}\underset{*}{\text{C}}\blacktriangleleft\text{H} \\
\text{Ph} \quad\quad\quad \text{D} \\
\text{(XXI)}
\end{array}
$$

deuteration can take place *without* tautomerisation by the reversal of (i) and so should proceed the faster. In practice, both *are* found to take place at the same rate so, knowing the reaction is reversible, it can be said with confidence that it proceeds via the concerted mechanism.

Which mechanism is at work in a particular case is also influenced by the medium involved, polar solvents, not surprisingly, favouring the stepwise mode. Although not relevant to carbanions, it should perhaps be emphasised that keto-enol interconversions can be catalysed by acids, e.g. **HA**, as well as by bases. This is another example of *general* acid catalysis (*cf.* p. 161):

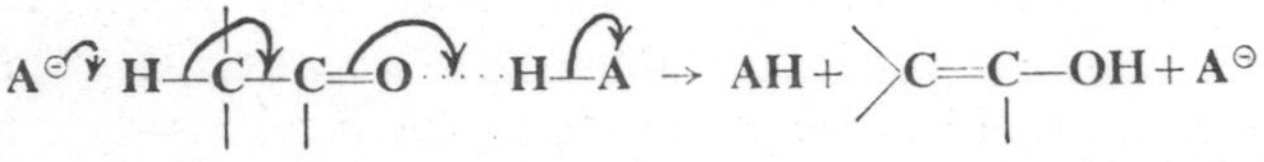

$$A^{\ominus} \; H \text{---} \overset{|}{\underset{|}{C}} \text{---} C \text{==} O \; \cdots \; H \text{---} A \;\to\; AH + \;\rangle C \text{==} C \text{---} OH + A^{\ominus}$$

The role played above by the acid anion, $A^{\ominus}$, can equally well be played by a solvent molecule in many cases.

(ii) Rate of tautomerisation

It should perhaps be emphasised that in the tautomerisations about which we have been speaking a **C—H** bond must undergo dissociation; so that although a number of the conversions are fairly rapid they are not like ionic reactions where no such bond-breaking is involved. The actual rates of a number of these conversions can, as implied in the last section, be followed by measuring the rate at which the compounds involved will incorporate deuterium from **D$_2$O, EtOD**, etc. When base is added to a pure tautomer it is, in the more familiar examples, usually the rate of formation of the anionic intermediate that is being observed and, on subsequent acidification, the rate of re-formation of one or both tautomers from the ion:

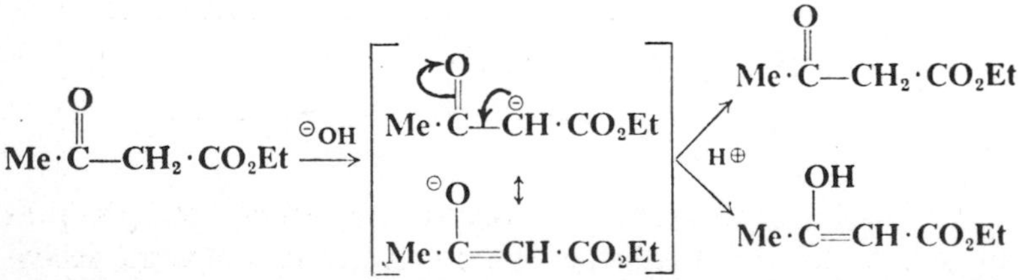

The correlation of relative rates of tautomerisation with structure is not quite so simple as might have been expected and while it is broadly true that structural features leading to greater acidity, i.e. readier loss of proton, lead to more rapid reactions, this is by no means universally the case.

(iii) Structure and position of equilibrium

Most information is available on this subject for keto/enol tautomers and their near relatives and we shall confine ourselves to them. Normally speaking, the occurrence of a significant amount of the enol form in the keto/enol equilibrium mixture requires the presence of a group or groups capable of stabilising the enol by delocalisation of the π electrons of its carbon–carbon double bond:

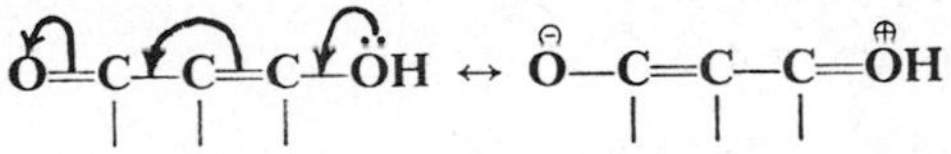

$$\overset{\ominus}{O}=C-C=C-\overset{..}{O}H \leftrightarrow \overset{\ominus}{O}-C=C-C=\overset{\oplus}{O}H$$

Thus the proportion of enol in acetone is almost negligible while with a β-diketone it is present as the major species:

	Percentage enol
Me·CO·CH$_3$	0·00025
Me·CO·CH$_2$·CO$_2$Et (XXII)	7·5
Me·CO·CHPh·CO$_2$Et (XXIII)	30
Me·CO·CH$_2$·CO·Me (XXIV)	80

The relative effectiveness to this end of a second keto group as opposed to the $>$C=O of an ester group is seen in comparing acetylacetone (XXIV) with ethyl acetoacetate (XXII), and the further delocalisation effected, by the introduction of a phenyl group on the methylene carbon atom by comparing ethyl acetoacetate (XXII) with its α-phenyl derivative (XXIII).

Another factor is also contributing to the stabilisation of the enol compared with the keto form in such species, however, namely internal hydrogen bonding:

219

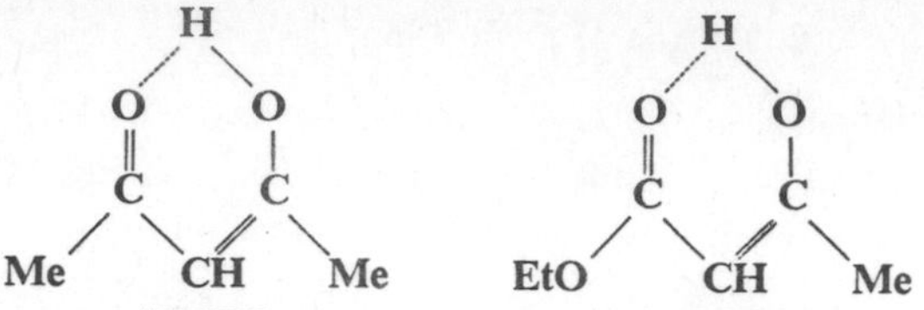

$$\underset{\text{(XXIV)}}{\text{Me}\diagdown\underset{\displaystyle \text{CH}}{\text{C}}\diagup\text{Me}} \qquad \underset{\text{(XXII)}}{\text{EtO}\diagdown\underset{\displaystyle \text{CH}}{\text{C}}\diagup\text{Me}}$$

Apart from the further stabilisation thereby effected, this hydrogen bonding leads to a decrease in the polar character of the enol and a compact, 'folded up' conformation for the molecule (by contrast to the extended conformation of the keto form) with the rather surprising result that, where the keto and enol forms can actually be separated, the latter usually has the lower boiling point of the two despite its hydroxyl group. The part played by such hydrogen bonding in effecting stabilisation is seen by comparing the proportion of the enol form of acetylacetone (XXIV) in water and in a non-hydroxylic solvent such as hexane. In the latter there is 92 per cent enol whereas in the former where the keto form can also form hydrogen bonds—with the solvent water molecules—the proportion of the enol is down to 15 per cent.

In the above examples, the composition of the equilibrium mixture is governed by the relative thermodynamic stabilities of the two forms under the particular circumstances being considered and this will, of course, ultimately always be the case. An interesting situation arises with aliphatic nitro-compounds such as phenylnitromethane (XXV), however:

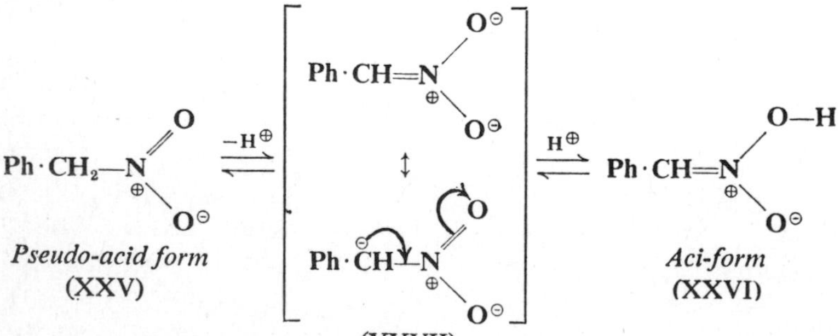

Here the normal nitro- or pseudo-acid form (XXV) is thermo-dynamically the more stable of the two and at true equilibrium this form is present to the almost total exclusion of the aci-form (XXVI).

Nevertheless, on acidification of the sodium salt of the system, i.e. (XXVII), it is very largely (XXVI) that is obtained. This results from the more stable pseudo-acid (XXV) being formed *more slowly* from the mesomeric ion than is the aci-form (XXVI), for the transition state between (XXVII) and (XXV) is at a considerably *higher* energy level than that between (XXVII) and (XXVI), reflecting the greater difficulty of breaking a C—H bond rather than an O—H bond. The reaction is thus said to be *kinetically* rather than *thermodynamically* controlled, leading to (XXVI) rather than (XXV).

Although the *immediate* result is the preferential formation of the aci-form (XXVI), slow, spontaneous re-ionisation of (XXVI) leads inexorably to the formation of (XXV), so that the position of *ultimate* equilibrium is *thermodynamically* controlled.

REACTIONS OF CARBANIONS

(i) Addition reactions

Carbanions take part in a wide variety of addition reactions, many of which involve additions to carbonyl systems. Thus Grignard and acetylide ion additions have already been considered (p. 170), as have aldol (p. 172), Perkin (p. 176), Claisen ester (p. 176), and benzoin (p. 179) reactions and carbanion addition to αβ-unsaturated carbonyl systems in the Michael reaction (p. 155).

(ii) Displacement reactions

Carbanions are also involved in a number of displacement reactions.

(a) **Alkylation:** Suitable carbanions, such as those derived from malonic ester, β-keto-esters, β-dicarbonyl compounds, etc., will effect ready displacement reactions with alkylating agents such as alkyl halides and other reactive halogen-containing compounds, this being a useful preparative method for the formation of carbon–carbon bonds. In most cases the carbanion is generated in non-aqueous solution by bases such as $EtO^{\ominus}$ and the reaction then follows a normal S_N2 course (see p. 222).

The S_N2 character has been confirmed kinetically in some examples and inversion of configuration has been shown to take place at the

$$\text{(EtO}_2\text{C)}_2\text{HC}^{\ominus} + \text{H---}\overset{\overset{\displaystyle H}{|}}{\underset{\underset{\displaystyle H}{|}}{\text{C}}}\text{---Br} \;\rightarrow\; \text{(EtO}_2\text{C)}_2\overset{\delta-}{\text{HC}}\text{------}\overset{\overset{\displaystyle H}{}}{\underset{\underset{\displaystyle H}{|}}{\text{C}}}\text{------}\overset{\delta-}{\text{Br}}$$

$$\uparrow {}^{\ominus}\text{OEt}$$

$$\text{(EtO}_2\text{C)}_2\text{HC---H} \qquad\qquad \text{(EtO}_2\text{C)}_2\text{HC---}\overset{\overset{\displaystyle H}{}}{\underset{\underset{\displaystyle H}{}}{\text{C}}}\text{---H} + \text{Br}^{\ominus}$$

carbon atom attacked. A similar reaction of preparative value occurs
with acetylide ion:

$$\text{HC}\equiv\text{CH} \underset{}{\overset{\ominus\text{NH}_2}{\rightleftharpoons}} \text{HC}\equiv\text{C}^{\ominus} + \text{RBr} \;\rightarrow\; \text{HC}\equiv\text{C}\cdot\text{R} + \text{Br}^{\ominus}$$

It should be remembered, however, that the above carbanions, and
particularly the acetylide ion, are derived from very weak acids and
are, therefore, themselves strong bases with the result that they can
induce elimination (p. 201) as well as displacement reactions; reaction
with tertiary halides thus commonly results in olefine formation to the
exclusion of alkylation.

(b) **Grignard and other organo-metallic reagents:** Grignard reagents
can be looked upon, formally, as providing a source of negative carbon though it is unlikely that they act as *direct* sources of carbanions
as such, and more than one molecule of the reagent may actually be
involved in their reactions as has been seen in discussing their addition to carbonyl groups (p. 170). They can also take part in displacement reactions as in the preparatively useful formation of aldehydes,
via their acetals, from ethyl orthoformate (XXVIII):

$$\overset{\delta-\;\;\;\delta+}{\text{R}\cdot\text{MgBr}} + \text{CH(OEt)}_3 \;\longrightarrow\; \text{R}\cdot\text{CH(OEt)}_2 \xrightarrow[\text{H}_2\text{O}]{\text{H}^{\oplus}} \text{R}\cdot\text{CHO}$$
$$\text{(XXVIII)}$$

Their reaction with esters to form ketones (which then react further
to form tertiary alcohols as the final product) could also, in theory,
be looked upon as a displacement reaction

$$\overset{\delta-\;\;\;\delta+}{\text{R}\cdot\text{MgBr}} + \text{R}'\text{---}\overset{\overset{\displaystyle O}{\|}}{\text{C}}\text{---OEt} \;\rightarrow\; \text{R}'\text{---}\overset{\overset{\displaystyle O}{\|}}{\text{C}}\text{---R} + \overset{\ominus}{\text{O}}\text{Et}$$

but it is doubtful in most cases, whether a sufficiently negative carbon is generated in $R^{\delta-}$ to expel $^{\ominus}OEt$ and addition, as with an ordinary carbonyl group (p. 171), followed by elimination, is probably more likely.

Of other organo-metallic compounds, there is some evidence that sodium and potassium derivatives, e.g. of di- and triphenylmethane, etc., do provide actual carbanions as the active species in the reactions in which they take part, though even here the carbanions may be present not as the simplest possible species but as dimers, trimers and higher aggregates. Lithium derivatives, which are synthetically more useful, correspond more closely to Grignard reagents in possessing a greater degree of covalent character not normally leading to the formation of free carbanions. They are not entirely analogous to Grignard reagents, however, as a number of cases are known where the two lead to different products from the same substrate.

(c) **Wurtz reaction:** A number of claims have been advanced that the Wurtz reaction proceeds via a radical mechanism:

$$R \cdot CH_2 \cdot CH_2Br + Na \cdot \; \rightarrow \; R \cdot CH_2 \cdot CH_2 \cdot + Br^{\ominus} + Na^{\oplus}$$

$$2R \cdot CH_2 \cdot CH_2 \cdot \; \rightarrow \; R \cdot (CH_2)_4 \cdot R$$

One of the pieces of supporting evidence quoted to corroborate this is that disproportionation is observed to take place as well as the expected dimerisation, an alternative reaction well known in radical chemistry (p. 235):

$$2R \cdot CH_2 \cdot CH_2 \cdot \; \rightarrow \; R \cdot CH_2 \cdot CH_3 + R \cdot CH{=}CH_2$$

While such a mechanism is probably valid in the vapour phase it is somewhat less likely in solution and reaction of alkyl chlorides with sodium in hydrocarbon solvents has been shown to lead to the formation of sodium alkyls, which can then be made to react with a second alkyl halide to give quite high yields of the mixed hydrocarbon:

$$R \cdot CH_2 \cdot CH_2Cl \xrightarrow{\ 2Na\ } Na^{\oplus} + Cl^{\ominus} + R \cdot CH_2 \cdot CH_2^{\ominus}Na^{\oplus} \xrightarrow{\ R'Cl\ } R \cdot CH_2 \cdot CH_2 \cdot R$$

Further, the disproportionation, which has often been taken as confirmation of a radical mechanism, can equally be explained, on a carbanion basis, by elimination. The carbanion acts as a base, abstracting a proton from the β-carbon atom of the halide, while chlorine is lost from the α-carbon atom under the influence of $Na^{\oplus}$:

223

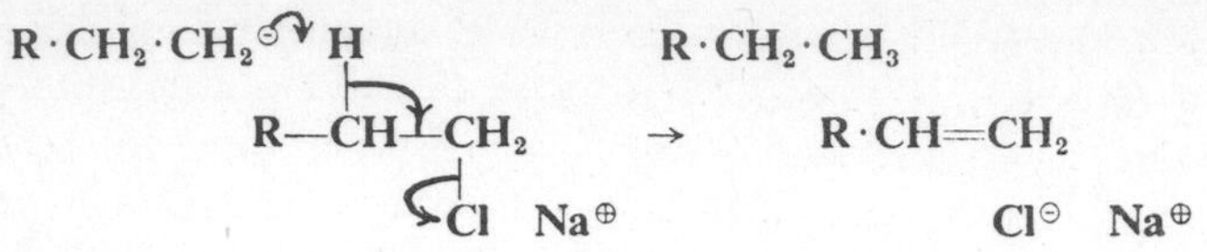

$$R \cdot CH_2 \cdot CH_2 \overset{\curvearrowleft}{} H \qquad\qquad R \cdot CH_2 \cdot CH_3$$

$$R - CH \overset{}{\underset{\underset{Cl}{|}}{-}} CH_2 \qquad \rightarrow \qquad R \cdot CH = CH_2$$

$$ Cl \quad Na^{\oplus} \qquad\qquad\qquad Cl^{\ominus} \quad Na^{\oplus}$$

Whether the process is actually initiated by $Na^{\oplus}$, $R \cdot CH_2 \cdot CH_2^{\ominus}$ or both is not certain, however.

Further support for such an ionic mechanism for the Wurtz reaction is provided by the behaviour of some optically active chlorides, the first formed carbanion attacking a second molecule of chloride by the S_N2 mechanism and leading to inversion of configuration at the carbon atom attacked.

(d) **Reimer-Tiemann reaction**: An example of a species which can lay claim to be a carbanion only because of the π delocalisation that results in the transfer of negative change from oxygen to carbon is the phenoxide ion (XXIX):

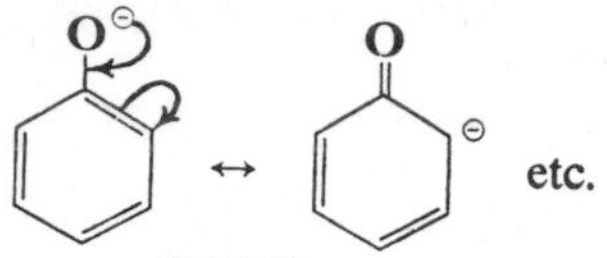

(XXIX)

This reacts with chloroform in the presence of strong bases to yield the *o*-aldehyde, salicaldehyde (XXX), in the Reimer-Tiemann reaction, the quasi-carbanion (XXIX) attacking the electron-deficient carbene CCl_2 obtained by partial hydrolysis of chloroform in the alkaline solution (*cf*. p. 206):

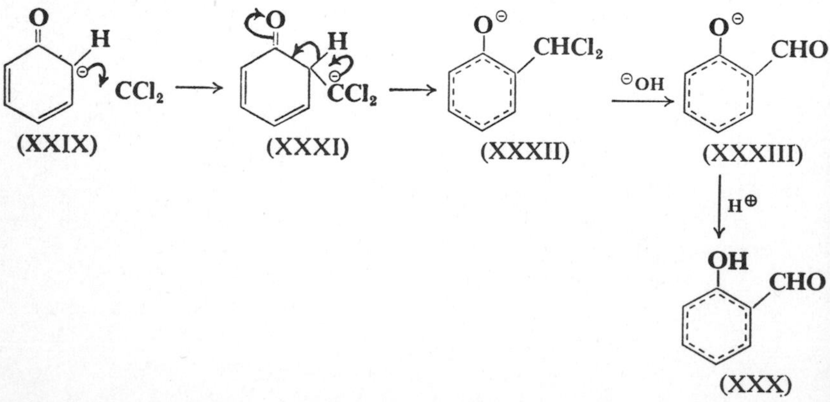

(XXIX)   (XXXI)   (XXXII)   (XXXIII)

(XXX)

224

Thus attack on CCl_2 yields (XXXI) which undergoes a proton shift to form (XXXII). This undergoes hydrolysis in the system to yield (XXXIII), the free aldehyde not being obtained until the reaction mixture is acidified after the reaction proper is over. Some *p*-hydroxybenzaldehyde is also obtained for the negative charge on the nucleus of (XXIX) is not of course confined to the *o*-position.

Some support for the above mechanism involving attack by dichloro-carbene is provided by the fact that when the reaction is carried out on the anion of *p*-cresol (XXXIV), in addition to the expected *o*-aldehyde (XXXV), it is also possible to isolate the unhydrolysed dichloro-compound (XXXVI) arising from attack by CCl_2 at the *p*-position:

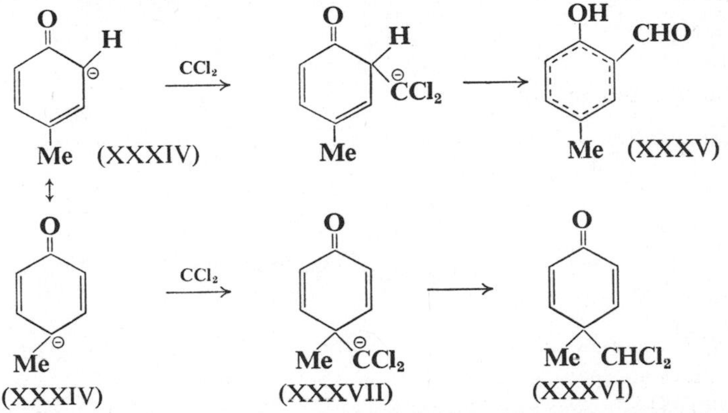

The initial product of the attack (XXXVII) has no hydrogen atom that can be eliminated as $H^{\oplus}$ from the relevant carbon atom to allow reformation of an aromatic structure, so the introduced $^{\ominus}CCl_2$ group acquires $H^{\oplus}$ from the solvent. The dichloro-compound (XXXVI) is somewhat resistant to further hydrolysis, probably due to its insolubility in aqueous alkali.

Somewhat analogous attack of CO_2 on sodium phenate (the Kolbe-Schmidt reaction) is used to prepare sodium salicylate:

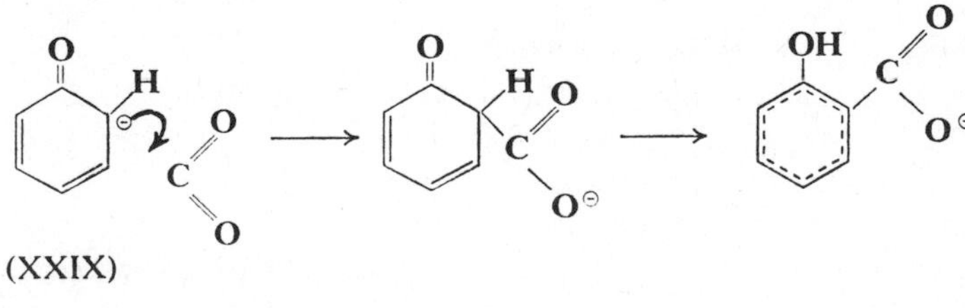

(iii) Halogenation of ketones

One of the earliest observations having a bearing on the subject of the occurrence of carbanions as reaction intermediates was that the bromination of acetone in the presence of base followed the kinetic equation

$$\text{Rate} \propto [\text{Me} \cdot \text{CO} \cdot \text{Me}]$$

and was independent of $[\text{Br}_2]$. The rate was, however, found to be proportional to [base] and this was subsequently interpreted as involving the formation of a carbanion as the rate-determining step, followed by rapid bromination:

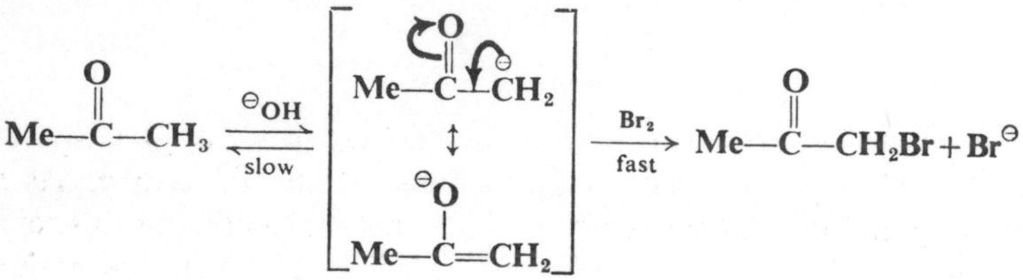

In support of this view it has subsequently been shown that under these conditions ketones undergo chlorination, iodination, deuterium exchange in D_2O and racemisation (if of suitable structure)

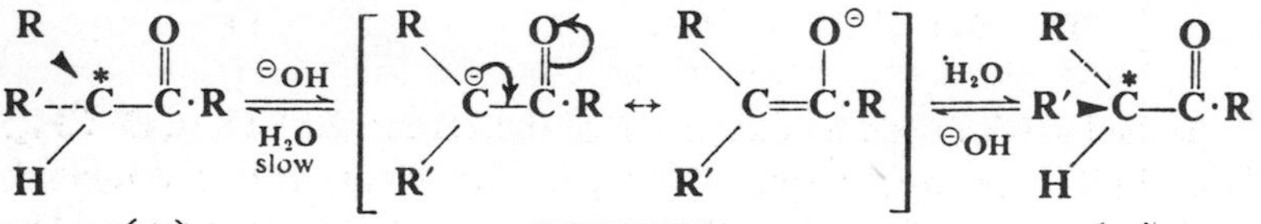

at exactly the same rate that they undergo bromination, indicating the participation of a common intermediate in all. The reconversion to the ketone of the planar intermediate (XXXVIII), or the enol derived from it (*cf.* p. 215), leads as readily to the D- as to the L- form and thus results in racemisation.

Further base-induced halogenation of a mono-halogenated ketone (XXXIX) will take place preferentially at the carbon atom that has already been substituted, provided that it still carries a hydrogen atom; for not only will the inductive effect of the halogen atom make the hydrogen atoms attached to the halogen-substituted carbon atom more acidic, and therefore more readily abstracted by base, but it will also help to stabilise the resultant carbanion, leading to the formation of (XL) rather than (XLI):

$$\underset{\text{(XXXIX)}}{CH_3-\overset{\overset{\displaystyle O}{\|}}{C}-\overset{\overset{\displaystyle H}{\downarrow}}{C}H\rightarrow-Br} \underset{\overset{\ominus}{OH}}{\rightleftharpoons} \underset{\text{(XL)}}{CH_3-\overset{\overset{\displaystyle O}{\|}}{C}-\overset{\ominus}{C}H\rightarrow-Br} \xrightarrow{Br_2} CH_3-\overset{\overset{\displaystyle O}{\|}}{C}-CHBr_2+Br^{\ominus}$$

$$\Updownarrow {\ominus}OH$$

$$\underset{\text{(XLI)}}{{\ominus}CH_2-\overset{\overset{\displaystyle O}{\|}}{C}-CH_2Br}$$

This is, of course, the reason for the exclusive production of $Me \cdot CO \cdot CX_3$ in the base-induced halogenation of acetone. As a final stage in the *haloform* reaction, this species then undergoes attack by base, e.g. ${\ominus}OH$, on the carbonyl carbon because of the highly positive character that that atom has now acquired:

$$Me-\overset{\overset{\displaystyle O}{\|}}{\underset{\overset{\displaystyle \curvearrowright}{\ominus OH}}{C}}\overset{Br}{\underset{Br}{\overset{\curvearrowleft}{C}-Br}} \rightarrow Me-C\overset{\displaystyle O}{\underset{OH}{\diagdown}} + {\ominus}CBr_3 \rightarrow Me-C\overset{\overset{\curvearrowright}{O}}{\diagdown}{\underset{O^{\ominus}}{}} + HCBr_3$$

In the base-induced halogenation of the ketone, $R \cdot CH_2 \cdot CO \cdot CH_3$, it is the methyl rather than the methylene group that is attacked, for the inductive effect of the R group will serve to decrease the acidity of the hydrogen atoms attached to the methylene group, while those of the methyl group are unaffected, thus leading to preferential formation of the carbanion (XXLII) rather than (XLIII):

$$\underset{\text{(XLII)}}{R\rightarrow-CH_2-\overset{\overset{\displaystyle O}{\|}}{C}-\overset{\ominus}{C}H_2} \qquad \underset{\text{(XLIII)}}{R\rightarrow-\overset{\ominus}{C}H-\overset{\overset{\displaystyle O}{\|}}{C}-CH_3}$$

The halogenation of ketones is also catalysed by acids, the reaction probably proceeding through the enol form of the ketone (*cf.* p. 218) whose formation is the rate-determining step of the reaction:

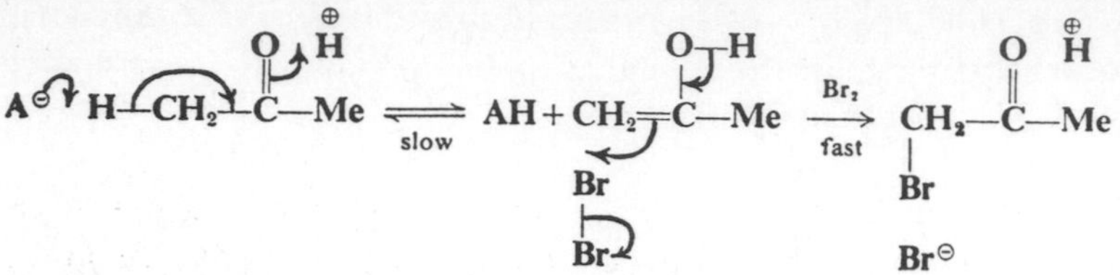

$$A \overset{\ominus}{\frown} H \overset{\frown}{-} CH_2 \overset{O}{\overset{\|}{-}} \overset{\oplus}{\overset{H}{C}} \overset{\frown}{-} Me \underset{\text{slow}}{\rightleftharpoons} AH + CH_2 \overset{O-H}{=} C \overset{\frown}{-} Me \xrightarrow[\text{fast}]{Br_2} \overset{O}{\underset{Br}{CH_2-C-Me}} \overset{\oplus}{\overset{H}{}}$$

Here the effect of substitution by R and halogen on the rate and position of attack is exactly opposite to that observed in base-induced halogenation. Thus with the ketone $R \cdot CH_2 \cdot CO \cdot CH_3$, the enol (XLIV), rather than (XLV), will be stabilised by hyperconjugation arising from the α-hydrogens of the methyl group in addition to any in the R group, whereas only the methylene group will be operative in (XLV):

$$R \cdot CH = \overset{OH}{\underset{|}{C}} - CH_3 \xrightarrow{Br_2} R \cdot CH \overset{O}{\overset{\|}{-}} C - CH_3$$
$$\underset{Br}{|}$$

$$\text{(XLIV)} \qquad\qquad \text{(XLVI)}$$

$$R \cdot CH_2 - \overset{OH}{\underset{|}{C}} = CH_2 \xrightarrow{Br_2} R \cdot CH_2 \overset{O}{\overset{\|}{-}} C - CH_2 \cdot Br$$
$$\text{(XLV)} \qquad\qquad \text{(XLVII)}$$

This leads to the formation of (XLVI) rather than (XLVII), which would have been obtained in the presence of base. In the bromination of acetone the effect of the bromine atom in the first-formed $Me \cdot CO \cdot CH_2Br$ is to withdraw electrons, thus making the initial uptake of proton by the $>C=O$, in forming the enol, *less* ready in bromoacetone than in acetone itself, resulting in preferential attack on the acetone rather than the bromoacetone in the system. The net effect is that under acid conditions $Me \cdot CO \cdot CH_2Br$ can actually be isolated whereas under alkaline conditions of bromination it cannot for, as we have seen above, it brominates more readily than does acetone itself when base is present. Further bromination of $Me \cdot CO \cdot CH_2Br$ under acid conditions results in preferential attack on the methyl rather than the methylene group.

(iv) Decarboxylation

Another reaction involving carbanions is the decarboxylation of a number of carboxylic acids via their anions

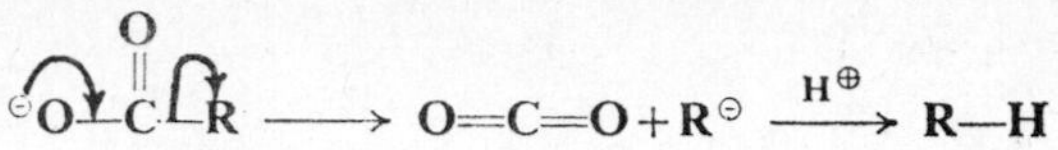

$$\overset{\ominus}{O}\overset{\overset{O}{\parallel}}{-}\overset{}{C}-R \longrightarrow O=C=O + R^{\ominus} \xrightarrow{H^{\oplus}} R-H$$

the resultant carbanion $R^{\ominus}$ subsequently acquiring a proton from solvent or other source. It would thus be expected that this mode of decarboxylation would be assisted by the presence of electron-withdrawing groups in **R** because of the stabilisation they would then confer on the carbanion intermediate. This is borne out by the extremely ready decomposition of nitroacetate

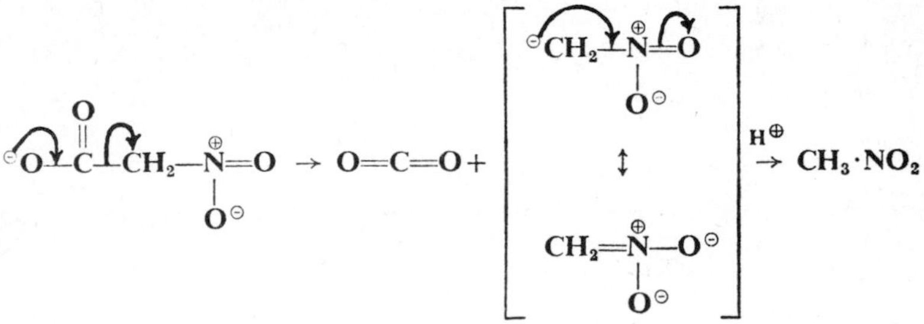

$$\overset{\ominus}{O}-\overset{\overset{O}{\parallel}}{C}-CH_2-\overset{\oplus}{N}=O \rightarrow O=C=O + \left[\begin{array}{c} ^{\ominus}CH_2-\overset{\oplus}{N}=O \\ \underset{O^{\ominus}}{\mid} \\ \updownarrow \\ CH_2=\overset{\oplus}{N}-O^{\ominus} \\ \underset{O^{\ominus}}{\mid} \end{array}\right] \xrightarrow{H^{\oplus}} CH_3 \cdot NO_2$$

and by the relative ease with which the decarboxylation of trihaloacetates and 2,4,6-trinitrobenzoates may be accomplished.

The decarboxylation of β-keto acids may also proceed via their anions and then through stabilised carbanions such as (XLVIII):

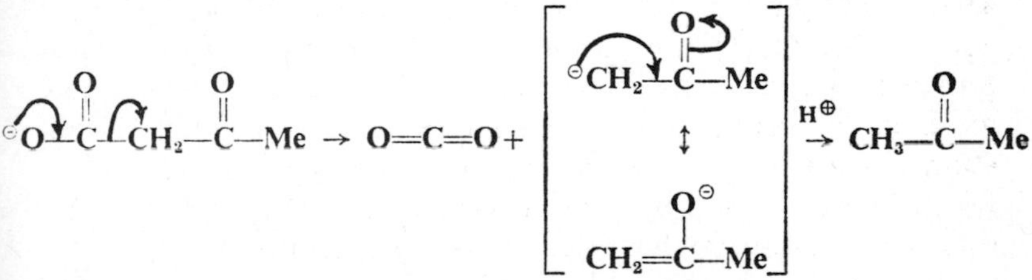

$$\overset{\ominus}{O}-\overset{\overset{O}{\parallel}}{C}-CH_2-\overset{\overset{O}{\parallel}}{C}-Me \rightarrow O=C=O + \left[\begin{array}{c} ^{\ominus}CH_2-\overset{\overset{O}{\parallel}}{C}-Me \\ \updownarrow \\ CH_2=\overset{\overset{O^{\ominus}}{\mid}}{C}-Me \end{array}\right] \xrightarrow{H^{\oplus}} CH_3-\overset{\overset{O}{\parallel}}{C}-Me$$

(XLVIII)

The overall rate law for the decarboxylation is, however, found to contain a term referring to [keto acid] itself as well as to the concentration of its anion; this is believed to be due to incipient transfer of proton to the keto group by hydrogen bonding:

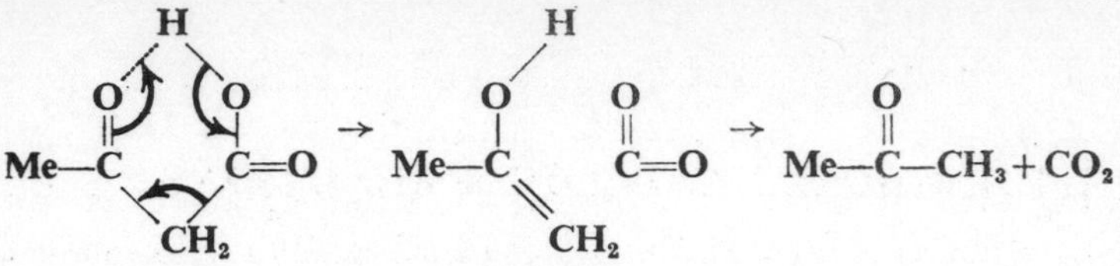

$$\underset{\underset{\textstyle CH_2}{}}{\overset{\overset{\textstyle H}{}}{Me-C}\underset{}{\overset{O\quad O}{}}C=O} \rightarrow \underset{\underset{\textstyle CH_2}{}}{Me-C}\overset{\overset{\textstyle H}{}}{\underset{}{\overset{O\quad O}{}}}C=O \rightarrow \underset{}{\overset{O}{Me-C}}-CH_3 + CO_2$$

(XLIX)

Confirmation of this mode of decarboxylation of the free acid has been obtained by 'trapping' the acetone-enol intermediate (XLIX).

10 RADICALS AND THEIR REACTIONS

MOST of the reactions that have been considered to date have involved the participation, however transiently, of charged intermediates, i.e. carbonium ions and carbanions, produced by the *heterolytic fission* of covalent bonds:

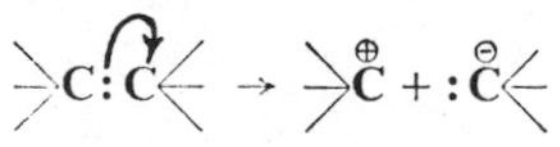

$$\ce{>C:C<} \rightarrow \ce{>\overset{\oplus}{C}} + \ce{:\overset{\ominus}{C}<}$$

But reactive intermediates possessing an unpaired electron, i.e. *radicals*, can also be generated if a covalent bond undergoes *homolytic fission*:

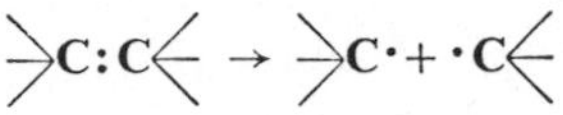

$$\ce{>C:C<} \rightarrow \ce{>C·} + \ce{·C<}$$

Reactions involving such radicals occur widely in the gas phase, but they also occur in solution, particularly if the reaction is carried out in non-polar solvents and if it is catalysed by light or the simultaneous decomposition of substances known to produce radicals, e.g. peroxides. Once a radical reaction has been started, it often proceeds with very great rapidity owing to the establishment of fast chain reactions (see below). These arise from the ability of the first formed radical to generate another on reaction with a neutral molecule, the new radical being able to repeat the process, and so the reaction is carried on. Thus in the bromination of a hydrocarbon, R—H, the reaction may need starting by introduction of the radical, **Ra·**, but once started it is self-perpetuating:

$$Ra· + Br—Br \rightarrow Ra—Br + ·Br$$
$$\downarrow$$
$$R—H + ·Br \rightarrow R· + H--Br$$
$$\uparrow \qquad \downarrow Br_2$$
$$·Br + R—Br$$

231

The chief characteristics of radical reactions are their rapidity, their initiation by radicals themselves or substances known to produce them (*initiators*), and their inhibition or termination by substances which are themselves known to react readily with radicals (*inhibitors*), e.g. hydroquinone, diphenylamine, iodine etc. Apart from the short-lived radicals that occur largely as reaction intermediates, some others are known which are more stable and which consequently have a longer life; these will be considered first.

LONG-LIVED RADICALS

The colourless solid hexaphenylethane, $Ph_3C—CPh_3$, is found to yield a yellow solution in non-polar solvents such as benzene. This solution reacts very readily with the oxygen of the air to form tri-phenylmethyl peroxide, $Ph_3C—O—O—CPh_3$, or with iodine to yield triphenylmethyl iodide, $Ph_3C—I$. In addition, the solution is found to be *paramagnetic*, i.e. to be attracted by a magnetic field, indicating the presence of unpaired electrons (compounds having only paired electrons are *diamagnetic*, i.e. are repelled by a magnetic field). These observations have been interpreted as indicating that hexaphenylethane undergoes reversible dissociation into triphenylmethyl radicals:

$$Ph_3C:CPh_3 \rightleftharpoons Ph_3C \cdot + \cdot CPh_3$$

In support of this hypothesis, it is significant that the $C—C$ bond energy in hexaphenylethane is only 11 kcals/mole compared with 83 kcals/mole for this bond in ethane itself.

The degree of dissociation of a 3 per cent solution in benzene has been estimated as about $0 \cdot 02$ at $20°$ and about $0 \cdot 1$ at $80°$. The reason for this behaviour, in contrast to hexamethylethane which does not exhibit it, has been ascribed to the stabilisation of the triphenylmethyl radical, with respect to undissociated hexaphenylethane, that can arise from the delocalisation of the unpaired electron via the π orbitals of the benzene nuclei:

A number of contributing structures of this kind can be written, but the stabilisation thereby promoted is not so great as might, at first sight, be expected, as interaction between the hydrogen atoms in the *o*-positions prevents the nuclei attaining coplanarity. The radical is thus not flat, but probably more like a three-bladed propeller with angled blades, so that delocalisation of the unpaired electron, with consequent stabilisation, is considerably inhibited.

The ready formation and stability of the radicals are, indeed, due in no small measure to the steric crowding in hexaphenylethane that can be relieved by dissociation. In support of this explanation, it is found that the C—C distance in this compound is significantly longer (by *ca.* 0·04 Å) than in ethane. Also, while the introduction of a variety of substituents into the nuclei promotes dissociation, this is particularly marked when substituents are in the *o*-positions where they would be expected to contribute most to steric crowding. Further, it is found that the compound (I)

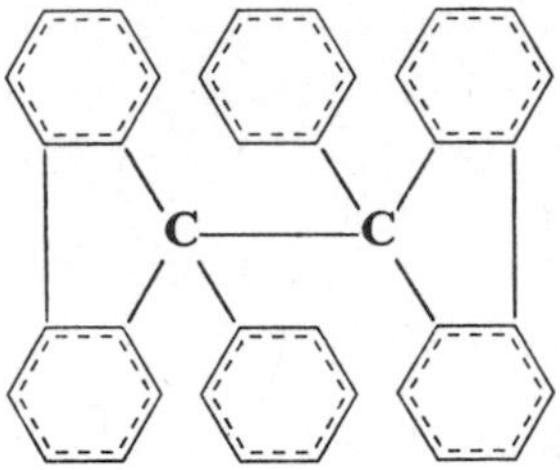

(I)

in which two of the benzene nuclei on each carbon atom are bonded to each other and so held back from 'crowding' near the C—C bond, is not dissociated at room temperature though the possibilities of stabilising the radical, that could be obtained from (I), by delocalisation are at least as great as those for triphenylmethyl.

Somewhat less stable radicals may be obtained by warming tetra-arylhydrazines in non-polar solvents, green solutions being obtained:

$$2Ph_2NH \xrightarrow{\text{KMnO}_4} Ph_2N:NPh_2 \rightleftharpoons Ph_2N\cdot + \cdot NPh_2$$

Here, promotion of dissociation by steric crowding is clearly less important than with hexaphenylethane; stabilisation of the radical due to delocalisation may be more significant, but dissociation is certainly favoured by the lower energy of the N—N bond.

Similarly, solutions of diphenyl disulphide become yellow on heating

$$PhS:SPh \rightleftharpoons PhS \cdot + \cdot SPh$$

and the radicals formed may be detected by the classical device of adding a second radical and isolating a mixed product:

$$PhS \cdot + \cdot CPh_3 \rightarrow PhS:CPh_3$$

The sulphide obtained is, however, rapidly decomposed in the presence of air. The best radical to use for such detection is 1,1-diphenyl-2-picrylhydrazyl (II)

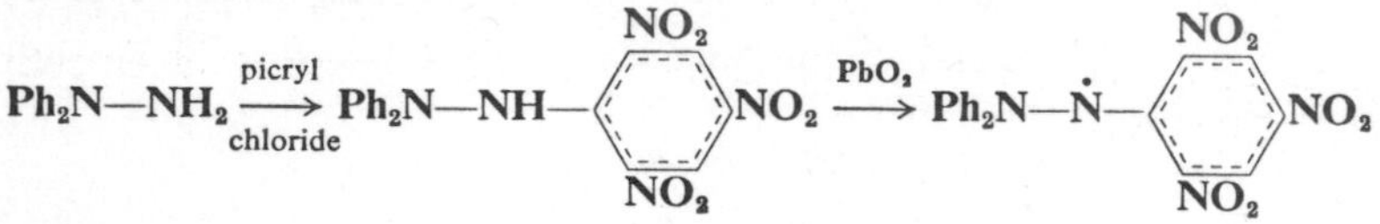

(II)

for this is very stable (due to delocalisation of the unpaired electron) and forms stable, isolable products with many radicals. In addition, its solutions are bright violet in colour and its reaction with other radicals to yield colourless products can thus be readily followed colorimetrically.

SHORT-LIVED RADICALS

The short-lived radicals, e.g. $Me \cdot$, though more difficult to handle, are of much greater importance as participants in chemical reactions; as their short life suggests, they are extremely reactive.

The relative stability of simple alkyl radicals is found to be in the same order as that of the corresponding carbonium ions (p. 62)

$$R_3C \cdot > R_2CH \cdot > RCH_2 \cdot > CH_3 \cdot$$

the sequence reflecting decreasing stabilisation by hyperconjugation as the series is traversed. As might be expected, however, the differences in stability between the radicals is less marked than between corresponding carbonium ions. Radicals involving allylic or benzylic positions show greatly enhanced stability arising from the delocalisation via π orbitals that is then possible:

$$CH_2 \overset{\curvearrowleft}{=} CH \overset{\curvearrowleft}{-} \dot{C}H_2 \leftrightarrow \dot{C}H_2 - CH = CH_2$$

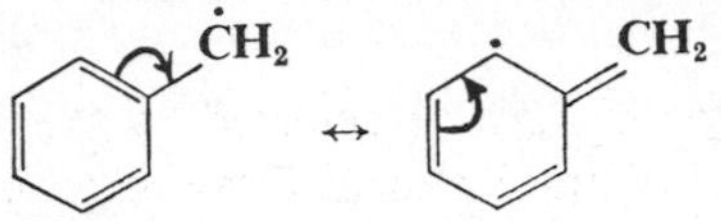

etc.

(i) Methods of formation

There are numerous methods by which short-lived radicals may be formed, of which the most important are the thermal and photochemical fission of bonds, oxidation/reduction reactions by inorganic ions resulting in single electron transfers, and electrolysis.

(a) **Photochemical fission:** A well-known example is the decomposition of acetone in the vapour phase by light having a wavelength of ≈ 3000 Å:

$$\underset{\overset{\|}{O}}{Me-C-Me} \rightarrow Me\cdot + \cdot\underset{\overset{\|}{O}}{C-Me} \rightarrow CO + \cdot Me$$

Another classic example is the conversion of molecular chlorine to chlorine atoms by sunlight

$$Cl-Cl \rightarrow Cl\cdot + \cdot Cl$$

that occurs as the first step in a number of photo-catalysed chlorinations (p. 248). Normally speaking, such photochemical decomposition may only be effected by visible or ultraviolet light of definite wavelengths corresponding—hardly surprisingly—to absorption maxima in the spectrum of the compound. Reactions of this type also occur in solution, but the life of the radical is then usually shorter owing to the opportunities afforded for reaction with solvent molecules (see below).

(b) **Thermal fission:** Much of the early work on short-lived radicals, including studies of their half-lives, was carried out on the products obtained from the thermal decomposition of metal alkyls:

$$Pb(CH_2-CH_3)_4 \rightarrow Pb + 4\cdot CH_2-CH_3$$

Further reference is made to this work when the methods for detecting short-lived radicals are discussed below. In the vapour phase, the life of such radicals can be ended not only by dimerisation

$$CH_3-CH_2\cdot + \cdot CH_2-CH_3 \rightarrow CH_3-CH_2-CH_2-CH_3$$

235

but also by disproportionation:

$$CH_3\text{—}CH_2\cdot + CH_3\text{—}CH_2\cdot \rightarrow CH_3\text{—}CH_3 + CH_2\text{=}CH_2$$

The use of lead tetraethyl as an anti-knock agent depends in part on the ability of the ethyl radicals that it produces to combine with radicals resulting from the over-rapid combustion of petrol, thus terminating chain reactions which are building up towards explosion.

In solution, of course, the relative abundance of solvent molecules means that the initial radicals most commonly meet their end by reaction with solvent

$$CH_3\text{—}CH_2\cdot + H\text{—}R \rightarrow CH_3\text{—}CH_3 + \cdot R$$

but a new radical is then obtained in exchange and this may possibly be capable of establishing a new reaction chain.

The thermal fission of carbon–carbon bonds is seen in the radical-induced cracking of long-chain hydrocarbons where the initial radicals introduced into the system act by abstracting a hydrogen atom from a $-CH_2-$ group of the chain. The radical so formed then undergoes fission at the β-position yielding an olefine of lower molecular weight and also a new radical to maintain the reaction chain:

$$\begin{array}{ccc} Ra\cdot \;\; H & & Ra\text{—}H \\ | & & \bullet \\ R\text{—}CH_2\text{—}CH\text{—}CH_2\text{—}CH_2\text{—}R' & \rightarrow & R\text{—}CH_2\text{—}CH\text{—}CH_2\text{—}CH_2\text{—}R' \\ & & \downarrow \\ & & R\text{—}CH_2\text{—}CH\text{=}CH_2 + \cdot CH_2\text{—}R' \end{array}$$

Termination of the reaction by mutual interaction of radicals will tend not to take place to any marked extent until the concentration of long-chain hydrocarbons has dropped to a low level.

Bonds involving some elements other than carbon may undergo easier thermal fission. Thus diazomethane yields methylene diradicals on heating, the reaction chain readily building up to explosion:

$$\left[CH_2\text{—}\overset{\oplus}{N}\text{—}\overset{\ominus}{\underset{..}{N}} \;\leftrightarrow\; \overset{\ominus}{C}H_2\text{—}\overset{\oplus}{N}\text{≡}N \right] \rightarrow \overset{\bullet}{\underset{\bullet}{C}}H_2 + N_2$$

Organic peroxides are particularly readily decomposed at quite low temperatures and, because of the ease with which they will form radicals, are much used as initiators:

$$\begin{array}{cccc} O & O & O & O \\ \parallel & \parallel & \parallel & \parallel \\ Ph\text{—}C\text{—}O\text{—}O\text{—}C\text{—}Ph & \rightarrow & Ph\text{—}C\text{—}O\cdot + \cdot O\text{—}C\text{—}Ph \end{array}$$

The decomposition of benzoyl peroxide is discussed in more detail below (p. 240).

(c) **Oxidation/reduction by inorganic ions:** Perhaps the best-known example is the use of ferrous ion to catalyse oxidations with hydrogen peroxide, the mixture being known as Fenton's reagent:

$$H_2O_2 + Fe^{\oplus\oplus} \rightarrow HO\cdot + {}^{\ominus}OH + Fe^{\oplus\oplus\oplus}$$

The ferrous ion goes to the ferric state and a hydroxyl radical is liberated. The latter acts as the effective oxidising agent in the system, usually by abstracting a hydrogen atom from the substrate that is to be oxidised:

$$HO\cdot + H{-}X \rightarrow H_2O + \cdot X$$

A rather similar reaction, but involving reduction of the inorganic ion, may take place as the first step in the autoxidation of benzaldehyde (p. 253), which is catalysed by a number of heavy metal ions capable of one-electron transfers:

$$\underset{(III)}{Ph{-}\overset{\overset{\textstyle O}{\|}}{C}{-}H} + Fe^{\oplus\oplus\oplus} \rightarrow Ph{-}\overset{\overset{\textstyle O}{\|}}{C}\cdot + H^{\oplus} + Fe^{\oplus\oplus}$$

(d) **Electrolysis:** The most common example is in the Kolbe electrolytic synthesis of hydrocarbons:

$$2R{-}\overset{\overset{\textstyle O}{\|}}{C}{-}O^{\ominus} \xrightarrow{-2e^{\ominus}} 2R{-}\overset{\overset{\textstyle O}{\|}}{C}{-}O\cdot \xrightarrow{-2CO_2} 2R\cdot \xrightarrow{\text{dimerisation}} R{-}R$$

$$\qquad\quad(III)\qquad\qquad\quad(IV)\qquad\qquad(V)$$

The carboxyl anion gives up an electron on discharge at the anode to yield the carboxyl radical (III) which rapidly decarboxylates to form the alkyl radical (IV). These alkyl radicals then dimerise, in part at any rate, to yield the expected hydrocarbon (V).

Electrolysis of ketones in aqueous acid solution results in their reduction to pinacols (VII) via the radical ion (VI)

$$2R_2C{=}O \xrightarrow{+2e^{\ominus}} 2R_2\overset{\cdot}{C}{-}O^{\ominus} \xrightarrow{\text{dimerisation}} \begin{array}{c} R_2C{-}O^{\ominus} \\ | \\ R_2C{-}O^{\ominus} \end{array} \xrightarrow{H^{\oplus}} \begin{array}{c} R_2C{-}OH \\ | \\ R_2C{-}OH \end{array}$$

$$\qquad\qquad\qquad\qquad\quad(VI)\qquad\qquad\qquad\qquad\qquad(VII)$$

which has already been encountered in the reaction of aromatic ketones with sodium in the absence of air (p. 169); it also resembles the radical ion obtained in the first stage of the acyloin reaction (p. 169). The above are but two cases of electrolytic reaction, several examples of which have considerable synthetic importance.

(ii) Methods of detection

The classical work on the detection of short-lived radicals was done by Paneth using thin metal, e.g. lead, mirrors deposited on the inside wall of glass tubes. These mirrors disappeared when attacked by radicals, so by varying (*a*) the distance of the mirrors from the point where the radicals were generated (by thermal decomposition of metal alkyls), and (*b*) the velocity of the inert carrier gas by which the radicals were transported, it was possible to estimate their half-lives. That of methyl, under these conditions proved to be *ca.* 8×10^{-3} seconds.

Some, more stable, radicals, e.g. $Ph_3C\cdot$, may be detected by molecular weight determinations, but it is only rarely that this can be accomplished satisfactorily. Several radicals are coloured, though the compounds from which they are derived are not, so that colorimetric estimation may be possible; and even though the radicals themselves may not be coloured, the rate at which they discharge the colour of the stable radical, diphenylpicrylhydrazyl (II), may serve to determine their concentration. This is an example of the 'use of a radical to catch a radical' already mentioned (p. 234), the evidence being strengthened by the isolation of the mixed product formed by mutual interaction of the two radicals, if that is possible. Another chemical method of detection involves the ability of radicals to initiate polymerisation of, for example, olefines; reference is made to this below (p. 247).

The use of magnetic fields to detect the paramagnetism arising from the presence of unpaired electrons in radicals has already been referred to (p. 232). Though simple in essence, it can be fraught with much difficulty in practice, and other physical methods of detection are commonly preferred. The most useful of these to date is electron spin resonance spectroscopy, which again depends for its utility on the presence of unpaired electrons in radicals.

Where it is desired merely to try and discover whether a particular reaction proceeds via radical intermediates or not, one of the simplest procedures is to observe the effect on the rate of the reaction of

adding (*a*) compounds that readily form radicals, e.g. organic peroxides, and (*b*) compounds known to react readily with radicals, i.e.
inhibitors such as hydroquinone.

(iii) Stereochemistry

A good deal of attention has been devoted to the question of whether
radicals in which the unpaired electron is on carbon have a planar
(VIII) or a pyramidal (IX) structure

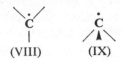

i.e. whether the presence of the unpaired electron preserves the quasi-
tetrahedral state or not. There is little doubt that in radicals that may
be considerably stabilised by delocalisation of the unpaired electron,
the three bonds attached to the carbon atom will be coplanar. Thus
in triphenylmethyl, although, as has been said already (p. 233), interference between the *o*-hydrogen atoms of the benzene nuclei prevents
the latter from lying in a common plane, the bonds joining the radical
carbon atom to the three phenyl groups are almost certainly coplanar, for movement of one of these bonds out of the common plane
would lower delocalisation possibilities without any compensating
relief of steric strain. The benzene nuclei are angled to this common
plane like the blades of a propeller so as to relieve as much steric
strain as possible, while losing the minimum amount of delocalisation
stabilisation due to their non-coplanarity.

By contrast, radicals in which the radical carbon atom constitutes
the bridgehead of a rigid cyclic system will have the pyramidal configuration forced upon them, e.g. the apocamphyl radical (X):

Me
Me

(X)

There is, however, evidence that such radicals are considerably less
stable than simple tertiary aliphatic radicals upon which no such
stereochemical restraint is imposed.

For radicals which do not have their configuration thrust upon them in this way, or which are not notably stabilised by delocalisation, the evidence available to date while not conclusive is certainly suggestive. Thus spectroscopic evidence indicates that the methyl radical and its deutero-derivative are planar or nearly so and with other simple alkyl radicals any stabilisation by hyperconjugation that may be possible will tend to favour the planar configuration; though this tendency is presumably less marked than with the corresponding carbonium ions as the stabilisation of the radicals is less pronounced than that of the ions.

(iv) Reactions

As with the carbonium ions and carbanions that have already been considered, radicals, once formed, can take part in three principal types of reaction: addition, displacement, and rearrangement, the latter normally being followed by one or other of the former. Before these reaction types are considered in detail, however, reference will be made to the formation and behaviour of a typical radical to illustrate the complexity of the secondary reactions that may result and, consequently, the wide variety of products that may be formed.

(a) The thermal fission of benzoyl peroxide: Benzoyl peroxide (a crystalline solid obtained by the reaction of benzoyl chloride with hydrogen peroxide in alkaline solution under Schotten-Baumann conditions) undergoes extremely ready thermal decomposition to yield benzoate radicals:

$$Ph-\overset{O}{\overset{\|}{C}}-O-O-\overset{O}{\overset{\|}{C}}-Ph \rightarrow Ph-\overset{O}{\overset{\|}{C}}-O\cdot + \cdot O-\overset{O}{\overset{\|}{C}}-Ph$$

It can be looked upon as consisting of two dipoles joined negative end to negative end as indicated above, and part, at least, of its inherent instability may stem from this cause. It would thus be expected that substitution of the benzene nucleus with electron-donating groups would enhance this instability leading to even more ready decomposition and this is, in fact, found to be the case. Electron-withdrawing groups are, correspondingly, found to exert a stabilising influence as compared with the unsubstituted compound.

Even at room temperature, and particularly as the temperature is raised, solutions of the peroxide are observed to liberate CO_2 due to:

$$\underset{\substack{\| \\ O}}{Ph-C}-O\cdot \rightarrow Ph\cdot + CO_2$$

Thus, phenyl radicals will be present as well as benzoate radicals and often in quite considerable concentration; this is, indeed, one of the most useful sources of phenyl radicals. Production of the radicals in solution, as is the normal practice, can lead to further complications. Thus with benzene as solvent, the following initial reactions can, in theory, take place:

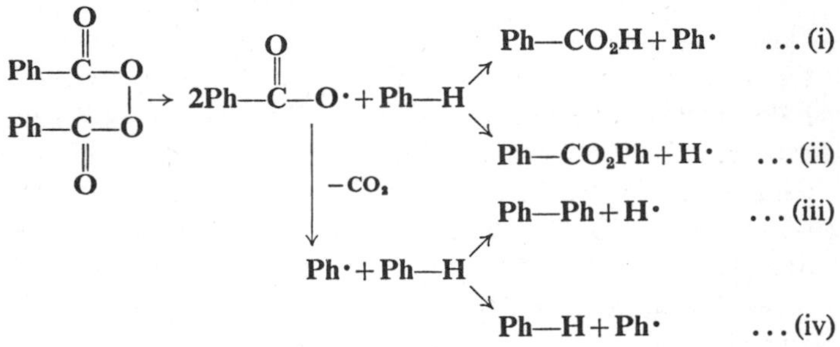

$$
\begin{array}{c}
Ph-C-O \\
\underset{\substack{| \\ Ph-C-O}}{\overset{\overset{\| \\ O}{}}{}} \rightarrow 2Ph-\overset{\overset{O}{\|}}{C}-O\cdot + Ph-H
\begin{array}{l}
\nearrow\; Ph-CO_2H + Ph\cdot \quad \ldots (i) \\
\searrow\; Ph-CO_2Ph + H\cdot \quad \ldots (ii)
\end{array}
\end{array}
$$

$$
\Big\downarrow{-CO_2}
\qquad
\begin{array}{l}
\nearrow\; Ph-Ph + H\cdot \quad \ldots (iii)
\end{array}
$$

$$
Ph\cdot + Ph-H
\begin{array}{l}
\nearrow \\
\searrow\; Ph-H + Ph\cdot \quad \ldots (iv)
\end{array}
$$

Reaction (iv) will, of course, not be directly detectable, but would serve to prolong the apparent life of phenyl radicals in the solution. In fact, (i) is found to be the main reaction taking place. It should be emphasised, however, that the above is only the *first stage*, for either

$\underset{\substack{\| \\ O}}{Ph-C}-O\cdot$ or $Ph\cdot$ can then attack the products derived from (i), (ii), and (iii). Thus, further attack on diphenyl from (iii) by $Ph\cdot$ leads to the formation of ter- and quater-phenyl, etc. It should, however, be pointed out that reactions (ii) and (iii) are almost certainly not direct displacements as shown, but proceed by addition followed by removal of a hydrogen atom from the addition product by another radical (*cf.* p. 256):

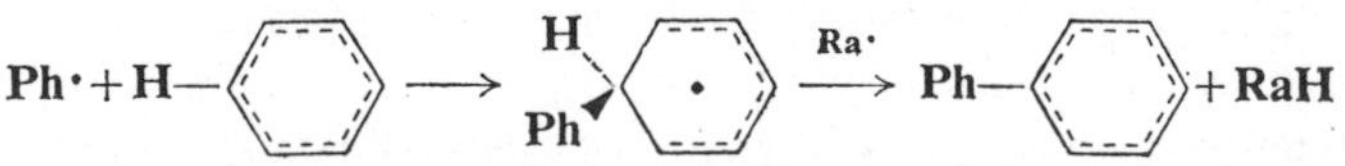

A further possibility is the attack of benzoate or phenyl radicals on as yet undecomposed benzoyl peroxide leading to the formation in the system of new radicals, $X-C_6H_4-\overset{\overset{O}{\|}}{C}-O\cdot$ and $X-C_6H_4\cdot$, which can give rise to a further range of possible products. As this is only a simple case, the possible complexity of the mixture of products that may result from radical reactions in general will readily be realised.

The most important group of radical reactions are probably those involving addition.

(b) Addition reactions: *(i) Halogens.* As has already been mentioned (p. 137) the addition of halogens to unsaturated systems can follow either an ionic or a radical mechanism. In the vapour phase in sunlight, it is almost entirely radicals that are involved, provided the containing vessel has walls of a non-polar material. The same is true in solution in non-polar solvents, again in the presence of sunlight. In more polar solvents, in the absence of sunlight, and particularly if catalysts, e.g. Lewis acids, are present, the reaction proceeds almost entirely by an ionic mechanism. It thus follows that in solution in non-polar solvents in the absence of sunlight or catalysts, little or no reaction takes place between olefines and halogens as neither ionic species nor radicals will normally be formed under these conditions without some specific initiating process.

The photochemically catalysed addition of chlorine to tetrachloro-ethylene (XI), for example, may be formulated as:

$$Cl-Cl$$
$$\downarrow hv$$
$$CCl_2{=}CCl_2 + \cdot Cl \;\rightarrow\; \cdot CCl_2{-}CCl_3 \quad (XII)$$
$$(XI) \qquad \uparrow \qquad \downarrow Cl_2$$
$$\cdot Cl \;+\; CCl_3{-}CCl_3 \quad (XIII)$$

It will be seen that the initiating step, the photochemical fission of a molecule of chlorine, will lead to the formation of *two* reactive entities, i.e. free chlorine atoms, which are, of course, radicals. In support of this it is found that

$$\text{Rate} \propto \sqrt{\text{Intensity of absorbed light}}$$

i.e. each quantum of energy absorbed did, in fact, lead to the initiation of *two* reaction chains. The addition of a free chlorine atom to the unsaturated compound results in the formation of a second radical (XII) which is capable of undergoing a radical displacement reaction with a molecule of chlorine to yield the final addition product (XIII) and a free chlorine atom. This is capable of initiating a similar reaction cycle with a second molecule of unsaturated compound and so the process goes on, i.e. an extremely rapid, continuing chain reaction is set up by *each* initiating chlorine atom produced photochemically. Such a continuing chain reaction, self-perpetuating once initiated, is perhaps the most characteristic feature of reactions proceeding via a radical mechanism. In support of the above reaction scheme, it is found that each quantum of energy absorbed leads to the conversion of several thousand molecules of (XI) → (XIII). Until the later stages of the reaction, i.e. when nearly all the unsaturated compound, (XI), is used up, the concentration of $Cl \cdot$ will always be very low compared to that of $Cl_2C{=}CCl_2$, so that termination of reaction chains owing to

$$Cl \cdot + \cdot Cl \rightarrow Cl_2$$

or mutual interaction of other active intermediates, e.g. of (XII), will be a very uncommon happening, and hence chain termination relatively infrequent. The reaction is inhibited by oxygen as the latter's molecule contains two unpaired electrons, $\cdot O{-}O \cdot$, causing it to behave as a diradical, albeit a not very reactive one. It can thus act as an effective inhibitor by converting highly active radicals to the much less reactive peroxy radicals, $Ra{-}O{-}O \cdot$. That the oxygen is reacting largely with pentachloro-ethyl radicals (XII) is shown by the formation of trichloro-acetyl chloride, $Cl_3C{-}\overset{\overset{\textstyle O}{\|}}{C}{-}Cl$, when the addition of chlorine to tetrachloro-ethylene is inhibited by oxygen. Photochemical addition of bromine is usually slower as the reaction chains are shorter.

The addition of chlorine to many unsaturated compounds is found to be irreversible at room temperature and for some way above (*cf.* p. 250), whereas the addition of bromine is often readily reversible. This results in the use of bromine radicals for the *cis* → *trans* isomerisation of geometrical isomerides:

$$
\underset{\text{(XV)}}{\overset{\displaystyle \text{Br} \qquad \text{Br}}{\underset{\displaystyle \text{H} \qquad \text{H}}{\text{C}{=}\text{C}}}}
\;\overset{\text{Br}\cdot}{\rightleftharpoons}\;
\underset{\text{(XIV)}}{\overset{\displaystyle \text{Br} \qquad \text{Br}}{\underset{\displaystyle \text{Br} \qquad \text{H}}{\text{H}{\blacktriangleright}\text{C}{-}\text{C}\cdot}}}
\;\overset{-\text{Br}\cdot}{\rightleftharpoons}\;
\underset{\text{(XVI)}}{\overset{\displaystyle \text{H} \qquad \text{Br}}{\underset{\displaystyle \text{Br} \qquad \text{H}}{\text{C}{=}\text{C}}}}
$$

The radical (XIV) formed initially can then eliminate **Br·** very rapidly and so be reconverted to the *cis* starting material, (XV), or rotation about the C—C bond can take place first followed by subsequent elimination of **Br·** to yield the *trans* isomeride, (XVI). As the latter is the more stable, it will come to preponderate, leading to an overall conversion of (XV)→(XVI). The addition of iodine is even more readily reversible at room temperature.

The addition of chlorine to benzene—one of the few addition reactions of an unactivated benzene nucleus—has also been shown to proceed via a radical mechanism, i.e. it is catalysed by light and the presence of peroxides, and is slowed or prevented by the usual inhibitors. This presumably proceeds:

A mixture of several of the eight possible geometrical isomers of hexachlorocyclohexane is obtained. In the absence of sunlight and radicals, no addition of chlorine can take place, while if catalysts are present (p. 106) electrophilic substitution occurs. With toluene, under radical conditions, attack on the methyl group offers an easier reaction path leading to predominant side-chain chlorination (substitution), rather than addition to the nucleus as with benzene, because of the stability and consequent ease of formation of the initial product, the benzyl radical, $\text{PhCH}_2\cdot$.

(ii) Hydrogen halide. The addition of hydrogen bromide to propylene via ionic intermediates to yield isopropyl bromide, has already been referred to (p. 141). In the presence of peroxides or other radical sources, however, the addition proceeds via a rapid chain reaction to yield n-propyl bromide (XVII) (i.e. the so-called 'anti-Markownikov' addition or the *peroxide effect*). The difference in product under differing conditions is due to the fact that in the former case the addition is initiated by $\text{H}^{\oplus}$, while in the latter it is initiated by **Br·**:

$$Ra \cdot (\text{ex peroxides}) + HBr \rightarrow Ra—H + \cdot Br$$

$$Me—CH{=}CH_2 + \cdot Br \rightarrow Me—\overset{\cdot}{C}H—CH_2—Br \quad \text{(XVIII)}$$

$$\cdot Br + Me—CH_2—CH_2—Br \quad \text{(XVII)}$$

In the addition of **Br·** to propylene, the radical (XVIII) is formed rather than the possible alternative, **Me—CHBr—CH$_2$·**, since a secondary radical is more stable than a primary one (p. 234).

The addition reaction may not need the presence of added radicals to initiate it, however, for olefines absorb oxygen from the air forming peroxides which can then themselves sometimes act as initiators. Such auto-initiation can be avoided by rigorous purification of the olefine prior to reaction, but this is not easy to achieve in practice, and formation of isopropyl bromide, i.e. predominance of the ionic reaction leading to so-called normal or Markownikov addition, is more easily secured by the addition of radical acceptors such as hydroquinone, etc., to absorb any radicals that may be present in the system and so prevent the occurrence of the rapid chain reaction.

It should not be thought that the presence of radicals in any way inhibits the ionic mechanism; it is merely that the radical reaction which they initiate, being a chain reaction, is so very much more rapid that it results in the vast majority of the propylene being converted to n-propyl bromide, (XVII), despite the fact that the ionic reaction is proceeding simultaneously. The virtually complete control of orientation of addition of **HBr** that can be effected by introducing radicals *or* radical acceptors into the reaction is very useful preparatively; it is not confined to propylene and applies to a number of other unsymmetrical unsaturated compounds, e.g. allyl bromide, **CH$_2$=CH—CH$_2$—Br**, which can be converted into 1,2- or 1,3-dibromopropane at will. In some cases, however, the ionic mechanism of addition is sufficiently fast to compete effectively with that induced by radicals and clear-cut control cannot then, of course, be effected.

It should, moreover, be emphasised that the reversal of the normal orientation of addition in the presence of peroxides is confined to **HBr**. This is due to the fact that with **HBr** the formation of (XVIII) and its subsequent conversion to (XVII), i.e. the steps propagating the chain-reaction, are both exothermic, while with **HF** too much energy is required to produce **F·**, and though with **HI**, **I·** is formed readily enough, it is then not sufficiently reactive to proceed further, i.e. the energy gained in forming a carbon–iodine bond is so much smaller than that lost in breaking a carbon–carbon double bond as to make the reaction energetically not worth while. With **HCl** the energetics more closely resemble those with **HBr** and radical additions have been observed in a few cases, but the radical reaction is not very rapid, as the reaction chains are short at ordinary temperatures, and it competes somewhat ineffectively with the ionic mechanism.

Nothing has so far been said about the stereochemistry of the addition of radicals to unsaturated compounds. It has been found, however, that the radical addition of **HBr** to substituted cyclohexenes proceeds stereospecifically *trans*. Thus with 1-methylcyclohexene (XIX)

cis-1-bromo-2-methylcyclohexane (XX) is obtained, i.e. the bromine and hydrogen have entered *trans* to each other. It might be expected that the first formed radical would be (XXI), but it has been suggested that the observed *trans* addition arises from the contribution of (XXII), corresponding to a bromonium ion (p. 138) plus an extra electron. As with a bromonium ion, attack (by **HBr**) would then take place 'from the back' leading to inversion of configuration on the carbon atom attacked with formation of (XX)—an overall *trans* addition. Though the occurrence of *trans* addition has been explained in this way, (XXII) contains a bromine atom with nine electrons, a not very likely happening, and alternative explanations of stereospecific *trans* addition have accordingly been put forward.

With simple acyclic olefines no such stereospecific addition of **HBr** is observed at room temperature owing to ready rotation about the **C—C** single bond in the first-formed radical intermediate (*cf.* p. 243). When such a radical addition is carried out at −78°, however, it has been found to proceed very largely *trans* owing to the much less free rotation about the C—C bond at this lower temperature. Thus under these conditions *cis*-2-bromobut-2-ene was found to yield 92 per cent of the *meso*-dibromide.

The addition of thiols, **RSH**, to olefines closely resembles that of **HBr** in many ways. Heterolytic addition (of **RS**$^\ominus$) can take place but radical additions may be initiated by the presence of peroxides and, as with **HBr**, the two mechanisms generally lead to opposite orientations of addition.

(iii) Vinyl polymerisation. This reaction has probably received more attention than any other involving radicals, not least because of its commercial implications in the manufacture of polymers. It can be said to involve three phases:

(a) *Initiation:* Formation of **Ra·** from peroxides, etc.
(b) *Propagation:*

$$\text{Ra·} + \text{CH}_2 = \text{CH}_2 \ \rightarrow \ \text{RaCH}_2 - \text{CH}_2 \cdot \xrightarrow{\ \text{CH}_2 = \text{CH}_2\ } \text{Ra(CH}_2)_4 \cdot \quad \text{etc.}$$

(c) *Termination:*
   (i) $\text{Ra(CH}_2)_{n-1}\text{CH}_2 \cdot + \cdot \text{Ra} \ \rightarrow \ \text{Ra(CH}_2)_n\text{Ra}$
   (ii) $\text{Ra(CH}_2)_{n-1}\text{CH}_2 \cdot + \cdot \text{CH}_2(\text{CH}_2)_{n-1}\text{Ra} \ \rightarrow \ \text{Ra(CH}_2)_{2n}\text{Ra}$

The propagation stage is usually extremely rapid.

As the olefine monomers readily absorb oxygen from the air, forming peroxides which can themselves form radicals and so act as initiators of polymerisation, it is usual to add some inhibitor, e.g. quinone, to the monomer if it is to be stored. When, subsequently, the monomer comes to be polymerised sufficient radicals must be produced to 'saturate' this added inhibitor before any become available to initiate polymerisation; thus an induction period is often observed before polymerisation begins to take place.

The radicals acting as initiators cannot properly be looked upon as catalysts—though often referred to as such—for each one that initiates a polymerisation chain becomes irreversibly attached to the chain and, if of suitable chemical structure, may be detected in the final polymer. The efficiency of some radicals as initiators may be so great that, after any induction period, every radical formed leads to a polymer chain; the concentration of initiator radicals may thus be kept very low.

Termination of a growing chain can result from reaction with either an initiator radical or a second growing chain, but of these the latter is normally the more important as the initiator radicals will have been largely used up in setting the chains going in the first place. It should be emphasised that such mutual interaction of radicals can result not only in reaction as above but also lead to disproportionation (p. 236). The chain length, i.e. the molecular weight, of the polymer may be controlled by addition of terminators or of *chain transfer agents*. These are usually compounds, **XH**, which react with a growing chain by loss of a hydrogen atom, so terminating the chain:

$$\mathbf{Ra(CH_2)_nCH_2\cdot + HX \rightarrow Ra(CH_2)_n\,CH_3 + \cdot X}$$

A new radical, **X·**, is formed and in the case of terminators **X** is chosen so that this radical is of low reactivity and hence not capable of initiating addition polymerisation in more monomer. In the case of chain transfer agents, however, **X** is chosen so that **X·** is reactive enough to initiate a new reaction chain so that the length (molecular weight) of individual chains is then controlled without at the same time slowing down the overall rate at which monomer undergoes polymerisation. Thiols, **RSH** are often used as chain transfer agents yielding **RS·** radicals as the initiators of the new chains.

Vinyl polymerisation, proceeding via ionic mechanisms, may also be initiated by acids and bases and by Lewis acids, e.g. **BF₃**, etc. These reagents have recently become of increasing importance in the manufacture of oriented polymers, e.g. polypropylene in which the methyl substituents are arranged in a regular pattern on the same side of the 'backbone' chain of carbon atoms (*isotactic* polymers). Such oriented polymers have notable advantages in crystalline structure, melting point, mechanical strength etc. over comparable species in which the alkyl substituents are arranged at random (*atactic* polymers).

(c) **Displacement reactions:** *(i) Halogenation.* The displacement reactions on carbon that proceed via a radical mechanism are not in fact *direct* displacements or substitutions but involve two separate stages. This may be seen in the photochemically catalysed chlorination of a hydrocarbon:

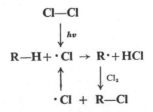

The reaction may also be initiated in the dark by heating but considerably elevated temperatures are required to effect **Cl—Cl →** **Cl· + ·Cl**; thus the rate of chlorination of ethane in the dark at 120° is virtually indetectable. The reaction becomes extremely rapid, however, on the introduction of small quantities of **Pb(Et)₄** which undergoes decomposition at this temperature to yield ethyl radicals (*cf.* p. 235) capable of acting as initiators:

$$\text{Et· + Cl—Cl} \rightarrow \text{Et—Cl + ·Cl}$$

As is well known, the hydrogen atom on a tertiary carbon is more readily displaced than those on a secondary carbon and these, in their turn, more readily than those on a primary carbon; this reflects the relative stability of the radical, **R·**, that will be formed in the first instance (p. 234). The difference is often not sufficiently great, however, to avoid the formation of mixtures of products from hydrocarbons containing more than one position that may undergo attack; further, what preferential attack there is may be in large part negatived by a statistical effect. Thus, in isobutane, **(CH₃)₃CH**, although the hydrogen atom on the tertiary carbon is more readily attacked than those on the primary, there are no less than *nine* of the latter to attack compared with only *one* of the former, thus further limiting the preparative, i.e. selective, use of photochemical chlorination.

The reaction is, however, also influenced by polar factors, for the electronegative **Hal·** as well as being a radical is at the same time an electrophilic reagent and will tend therefore to attack preferentially at a site where the electron density is high. Radical halogenation thus tends to be retarded by the presence of electron-withdrawing atoms or groups, e.g. a second halogenation on a carbon atom that has already been substituted is more difficult than the first.

If the carbon indirectly attacked is asymmetric, e.g. **RR′R″CH**, then a racemic chloride is obtained. This racemisation does not constitute proof of the planar nature of the radical formed, however, (*cf.* p. 239), for the same result would be obtained with a radical having a pyramidal configuration provided it could rapidly and reversibly turn itself 'inside out' as can the pyramidal molecules of ammonia and amines:

At elevated temperatures (*ca.* 450°) propylene, Me—CH=CH$_2$, is found to undergo chlorination to allyl chloride rather than addition of chlorine, for as the temperature rises the addition reaction becomes reversible (*cf.* p. 243) whereas the displacement reaction via a stabilised allyl radical does not:

$$Cl_2 + CH_3—CH=CH_2 \rightarrow Cl—CH_2—CH=CH_2 + HCl$$

At similarly elevated temperatures it is found that halogeno-benzenes undergo considerable chlorination and bromination in the *m*-position despite the presence in the nucleus of an *o/p*-directive halogen; thus bromobenzene yields 57 per cent of *m*-dibromobenzene at 500°. This is due to increasing homolytic attack by bromine atoms generated by thermal fission of molecules of bromine. Attack by Br· at such elevated temperatures will tend to be less selective and will be little influenced by relative electron availability at *o*-, *m*- and *p*-positions and the usual directive effect of a substituent already present will no longer apply: a characteristic feature of the homolytic substitution of aromatic systems at high temperatures.

Fluorination takes place with great readiness and though it appears to proceed via a radical mechanism, the reaction will often take place in the absence of light or initiators. Fluorine atoms are then believed to be produced, in the first instance, by the reaction:

$$\overset{\diagdown}{\underset{\diagup}{—C}}—H + F—F \rightarrow \overset{\diagdown}{\underset{\diagup}{—C}}· + H—F + ·F$$

The driving force of the reaction is provided by tne 100 kcals by which the bond energy of H—F exceeds that of F—F. Bromination is generally slower and less easy than chlorination as the stage in which a hydrogen atom is abstracted

$$\overset{\diagdown}{\underset{\diagup}{—C}}—H + ·Br \rightarrow \overset{\diagdown}{\underset{\diagup}{—C}}· + H—Br$$

is often endothermic, whereas in chlorination this stage is exothermic due to the greater bond energy of H—Cl as compared with H—Br.

The lower reactivity of bromine compared with chlorine is associated, as often happens, with greater selectivity in the position of attack, so that the difference in reactivity of tertiary, secondary and primary hydrogen is considerably more marked in bromination than chlorination. Direct iodination is not normally practicable, for though $I\cdot$ is readily formed it is not reactive enough to abstract a hydrogen atom, the bond energy of the H—I that would be formed being low.

Radical halogenation by reagents other than the halogens themselves, e.g. N-bromosuccinimide (XXIII), is of considerable synthetic importance. This reagent will brominate a number of positions but is especially useful for attack on hydrogen attached to a carbon atom α- to a double bond (an allylic carbon). Thus with cyclohexene (XXIV), 3-bromocyclohexene (XXV) is formed:

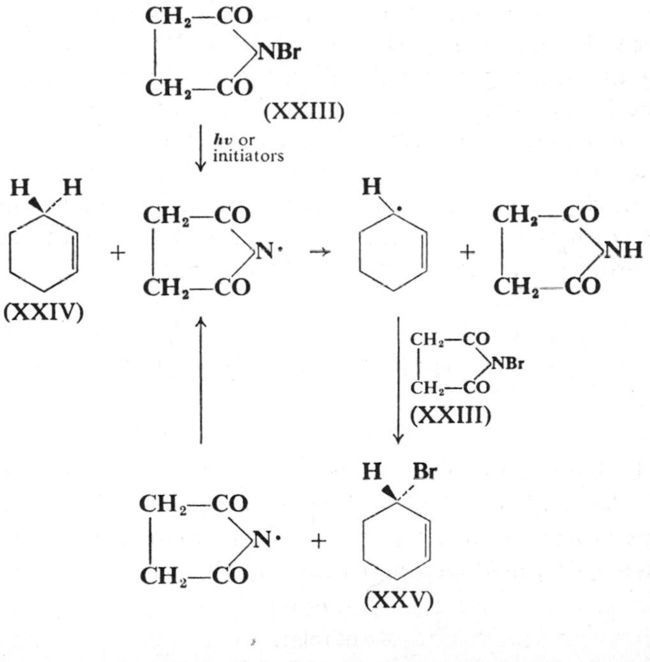

More recently, however, it has been suggested that the function of the N-bromosuccinimide, in some cases at any rate, is to act as a source of a *low* concentration of molecular bromine which itself effects the actual bromination. The particularly ready attack on an allylic, or on the similar, benzylic position, is due to stabilisation of

the first-formed radical by the delocalisation that can then take place
(*cf.* p. 234):

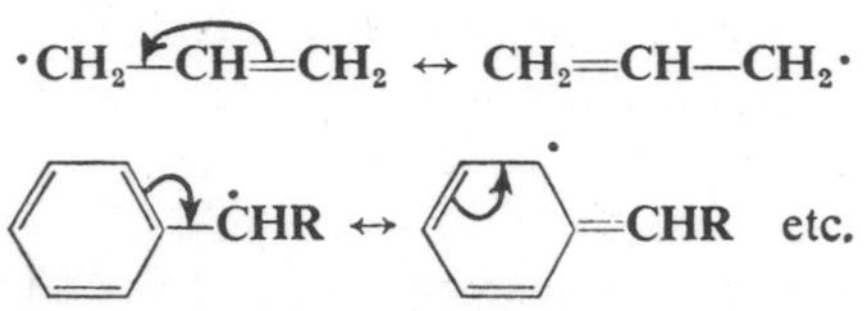

$$\cdot CH_2 \overset{\frown}{-} CH = CH_2 \leftrightarrow CH_2 = CH - CH_2 \cdot$$

$$\text{⬡} \cdot CHR \leftrightarrow \text{⬡} = CHR \quad \text{etc.}$$

(ii) *Autoxidation*. Another displacement reaction involving
radicals is autoxidation, the reaction of organic compounds with
oxygen under mild conditions. Substances often contain impurities,
e.g. trace metals, that can act as initiators so that the reaction then
proceeds spontaneously; but, as always, added peroxides act as very
powerful initiators. The decomposition of most organic compounds
exposed to air and sunlight is due to photosensitised oxidation. Thus
a number of hydrocarbons may be converted to hydroperoxides
(XXVI), molecules of oxygen reacting extremely readily with radicals
on account of their own diradical nature (*cf.* p. 243):

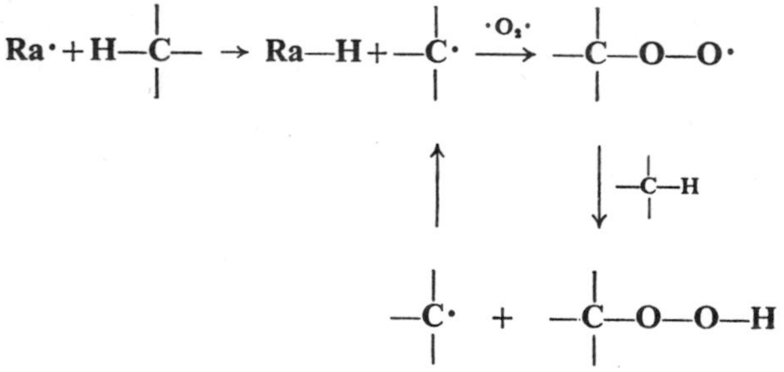

$$Ra\cdot + H-\overset{|}{\underset{|}{C}}- \rightarrow Ra-H + -\overset{|}{\underset{|}{C}}\cdot \xrightarrow{\cdot O_2 \cdot} -\overset{|}{\underset{|}{C}}-O-O\cdot$$

$$\uparrow \qquad \downarrow -\overset{|}{C}-H$$

$$-\overset{|}{\underset{|}{C}}\cdot + -\overset{|}{\underset{|}{C}}-O-O-H \quad (XXVI)$$

In some cases the hydroperoxide formed can itself act as an
initiator so that the reaction is autocatalysed.

As peroxy radicals, $RO_2\cdot$, are of relatively low reactivity they do not
readily abstract hydrogen from $>C-H$ and many autoxidation
reactions are highly selective. Thus tertiary hydrogens are usually the
only ones attacked in simple saturated hydrocarbons but allylic,
benzylic and other positions that can yield stabilised radicals are
attacked relatively easily. Thus decalin (decahydronaphthalene) yields

(XXVII), cyclohexene (XXVIII) and diphenylmethane, (XXIX), respectively:

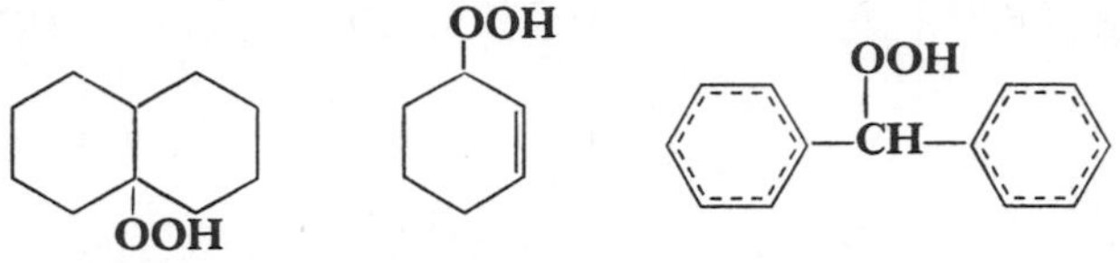

OOH

(XXVII)   (XXVIII)   (XXIX)

Reference has already been made to the large-scale conversion of cumene (isopropylbenzene) into phenol + acetone via the hydroperoxide (p. 100); the air oxidation of tetralin (tetrahydronaphthalene) to the ketone α-tetralone may also be accomplished preparatively via the action of alkali on the first-formed hydroperoxide:

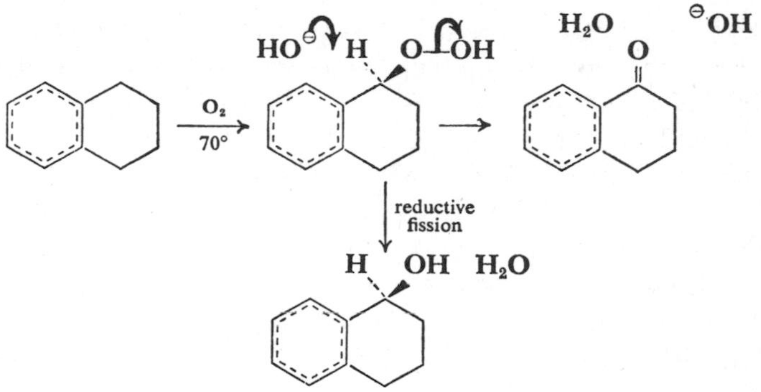

In addition, the corresponding alcohol α-tetralol may be obtained by reductive fissions of the hydroperoxide.

Aldehydes also readily autoxidise: thus benzaldehyde, in air, is extremely easily converted into benzoic acid (see p. 254). This reaction is catalysed by light and also by a number of metal ions, provided these are capable of a one electron oxidation/reduction transition (e.g. $Fe^{\oplus\oplus\oplus} \rightarrow Fe^{\oplus\oplus}$). The perbenzoate radical (XXXI), obtained by addition of $\cdot O_2 \cdot$ to the first-formed benzoyl radical (XXX), removes a hydrogen atom from a second molecule of benzaldehyde to form perbenzoic acid (XXXII) plus a benzoyl radical (XXX) to continue the reaction chain.

The perbenzoic acid reacts with a further molecule of benzaldehyde, however, to yield two molecules of benzoic acid. This reaction is

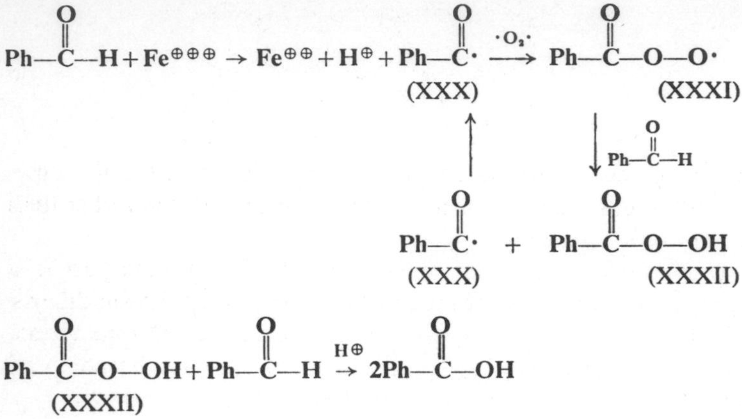

$$Ph-\overset{\overset{\displaystyle O}{\|}}{C}-H + Fe^{\oplus\oplus\oplus} \rightarrow Fe^{\oplus\oplus} + H^{\oplus} + Ph-\overset{\overset{\displaystyle O}{\|}}{C}\cdot \xrightarrow{\cdot O_2 \cdot} Ph-\overset{\overset{\displaystyle O}{\|}}{C}-O-O\cdot$$

$$(XXX) \qquad\qquad\qquad (XXXI)$$

$$Ph-\overset{\overset{\displaystyle O}{\|}}{C}-H \quad\downarrow$$

$$Ph-\overset{\overset{\displaystyle O}{\|}}{C}\cdot \quad + \quad Ph-\overset{\overset{\displaystyle O}{\|}}{C}-O-OH$$

$$(XXX) \qquad\qquad (XXXII)$$

$$Ph-\overset{\overset{\displaystyle O}{\|}}{C}-O-OH + Ph-\overset{\overset{\displaystyle O}{\|}}{C}-H \xrightarrow{H^{\oplus}} 2Ph-\overset{\overset{\displaystyle O}{\|}}{C}-OH$$

$$(XXXII)$$

catalysed by hydrogen ions and so is accelerated as the amount of benzoic acid formed increases. The presence of electron-donating groups in the benzene nucleus, as might be expected, facilitates removal of a hydrogen atom from the aldehyde to yield the initial radical, corresponding to (XXX).

The autoxidation of aldehydes may be lessened by very careful purification but more readily by the addition of anti-oxidants, such as phenols and aromatic amines, that react preferentially with any radicals that may be present.

An interesting autoxidation is the photo-oxidation of hydrocarbons such as anthracene (XXXV):

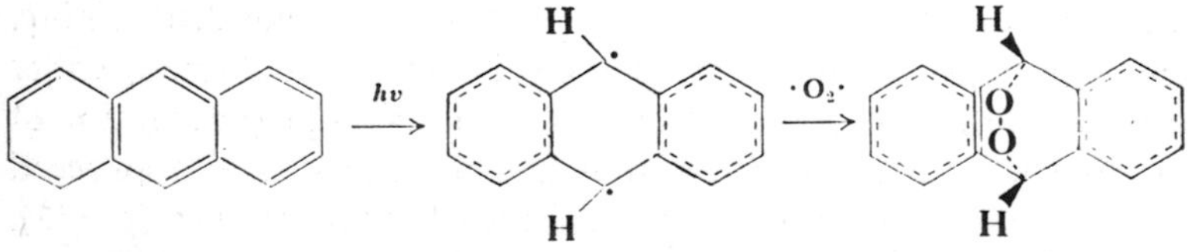

$$(XXXV) \qquad\qquad (XXXIII) \qquad\qquad (XXXIV)$$

The light absorbed converts the anthracene to an excited state, such as the di-radical (XXXIII) or something like it, which then adds on a molecule of oxygen to form the photo-oxide (XXXIV). This photo-oxidation proceeds so readily with higher *lin* aromatic hydrocarbons such as hexacene (XXXVI)

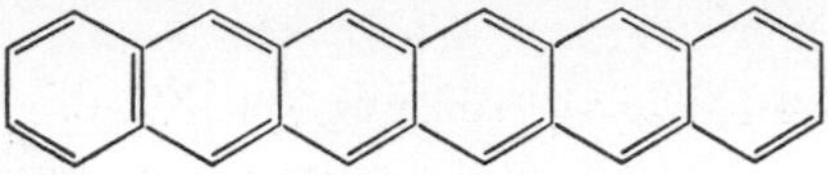

(XXXVI)

that it is impossible to work with them in sunlight. It should, however, be emphasised that this autoxidation is an addition rather than
a displacement reaction.

(iii) Arylation. Phenyl or other aryl radicals can take part in a
number of reactions, one of the most common being the Sandmeyer
reaction of a diazonium salt with cuprous chloride or bromide as a
complex ion, e.g. $CuCl_2^{\ominus}$. Here the aryl radical is believed to be
generated by an electron transfer, coupled with loss of nitrogen

$$ArN_2^{\oplus} + CuCl_2^{\ominus} \rightarrow Ar\cdot + N_2 + CuCl_2$$

which is then followed by a displacement reaction on a chlorine atom
of the cupric chloride:

$$Ar\cdot + Cl-Cu-Cl \rightarrow Ar-Cl + Cu-Cl$$

Again no reaction chain is set up as the reaction in which the radical
is consumed does not lead to the production of a second one in its
place. It is found that

$$\text{Rate} \propto [ArN_2^{\oplus}][CuCl_2^{\ominus}]$$

indicating that the first reaction is the slower, i.e. rate-determining,
one. The actual intervention of radicals can be confirmed, under
suitable conditions, by their initiation of the chain polymerisation of
acrylonitrile. Reactions of diazonium solutions can also proceed
through an ionic mechanism as has already been mentioned (p. 112).

Phenyl or other aryl radicals, generated in a number of ways, can
also react with aromatic species, e.g. the Gomberg-Bachmann reaction in which aryl radicals are generated by the decomposition of
diazo hydroxides (XXXVII), in contact with the aromatic compound
that is to be arylated:

$$Ar-N{=}N-OH \rightarrow Ar\cdot + N_2 + \cdot OH$$
(XXXVII)

255

It might be expected that the attack on the aromatic species, C_6H_5—X, would then proceed via a direct displacement:

$$Ar \cdot + C_6H_5—X \rightarrow Ar—C_6H_4—X + H \cdot$$

This would, however, involve the breaking of a carbon–hydrogen bond and the formation of a carbon–carbon bond and, as the former is usually considerably stronger than the latter, would thus lead to a high activation energy and so to a slow reaction: this is not what is actually observed. Also the addition of substances that would readily be reduced by free hydrogen atoms has never been found to result in such reduction, indicating that it is unlikely that hydrogen atoms ever do in fact become free. It seems more likely, therefore, that the reaction proceeds as a two-stage process:

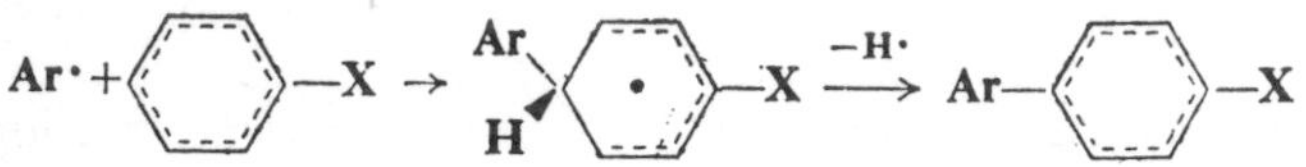

The hydrogen atom is removed by another radical or by attack on the original source of aryl radicals:

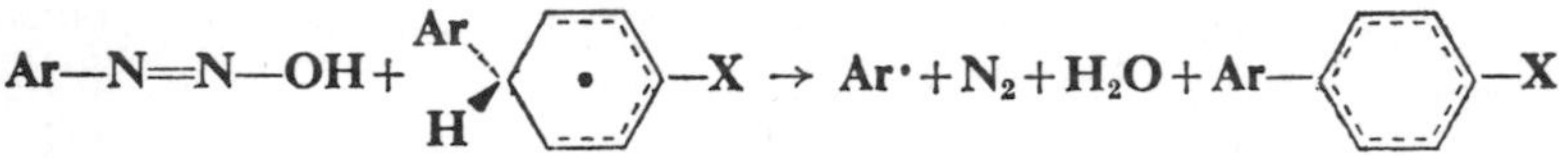

Evidence for such a mechanism is provided by the fact that such arylations show no isotope effect, i.e. deuterium and tritium are displaced as readily as hydrogen, indicating that arylation cannot be initiated by fission of a carbon–hydrogen (or deuterium or tritium) bond as the rate-determining step of the reaction.

The aryl group has here been shown entering the *p*-position to the group already present, but it could as well have been the *o*- or *m*-positions as the characteristic directing effect exerted by this group on an attacking electrophilic or nucleophilic reagent will apply with much less stringency to an uncharged aryl radical. Nevertheless, an entirely random choice of position of attack by the entering group is not observed. All substituents, irrespective of their nature, appear slightly to favour attack at the *o*- and *p*-positions. This may be due to the extra stabilisation of the intermediate by delocalisation that could result when attack is at the *o*- and *p*-, but not at the *m*-position

$$
\begin{array}{ccc}
\text{O}^\circleddash & & \text{O}^\circleddash \\
\text{O=N}^\oplus & & \cdot\text{O—N}^\oplus \\
\end{array}
$$

but it is by no means certain that this is the only factor involved.

Yields in this reaction tend to be low, partly owing to the two-phase, aqueous/organic, system involved. They may be improved by using substances such as N-nitroso-acetanilide, **PhN(NO)—CO—Me**, or dibenzoyl peroxide (heated) as sources of phenyl radicals, for the reaction may then be carried out in homogeneous solution using the substance to be phenylated as solvent, but mixed products and tarry by-products still result.

(d) Rearrangements: The few known rearrangement reactions of radicals nearly always involve aryl residues as migrants, and even then only from an atom on which the attached groups are strained by crowding. Thus the radical (XXXVIII) derived from the aldehyde, **Ph₂C(Me)—CH₂—CHO**, may be made to undergo loss of **CO**, but the products ultimately formed are derived from radical (XXXIX), not (XL):

$$
\underset{\text{(XXXVIII)}}{\text{Ph}_2\text{C(Me)—CH}_2\text{—}\overset{\cdot}{\text{C}}\text{=O}} \xrightarrow{-\text{CO}} \underset{\text{(XL)}}{\text{Ph}_2\text{C(Me)—}\overset{\cdot}{\text{C}}\text{H}_2} \longrightarrow \underset{\text{(XXXIX)}}{\text{Ph}\overset{\cdot}{\text{C}}\text{(Me)—CH}_2\text{Ph}}
$$

It has been suggested that the migration of phenyl rather than an alkyl group is encouraged by the possibility, with the former, of proceeding via an intermediate (XLI) that is stabilised by delocalisation:

$$
\underset{}{\text{>C—}\overset{\cdot}{\text{C}}\text{<}} \rightarrow \underset{\text{(XLI)}}{\text{>C—C<}} \rightarrow \underset{}{\cdot\text{>C—C<}}
$$

For in the above case it is migration of methyl rather than phenyl that would be expected to yield the more stable radical, **Ph₂Ċ—CH₂Me**, and the non-phenylated radical, **EtMe₂C—ĊH₂**, corresponding to (XL) is found not to rearrange at all.

But migration is not confined to shifts on to carbon; thus triphenyl-methyl peroxide (p. 232) undergoes the following changes on heating:

$$Ph_3C\text{—}O\text{—}O\text{—}CPh_3 \rightarrow 2Ph_3C\text{—}O\cdot \rightarrow 2Ph_2\overset{\bullet}{C}\text{—}OPh \rightarrow \quad \begin{array}{l} Ph_2C\text{—}OPh \\ | \\ Ph_2C\text{—}OPh \end{array}$$

The much less common occurrence of rearrangements among radicals as compared with carbonium ions (p. 86) probably reflects the smaller difference in stability observed between primary and tertiary radicals as compared with the corresponding carbonium ions.

(v) Diradicals

The oxygen molecule has already been referred to as a diradical, albeit an unreactive one, and another very simple species is the methylene radical obtained, for example, by the photo-chemical decomposition of ketene (XLII) or diazomethane (XLIII):

$$CH_2N_2 \rightarrow \overset{\bullet}{\underset{\bullet}{C}}H_2 \leftarrow CH_2\text{=}C\text{=}O$$
$$\text{(XLIII)} \qquad\qquad \text{(XLII)}$$

This by contrast is extremely reactive, adding with great readiness, and stereospecifically, to double bonds to form cyclopropane derivatives:

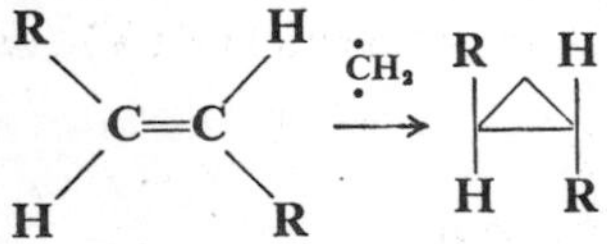

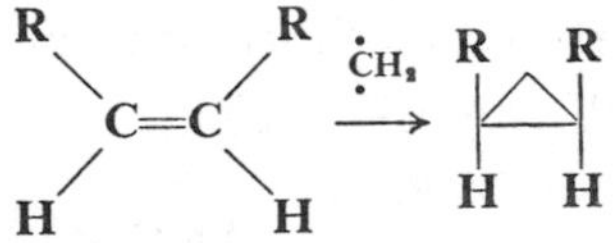

The photochemical excitation of anthracene and other *lin* aromatic hydrocarbons has already been referred to; if the excitation is carried out in the absence of air or oxygen, cyclisation takes place to a photo-dimer (XLIV):

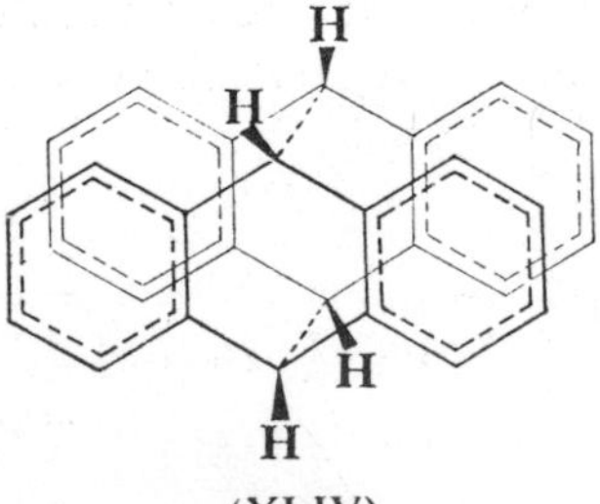

(XLIV)

258

The isomerisation of cyclopropanes to the corresponding propylene derivatives probably proceeds through diradicals:

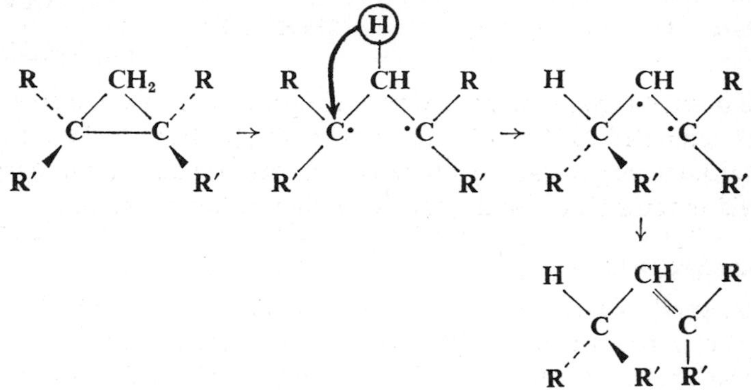

The driving force for the 1,2-hydrogen shift is provided by the possibility of electron pairing and consequent formation of a new bond that is thereby conferred.

Diradicals have also been encountered as intermediates in the reduction of ketones to pinacols (p. 168) and in the acyloin reaction on esters (p. 169). All these diradicals, with the exception of the oxygen molecule, are highly unstable but, surprisingly, a number of diradicals are known which are quite stable. Thus the hydrocarbon (XLV) exists in the diradical form:

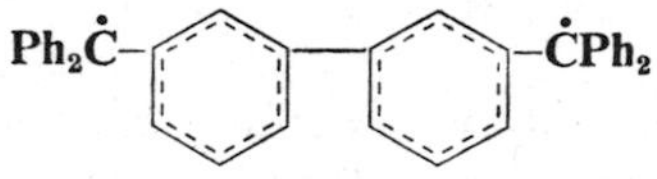

(XLV)

This is due to the fact that the diradical is very greatly stabilised by delocalisation and that a quinonoid structure embracing both nuclei, that would result in electron pairing, cannot be formed. The diradical (XLVI)

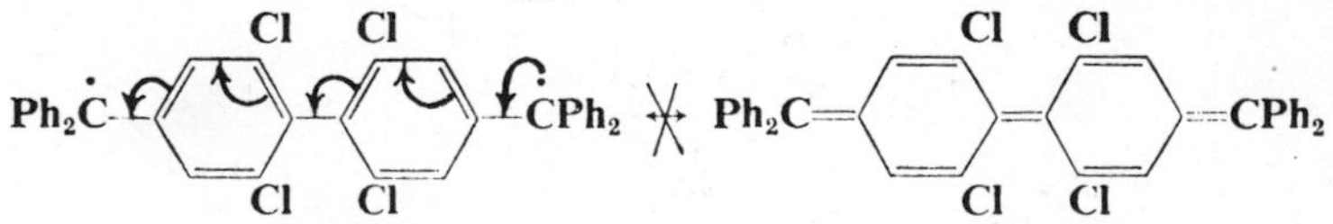

(XLVI)   (XLVII)

can, in theory, be converted to a quinonoid form (XLVII) in which its electrons are paired, but formation of the latter is inhibited as the bulky chlorine atoms prevent the two benzene nuclei from becoming coplanar, a necessary condition if there is to be the effective overlapping between their π orbitals that formation of (XLVII) requires. Both these diradicals undergo reversible association in solution, however.

(vi) Chemical action of X-rays

X-rays and other ionising radiations can react with water, in living tissues as well as *in vitro* systems, in the following way:

$$H_2O + h\nu \rightarrow [H_2O]^{\oplus} + e^{\ominus}$$
$$\downarrow \qquad\qquad \downarrow {\scriptstyle H_2O}$$
$$H^{\oplus} + \cdot OH \qquad HO^{\ominus} + \cdot H$$

Two radicals are formed by secondary processes, one involving a second molecule of water. As the ejected electron may not react immediately with a second molecule of water, the two radicals, and any reaction chains that they set in motion, may thus occur some distance apart.

Vinyl polymerisation in aqueous solution may be initiated in this way but the solution must be free from oxygen which acts as a powerful inhibitor. In living tissue, dissolved oxygen can lead to the formation of hydrogen peroxide

$$H\cdot + \cdot O_2\cdot \rightarrow HO_2\cdot \xrightarrow{H\cdot} H_2O_2$$

while dissolved nitrogen can similarly be converted to NH_3, etc. Many other reactions of great ultimate complexity can be set in train by radiation in this way.

SELECT BIBLIOGRAPHY

Valence and Chemical Bonding

CARTMELL, E., and FOWLES, G. W. A. *Valency and Molecular Structure* (Butterworths, 2nd Edition, 1961).

COTTRELL, T. L. *The Strength of Chemical Bonds* (Butterworths, 2nd Edition, 1958).

COULSON, C. A. *Valence* (O.U.P., 2nd Edition, 1961). Probably the best general account for the purpose.

MORTIMER, C. T. *Reaction Heats and Bond Strengths* (Pergamon, 1962).

PIMENTEL, G. C., and MCCLELLAN, A. L. *The Hydrogen Bond* (Freeman, 1960).

STREITWIESER, A. *Molecular Orbital Theory for Organic Chemists* (Wiley, 1961).

Structure and Reaction Mechanism

BANTHORPE, D. V. *Elimination Reactions* (Elsevier, 1963).

DE MAYO, P. (Ed.). *Molecular Rearrangements* (Interscience, Vol. I, 1963; Vol. II, 1964).

DEWAR, M. J. S. *Hyperconjugation* (Ronald Press, 1962).

ELIEL, E. L. *Stereochemistry of Carbon Compounds* (McGraw-Hill, 1962).

GOULD, E. S. *Mechanism and Structure in Organic Chemistry* (Holt-Dryden, 1959). The most readable and, overall, the most satisfactory text available.

HINE, J. *Divalent Carbon* (Ronald Press, 1964).

HINE, J. *Physical Organic Chemistry* (McGraw-Hill, 2nd Edition, 1962). Especially valuable for the kinetic aspects of the subject.

INGOLD, SIR C. K. *Structure and Mechanism in Organic Chemistry* (Bell, 1953). *The* great source of information to which all other authors must needs be indebted.

KEKULÉ SYMPOSIUM. *Theoretical Organic Chemistry* (Butterworths, 1959).

LEFFLER, J. E. *The Reactive Intermediates of Organic Chemistry* (Interscience, 1956).

LEFFLER, J. E., and GRUNWALD, E. *Rates and Equilibria of Organic Reactions* (Wiley, 1963).

MARE, P. B. D. DE LA, and RIDD, J. H. *Aromatic Substitution; Nitration and Halogenation* (Butterworths, 1959).

MELANDER, L. *Isotope Effects on Reaction Rates* (Ronald Press, 1960).

NEWMAN, M. S. (Ed.). *Steric Effects in Organic Chemistry* (Wiley, 1956).

Select Bibliography

NORMAN, R. O. C., and TAYLOR, R. E. *Electrophilic Substitution in Benzenoid Compound* (Elsevian, 1965).

STEWART, R. *Oxidation Mechanisms* (Benjamin, 1964).

STREITWIESER, A. *Solvolytic Displacement Reactions* (McGraw-Hill, 1962).

WALLING, C. *Free Radicals in Solution* (Wiley, 1957).

WATERS, W. A. *Mechanisms of Oxidation of Organic Compounds* (Methuen, 1964).

WHELAND, G. W. *Resonance in Organic Chemistry* (Wiley, 1955).

WIBERG, K. B. *Physical Organic Chemistry* (Wiley, 1964).

WILLIAMS, G. H. *Homolytic Aromatic Substitution* (Pergamon, 1960).

INDEX

Index